Bass Tab
WHITE PAGES

HLE

HAL LEONARD EUROPE

Distributed by Music Sales

Published by
Hal Leonard Europe
A Music Sales / Hal Leonard Joint Venture Company
14-15 Berners Street, London W1T 3LJ, UK.

Exclusive Distributors:
Music Sales Limited
Distribution Centre, Newmarket Road,
Bury St Edmunds, Suffolk IP33 3YB, UK.

Order No. HLE90001868
ISBN 0-7119-9862-0

Printed in the EU.

Addicted to That Rush

Words and Music by Billy Sheehan, Pat Torpey and Paul Gilbert

1st, 2nd Verses
Am7
N.C.
Am7
N.C.
D5/A
mf
1. When I was a young boy, (etc.)
2. Look a - round I stop and stare (etc.)
Am7
N.C.
Play Fill 1 2nd time
Am7
D5/A
E♭5/A
D5/A
N.C.
sl.
Am7
N.C.
Am7
N.C.
D5/A
sl.
Play Fill 2 2nd time
Am7
N.C.
sl.
P
H
Pre-chorus
C
D5
N.C.
C5
Whoa! (etc.)
Fill 1
sl.
P
Fill 2
H P sl.
sl.

D5 A5 C5 D5 F5
Em7 F5 G5
Chorus
N.C. A5 N.C.
. . (ad)-dic-ted to— that rush,— (etc.)
A5 N.C, A5
1. N.C. Am7
N.C. Am7 N.C. D5/A C5 A5 G5 E5
2. N.C. A5 N.C. A5
N.C. A5 N.C.
Guitar solo
N.C.(Bm)
sim.

8va
Pre-chorus
C5
loco
D5
A5
N.C.
C5
D5
A5
C5
D5
F5
Em7
F5
G5
A5
(steady gliss.)
Bridge
A5
N.C.
Once I thought her lov - in' was a
hab-it I could break. (etc.)

sl.
P
4
Full
grad.
bend
*A.H.
(15ma)
(steady gliss.)
*Rest thumb of picking hand on string in front
(toward neck) of picking finger to produce A.H.
Pre-chorus
C5
D5
A5
N.C.
F5
Em7
G5
Chorus

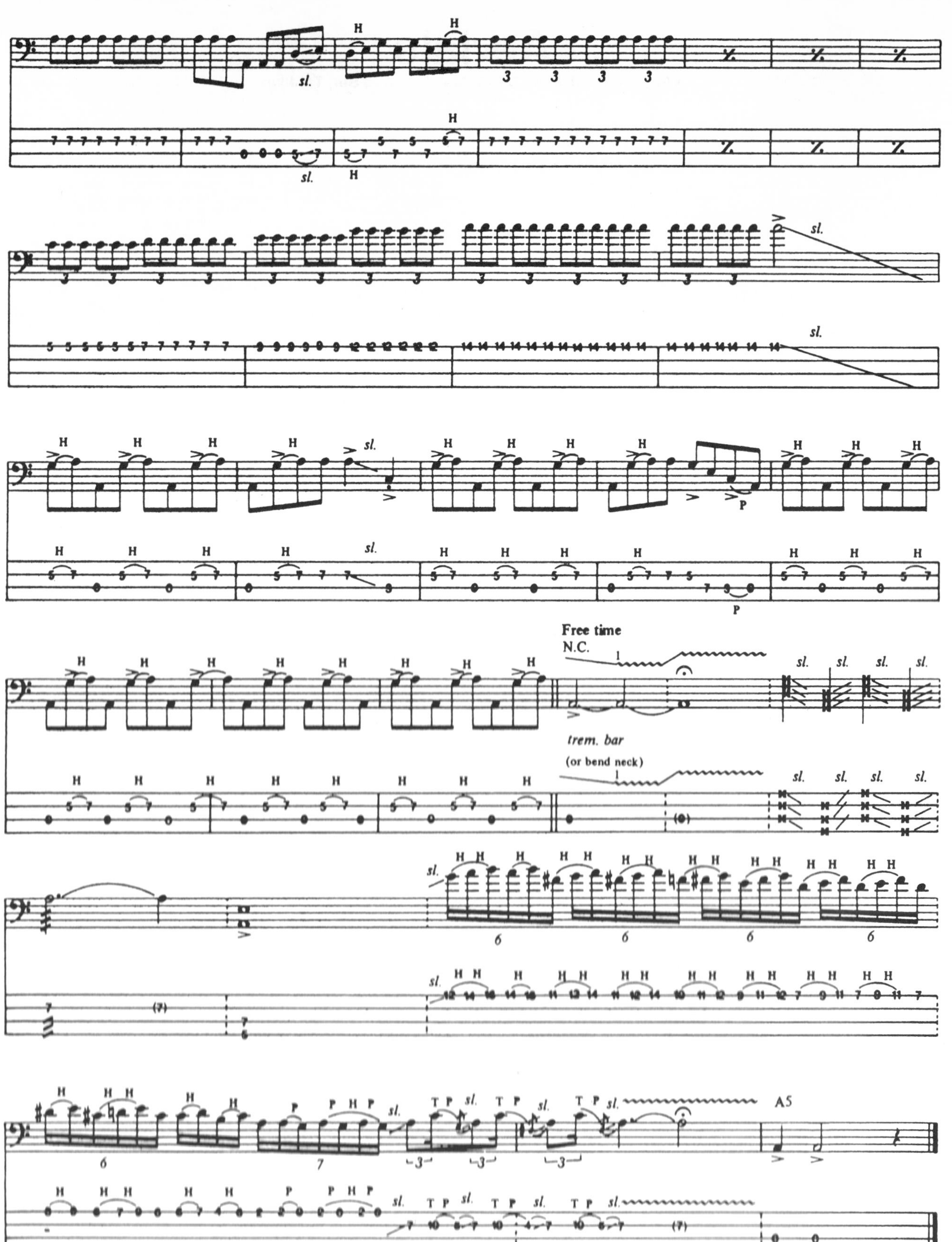
Free time
N.C.
trem. bar
(or bend neck)
A5

Aerials

Words and Music by Daron Malakian and Serj Tankian

Drop D tuning, down 1 step:
(low to high) C-G-C-F

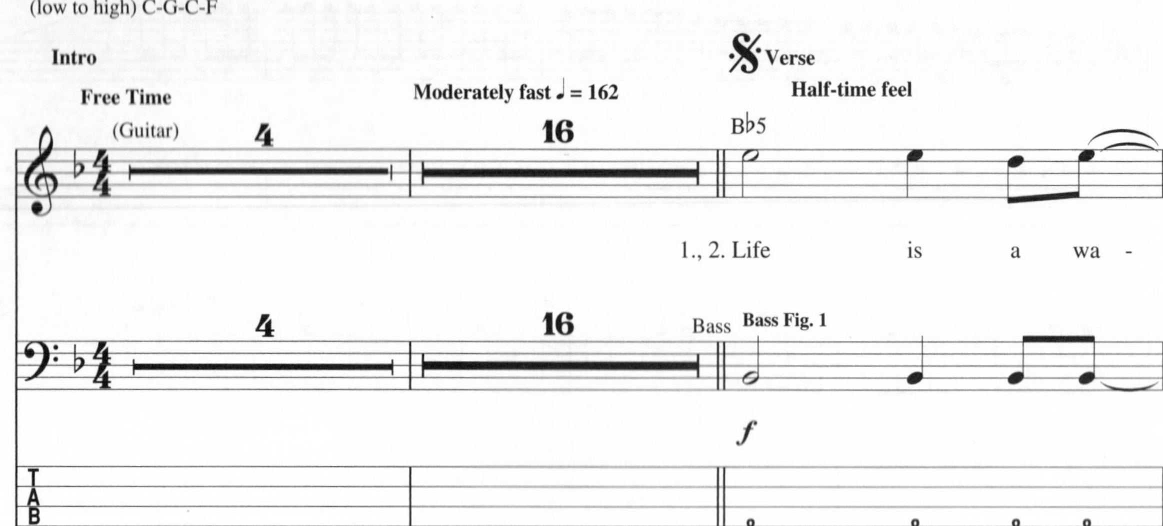

- ter - fall, we're one in the riv - er and one a - gain af - ter the fall.
we drink from the riv - er, then we turn a round and put up our walls.

(8) 8 8 8 8 8 8 8 8 8 8 8 8 8 8 8

D5 G5 D5 F5 D5 E5 D5

End Bass Fig. 1

0 0 0 0 10 0 0 0 0 8 0 0 0 0 7 0 0 0 0 5

Bass: w/ Bass Fig. 1 (2 1/2 times)
B♭5
Swim-ming through the void we hear the word, we lose our-selves but we
D5 G5 D5 F5 D5 E5 D5
find it all. 'Cause
B♭5
we are the ones that wan - na play, al - ways wan - na go but you
D5 G5 D5 F5 D5 E5 D5
B♭5
nev-er wan-na stay. And we are the ones that wan-
To Coda
- na choose, al - ways wan - na play but you nev - er wan - na lose.
Interlude
D5/F D5/E D5 D5/G D5/F D5/E
Bass Fig. 2
3 2 0 0 0 0 5 3 2 2 2 2
D5/F D5/G D5/A D5/B♭ D5/A D5/G D5/F D5/E D5
End Bass Fig. 2
3 5 7 8 7 5 3 2 0 0 0 0

Chorus

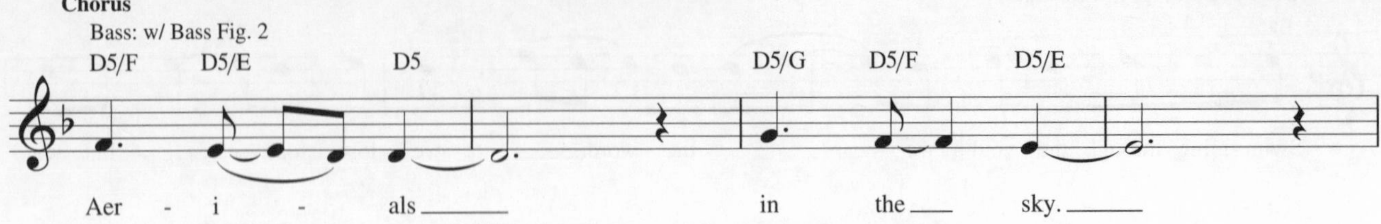
Bass: w/ Bass Fig. 2
D5/F D5/E D5 D5/G D5/F D5/E
Aer - i - als in the sky.

D.S. al Coda
D5/F D5/G D5/A D5/B♭ D5/A D5/G D5/F D5/E D5
When you lose small mind, you free your life.

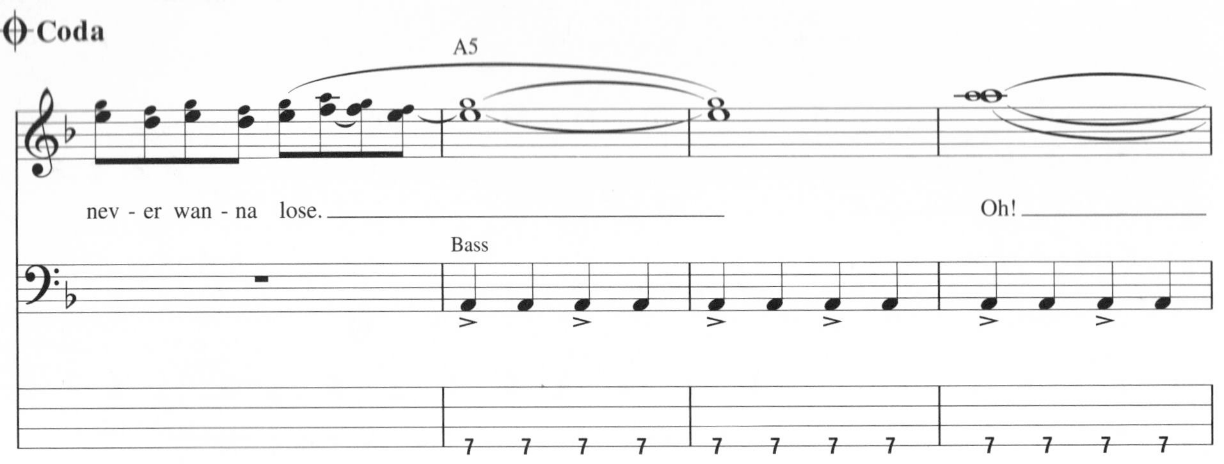
Coda
A5
nev - er wan - na lose.
Oh!
Bass
7 7 7 7 7 7 7 7 7 7 7 7

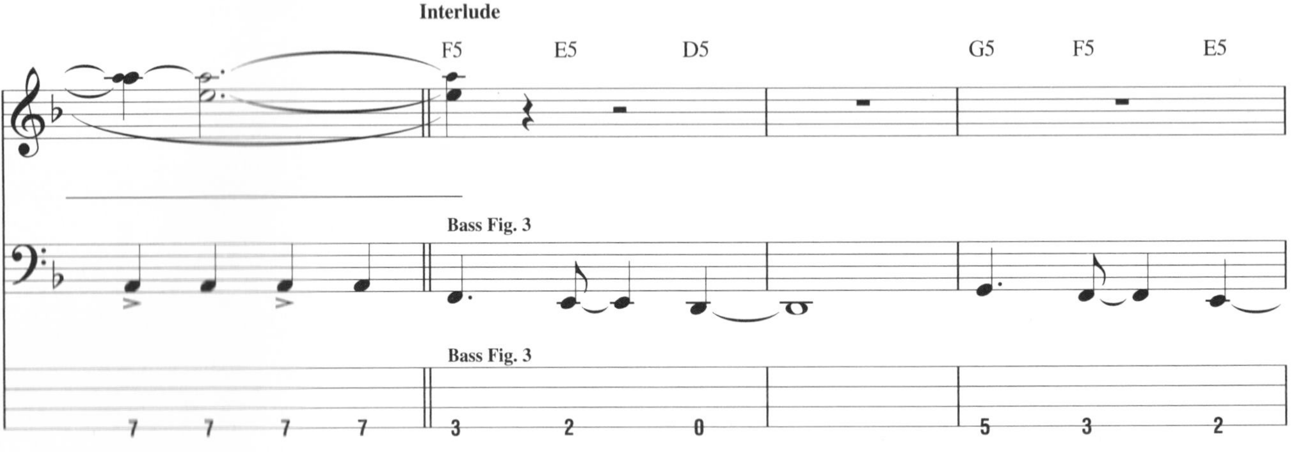
Interlude
F5 E5 D5 G5 F5 E5
Bass Fig. 3
Bass Fig. 3
7 7 7 7 3 2 0 5 3 2

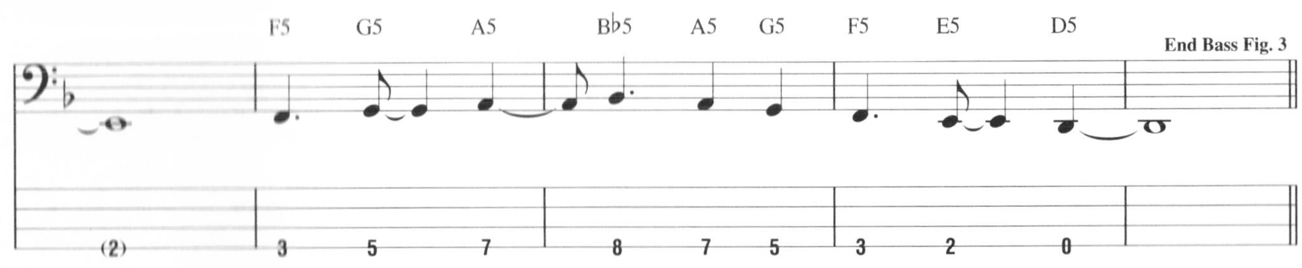
F5 G5 A5 B♭5 A5 G5 F5 E5 D5
End Bass Fig. 3
(2) 3 5 7 8 7 5 3 2 0

Chorus
Bass: w/ Bass Fig. 3 (2 times)
F5 E5 D5 G5 F5 E5
Aer - i - als in the sky.
Aer - i - als so up high.
F5 G5 A5 B♭5 A5 G5 F5 E5 D5
When you lose small mind, you free your life.
When you free your eyes, e - ter - nal prize.
Bass: w/ Bass Fig. 2 (2 times)
D5/F D5/E D5 D5/G D5/F D5/E
Aer - i - als in the sky.
Aer - i - als so up high.
D5/F D5/G D5/A D5/B♭ D5/A D5/G D5/F D5/E D5
When you lose small mind, you free your life.
When you free your eyes, e - ter - nal prize.
Outro
Bass; w/ Bass Fig. 2 (1 3/4 times)
D5/F D5/E D5 D5/F D5/E D5/E D5/F D5/G D5/A D5/B♭ D5/A D5/G
Ah, ah. Ah.
1.
D5/F D5/E D5
2.
D5/F D5/E D5
3 2 0

All Along the Watchtower

Words and Music by Bob Dylan

B A E5 C♯m B
I can't get no re - lief.
Busi-ness men, they ah, ah,
A B C♯m B A B C♯m B
drink my wine.
Plow man, dig my earth, uh.
None will lev-el on
A B C♯m B A
the line, uh,
no - bod - y of it is worth.
Hey, hey!
Guitar Solo
C♯m B A B C♯m B A
B C♯m B A B C♯m

Verse
B A B C♯m B
2. No rea - son to get ex - cit -
A B C♯m B A B
ed, uh, heh, the thief, he kind - ly spoke.
C♯m B A B C♯m B
There are man - y here a - mong us who feel that life is but a joke.
A B C♯m B A B
But uh, but you and I, we've been through that, but, ah,

C♯m
B
A
B
C♯m
B
and this is not our fate.
So let us not talk false-
A
B
C♯m
B
A
B
-ly now,
the ho-ur's get-tin' late, ah.
Hey!
Guitar Solo
C♯m
B
A
B
C♯m
B
A

C♯m
B
A
B
C♯m
B
A
B
C♯m
B
A
B
Hey!
C♯m
B
A
B
C♯m
B
A
B
C♯m
B
A
B
C♯m
B
A
B
C♯m
B
A
B
C♯m
B
A
B
C♯m

B A B C#m B A B
3. Well,
Verse
C#m B A B C#5 C#m B
all a - long the watch - tow - er, prin - ces kept the view.
A B C#5 C#m B A B C#5
While all the wo - men came and went,
C#m B A B C#5 C#m B
bare feet ser - vants too. Well, ah, oh, out - side in the cold

A B C#5 C#m B A B C#5
dis - tance, uh, a wild cat did growl.
C#m B A B C#m B
Two rid - ers were ap - proach - in' and the wind be - gan to howl.
Outro
A B C#m B A C#m
Hey! Ah.
C#m7 A C#7 C#m C#m7
All a - long the watch - tow - er

A
C♯7
C♯m
C♯m7
they __ say come in. Have you ev - er? Don't be way out
here.
B
Yeah.
Ah, babe.
Fade Out
Well, all a - long _ the watch - tow - er. __

All Right Now

Words and Music by Paul Rodgers and Andy Fraser

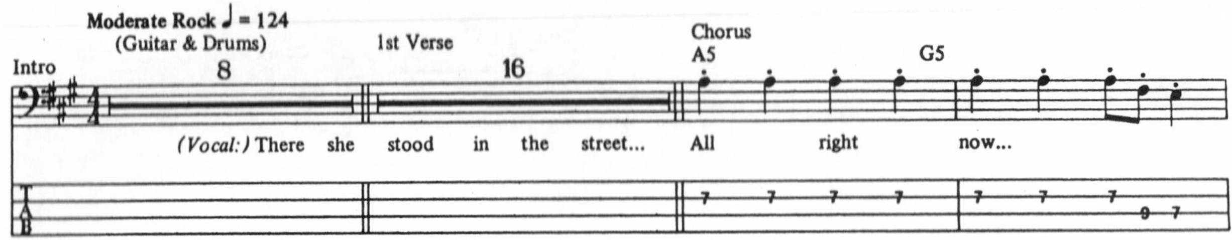

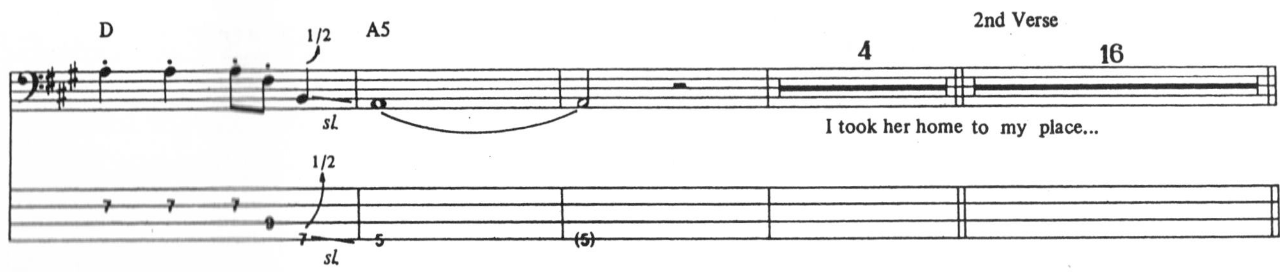

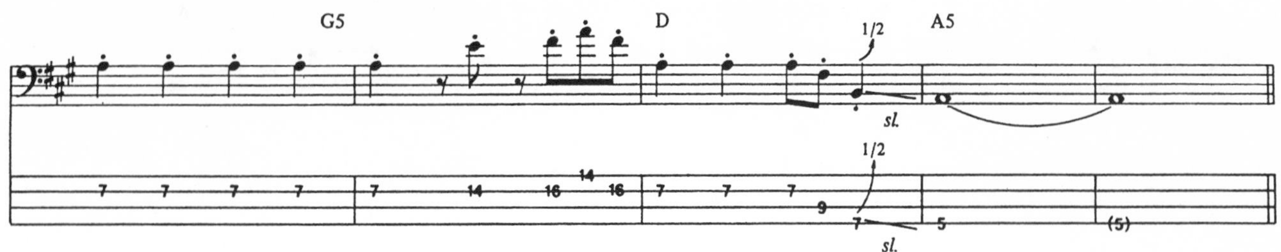
G5
D
1/2
A5
sl.
1/2
sl.

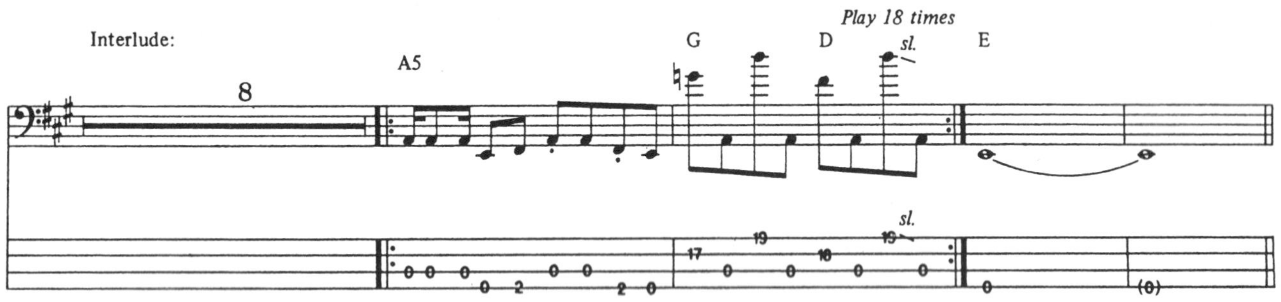
Interlude:
8
A5
Play 18 times
G
D
sl.
E
sl.

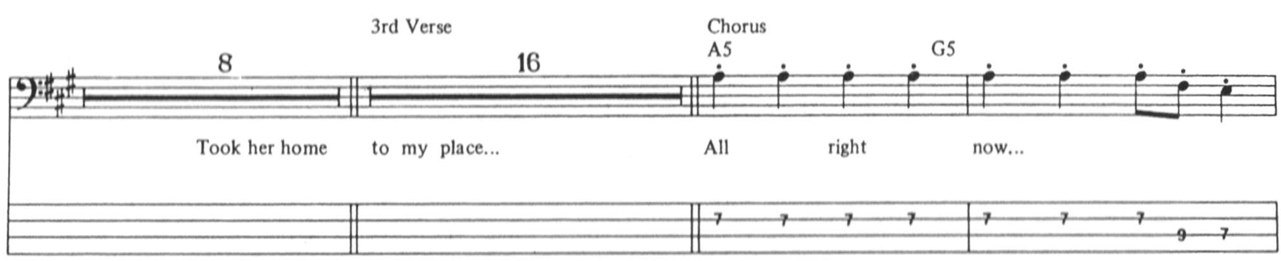
8
3rd Verse
16
Chorus
A5
G5
Took her home
to my place...
All
right
now...

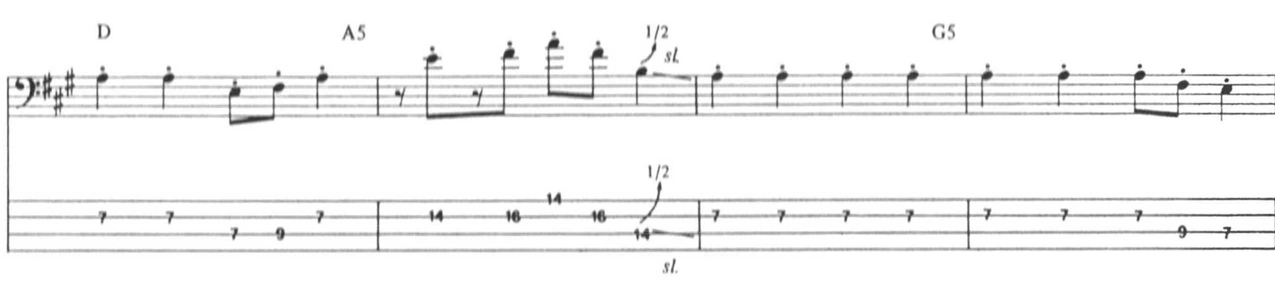
D
A5
1/2
sl.
G5
1/2
sl.

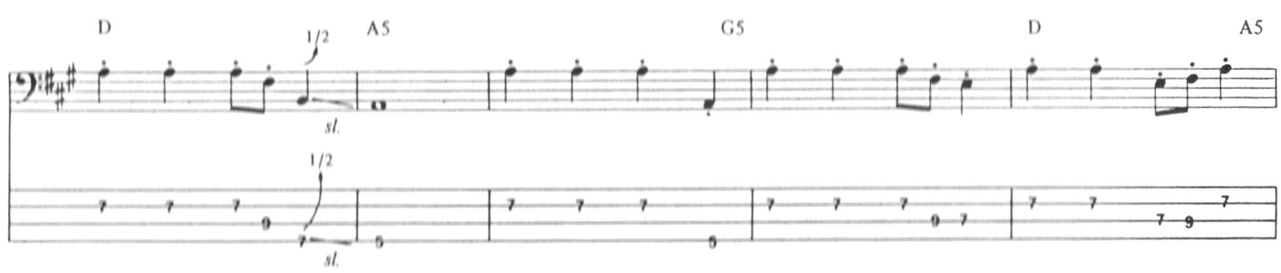
D
1/2
A5
G5
D
A5
sl.
1/2
sl.

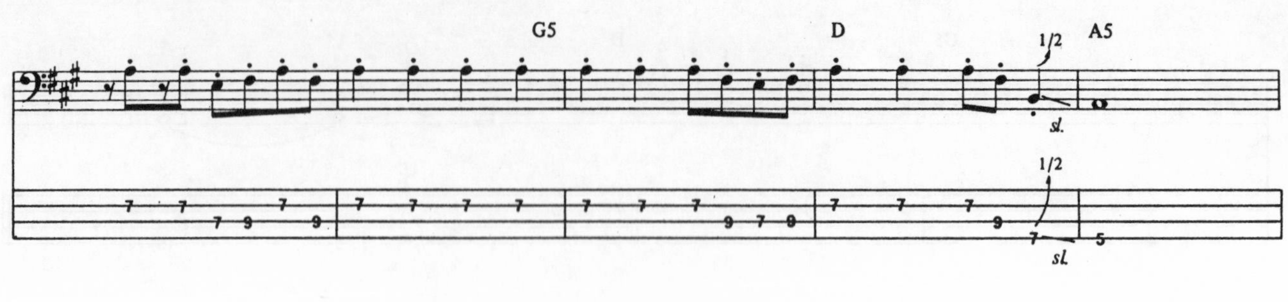
G5
D
1/2
A5
sl.
1/2
sl.

G5
D
A5
sl.
sl.

Bass I
G5
D
1/2
sl.
A5
Bass II
1/2
sl.

G5
D
A5

G5
D
H
sl.
A5
rit.
H
sl.

All Shook Up

Words and Music by Otis Blackwell and Elvis Presley

Moderate Rock (♩ = 152)

D
E
love I'm all shook up! ooh ooh yeah,
A
yeah, yeah. My hands are shak-y and my knees are weak. I
can't seem to stand on my own two feet, Who do you thank when you have such luck? I'm in
D
E
love! I'm all shook up! ooh, ooh, yeah,

A
D
yeah, yeah. Well, please don't ask what's on my mind, I'm a
tongue gets tired when I try to speak, my
A
D
lit - tle mixed up but I'm feel - in' fine When I'm near the girl that
in - sides shake like a leaf on a tree. There's on - ly one cure for this
E
I love best, My heart beats so it scares me to death! She
bod - y of mine, that's to have the girl that I love so fine! She
A
touched my hand what a chill I got, her kiss - es are like a vol -

can - o that's hot. I'm proud to say she's my but - ter - cup, I'm in
love! I'm all shook up! ooh, ooh, yeah,
D
E
1
2
A
A
yeah, yeah. My yeah, yeah; ooh
D
E
A
ooh yeah, yeah, I'm all shook up!

American Woman

Written by Burton Cummings, Randy Bachman, Gary Peterson and Jim Kale

E D E B D E D E B D
Don't come a-hang-ing a - round _ my door. ___ I don't wan-na see your face _ no more.
Don't come a-knock-ing a - round _ my door. ___ Don't wan - na see _ your shad-ow no more.
Don't come _ hang-ing a - round _ my door. ___ Don't wan - na see _ your face _ no more.
5 7 7 7 7 7 7 5 7 5 7 7 7 7 7 7 5 7 5
E D E B D E D E B D
I got more im - por - tant things to do ___ than spend my time _ grow-ing old _ with you. ___ Now
Col-ored lights _ can hyp - no - tize. ___ Spar-kle some - one _ else - 's eyes. ___ Now
I don't need _ you war ma - chines. _ I don't need _ your _ ghet - to scenes. _
5 7 7 7 7 7 7 5 7 5 7 7 7 7 7 7 5 7 5
E D E B D E D E B D
wom-an, I said stay a - way. ___ A - mer - i - can wom-
wom-an, I said get a - way. ___ A - mer - i - can wom-
Col-ored lights can hyp - no - tize. Spar - kle some - one else - 's eyes. Now
7 7 7 7 7 7 5 7 5 5 7 7 7 7 7 5 7 5
To Coda
E D E B D E D E B D
- an, lis - ten what I say. ___
- an, lis - ten what I say. ___
wom - an, get a - way from me. ___ A - mer - i - can
7 7 7 7 7 7 5 7 5 5 7 7 7 5 5 7 7 7 7 5 6 7

Guitar Solo
E
D E
B
D
Interlude

D.S. al Coda
D E
D E
3. A - mer - i - can wom-
Coda
Outro
E
D E
B
D
E
D E
B
D
wom-an,
ma-ma let me
be.
Go.
Got-ta get a-way,
got-ta get a - way
now
go, go,
go.
I'm gon-na
leave you wom - an.
Gon-na
leave you wom - an.
Bye,

E DE B D E DE B D E DE B D
bye. Bye, bye. Bye, bye. Bye,
E DE B D E DE B D E DE B D
bye. You're no good for me. I'm no good for you.
E DE B D E DE B D
Gon-na look you right in the eye, tell you what I'm gon-na do. You know I'm gon-na
Bass Fig. 1
End Bass Fig. 1
Bass: w/ Bass Fig. 1 (till fade)
E DE B D E DE B D
leave. You know I'm gon - na go. You know I'm gon - na
Begin fade
Fade out
E DE B D E DE B D
leave. I, I'm know gon - na go, wom - an. I'm gon - na...

As the Years Go Passing By

Words and Music by Deadric Malone

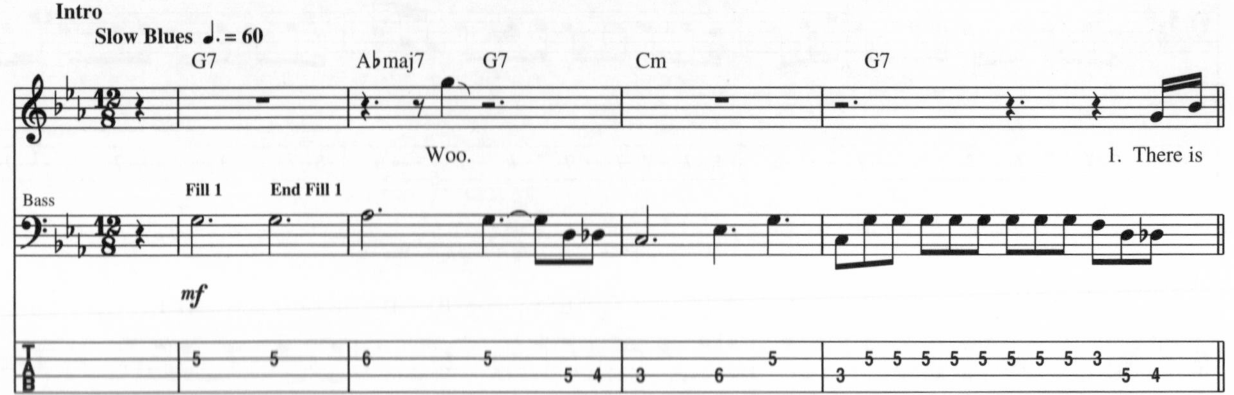

To Coda
Bass: w/ Fill1, 2nd time
Cm
G7
4:3
You know my love will fol - low you
Yes, my love will fol - low you
bye.
You know my
Ab maj7
G7
Cm
1.
G7
as the years go pass - ing by.
as the years go pass - ing by.
2. I'd give you
2.
Guitar Solo
G
Cm
Fm7
Cm
Fm7
Cm
G7
Ab maj7
G7
Cm

D.S. al Coda
Coda
G7
4:3
3. I'm gon-na
G7
love will fol-low you

A♭maj7
G7
Cm
G7
as the years go pass - ing by.
Mm,

Outro
Begin Fade
Cm
Fm7
mm.

Fade Out
Cm
Fm7
Mm.

Astronomy

Words and Music by Samuel Pearlman, Albert Bouchard and Joseph Bouchard

D C B
acid and oil on a madman's face, his reasons tend to
sl. sl.
let ring let ring
Em C G6
fly away. Like lesser birds on the four winds, yeah, like
let ring let ring
P sl. sl. sl.
C B7 Em D
silver scrapes in May. And now the sands become a crust and
H P sl. sl.
let ring let ring
C B Em
most of you have gone away. Oh yeah,
let ring let ring let ring
H

2nd Verse
Em
D
gone a - way.
Ah, come Su - sie dear, let's take a walk
sl.
let ring
H
C
B
Em
just out there up - on the beach.
I know you'll soon be mar - ried and you'll
let ring
want to know where winds come from.
Well, it's nev - er said at all on the
G6
P
B7
map that Car - ric reads
be - hind the clock back there, you know,

C
B
Em
at the Four Winds Bar.
Mm, yeah.
let ring
H
Interlude
Em
D
C
1/2
f
Yeah.
Hey!
Dsus2
E5
Bass Fig. 1
(end Bass Fig. 1)

Bridge
w/Bass Fig. 1 (3½ times)
Em C D Dsus2 E5
Four winds at the Four Winds Bar, two doors locked and win - dows barred.
Em C D Dsus2 E5
One door there to take you in, the oth - er one just mir - rors it.
Em C D Dsus2 E5 Em C
Hey! Hey! Yeah. Hey! Yeah.
w/Bass Fill 1
D Dsus2 E5
Hey! Ooh.
Bridge
w/Bass Fig. 1 (3½ times)
Em C
Hel - lish glare and in - fer - ence, the
D Dsus2 E5 Em C
oth - er one's a du - pli - cate. The queen - ly flux, e - ter - nal light,
D Dsus2 E5 Em C
or the light that nev - er warms. Yes, the light that nev - er,
D Dsus2 E5 Em C
nev - er warms. Yes, the light that nev - er,
D5 C5 D5 C5 D5 C5 D5 C5
nev - er warms, nev - er warms,
Bass Fill 1
H

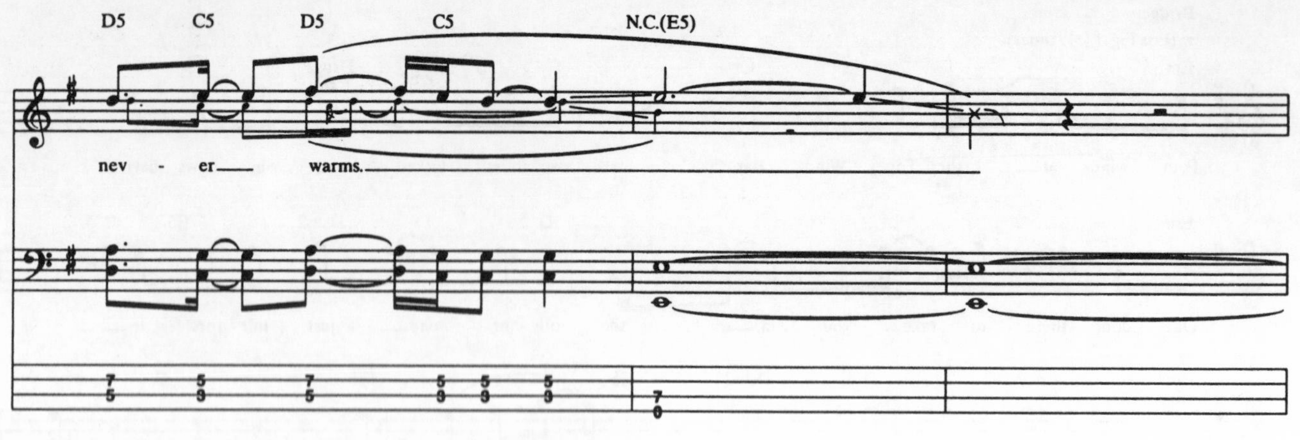
D5
C5
D5
C5
N.C.(E5)
nev - er warms.

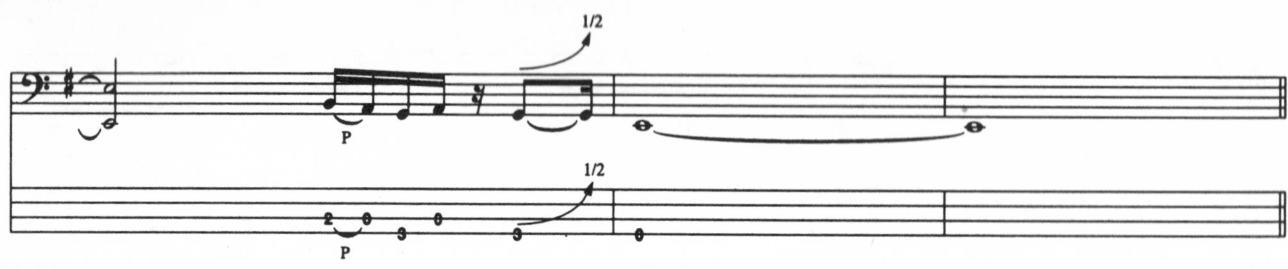
1/2
P
1/2
P

Em
The
H
mf
let ring
let ring
let ring
let ring
H
H

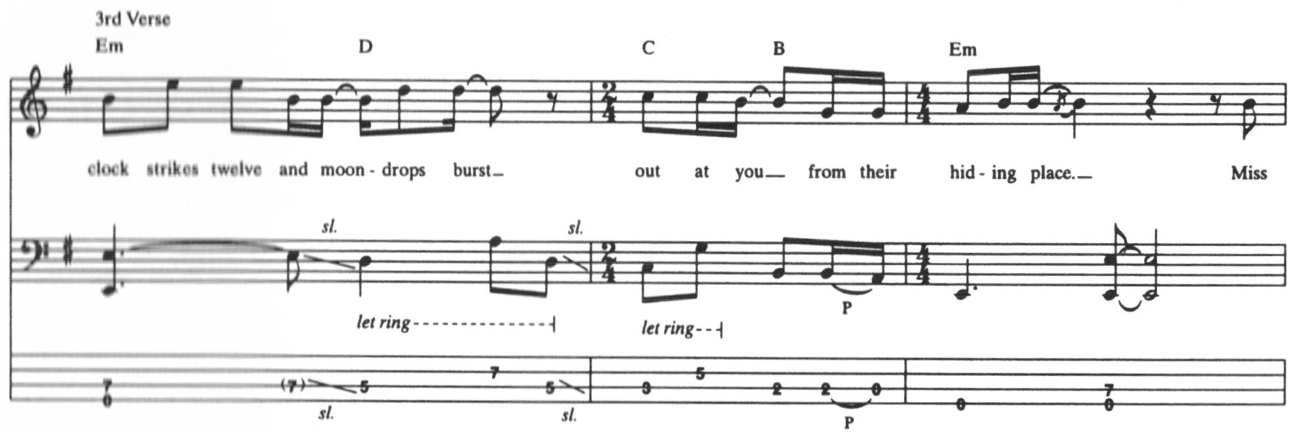
3rd Verse
Em
D
C
B
Em
clock strikes twelve and moon - drops burst out at you from their hid - ing place. Miss
sl.
sl.
let ring
let ring
P
sl.
sl.
P

D
C
B
Car - rie nurse and Su - sie dear would find them - selves at Four
sl.
let ring
Em
C
G6
Winds Bar.
It's the nex- us of the cri - sis and the
C
B7
Em
D
or - i - gin of storms,
just the place to hope - less - ly en -
C
B
Em
coun- ter time,
and then came me.
let ring
H

Interlude
Em
D
C
Em
D
C
Em
f
D
C
Em
D
C
Guitar solo
D
Em
C
No.
Hey!
H
H
D
Dsus2
E5
Em
C
Hey!
1.
D
Dsus2
E5
2.
D
Dsus2
E5

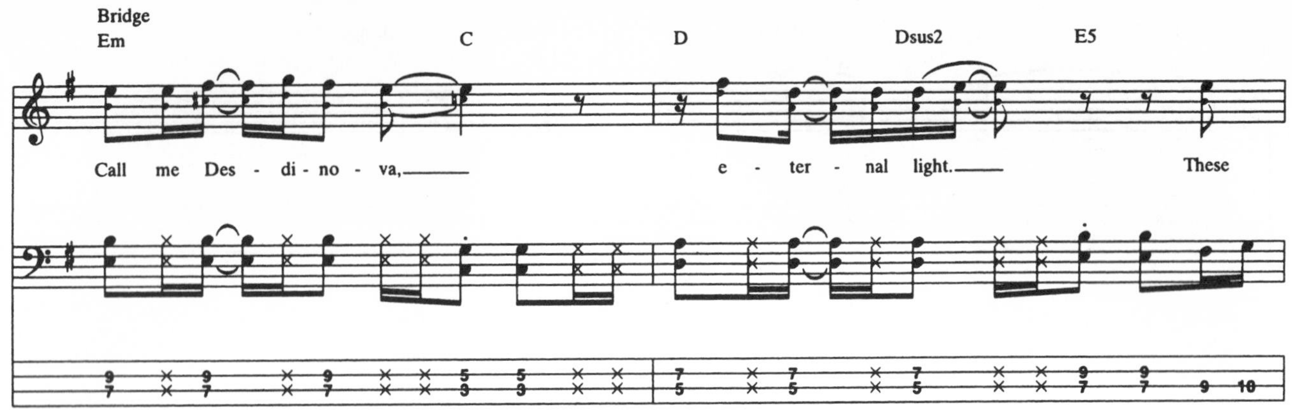
Bridge
Em
C
D
Dsus2
E5
Call me Des - di - no - va,
e - ter - nal light.
These

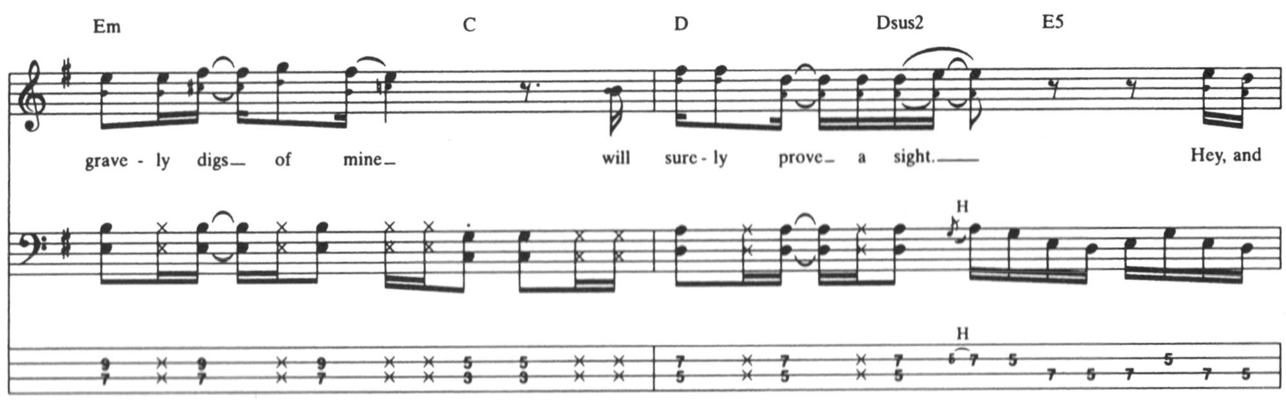
Em
C
D
Dsus2
E5
grave - ly digs of mine
will sure - ly prove a sight.
Hey, and
H
H

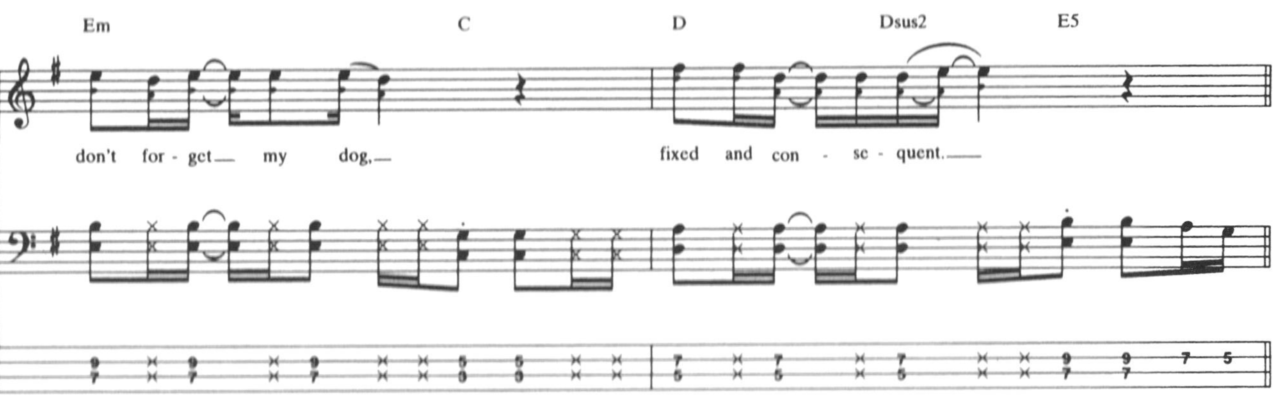
Em
C
D
Dsus2
E5
don't for - get my dog,
fixed and con - se - quent.

Interlude
N.C.(Em)
(C)
(Em)
(C/G)
sl.
P
H

Double time feel
Chorus/Outro solo

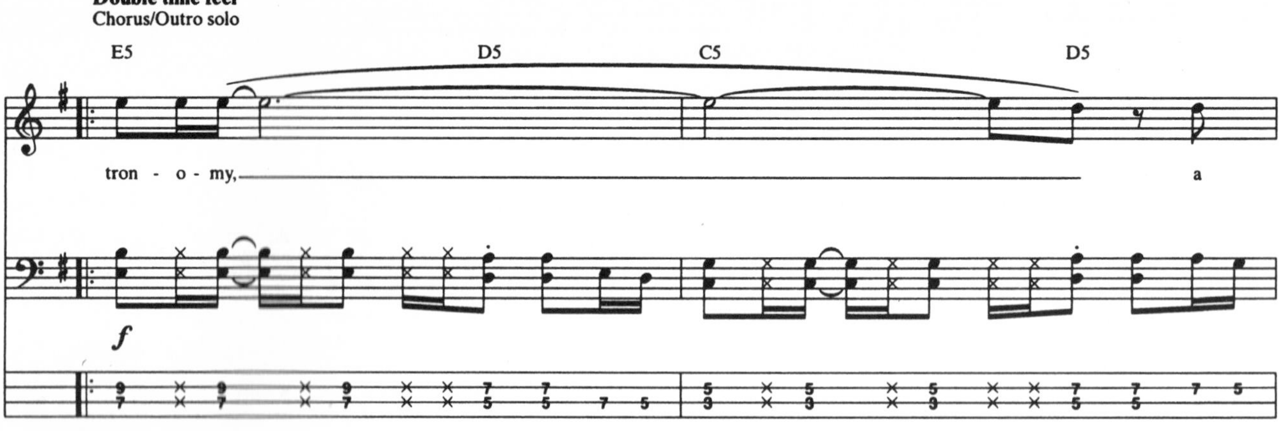

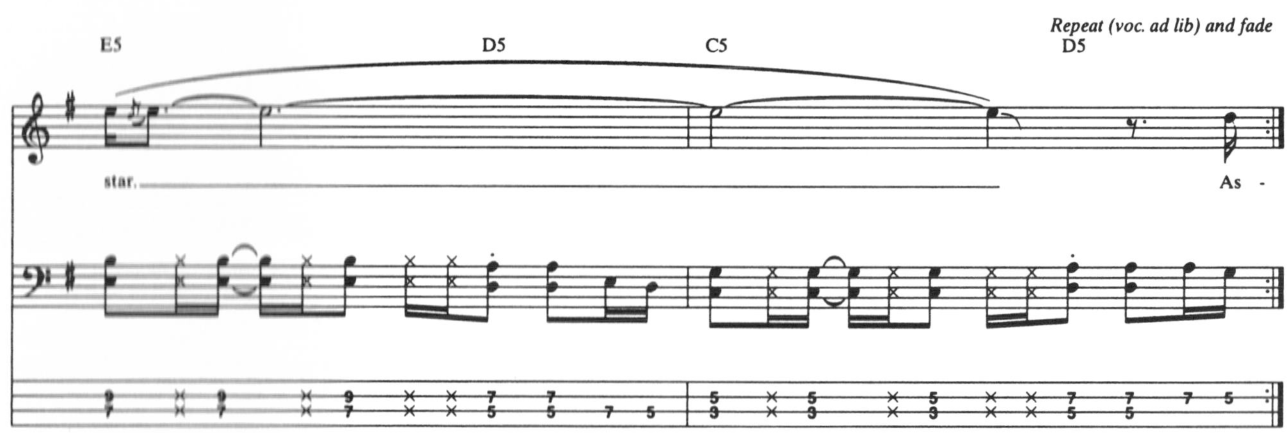

Back in the U.S.S.R.

Words and Music by John Lennon and Paul McCartney

2nd time, Bass: w/ Bass Fill 1
D6
C6
D6
on my knee. Man, I had a dread-ful flight.
pack my case. Hon - ey, dis-con-nect the phone.
I'm back in the U. S. S. R.,
Chorus
A6
C6
D6
you don't know how luck-y you are, boy.
1.
D7
A6
A
E7
Back in the U. S. S. R.
2.
E5
Emadd9
Back in the U. S.,
back in the U. S., back in the U. S. S. R.
A6
A7
Well, the
(Da, da, da.

Bridge
D
A7
U - kraine girls real - ly knock me out, they leave the west be - hind. And
Ooh. Da, da, da,
D
D♭
C
B
E7
Mos - cow girls make me sing and shout, that Geor - gia's al - ways on my mi - mi -
Ooh.)
D7
To Coda
A
A
B
E7
mi - mi - mi - mi - mi - mi mind.
Oh, come on!
Bass Fig. 1
End Bass Fig. 1
Guitar Solo
A6
Bass Fig. 2
D6
C6
1.
D6
End Bass Fig. 2

2.
Chorus
D6
A6
C6
I'm back in the U. S. S. R., you don't know how luck-y you are,
D6
D
A6
D.S. al Coda
boys. Back in the U. S. S. R.
Coda
Verse
Bass: w/ Bass Fig. 1
Bass: w/ Bass Fig. 1½ times)
A
B E7
A6
D6
3. Oh, show me 'round your snow peaked moun-tains way down south, take
C6
D6
A6
D6
me to your dad-dy's farm. Let me hear your bal-a-lai-kas ring-ing out. Come
Chorus
C6
D6
A6
and keep your com-rade warm. I'm back in the U. S. S. R. Hey!

C6
D6
D
You don't know how luck - y you are,
boys.
Back in the U. S. S. R.
A6
B
E7
Outro
A6
Aw,
let me tell you hon - ey!
Hey, I'm back!
(Oo, oo, oo.
Oo, oo,
oo.
N.C.

Badge

Words and Music by Eric Clapton and George Harrison

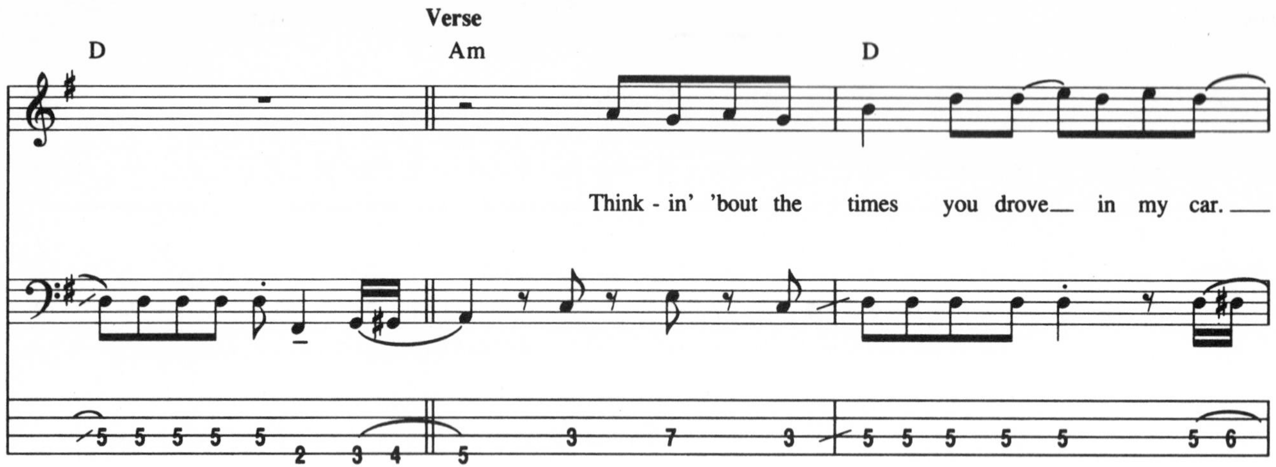

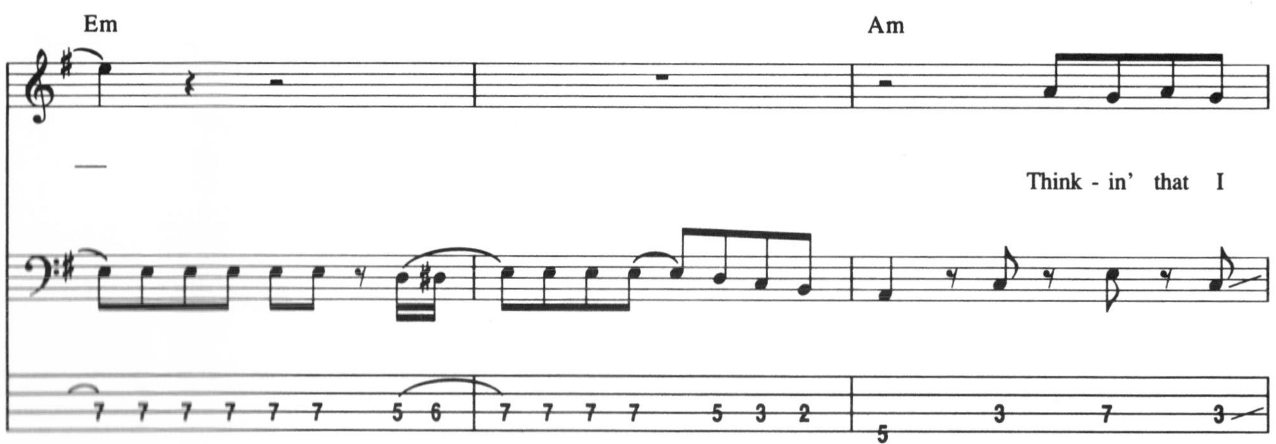

D
Em(add9)
Em
might have drove you too far.
C
Am
Bm
And I'm think-in' bout the love that you laid on my ta - ble.
Am(add9)
Second Verse
Am
I told you not to
D
Em(add9)
Em
wan - der 'round in the dark.

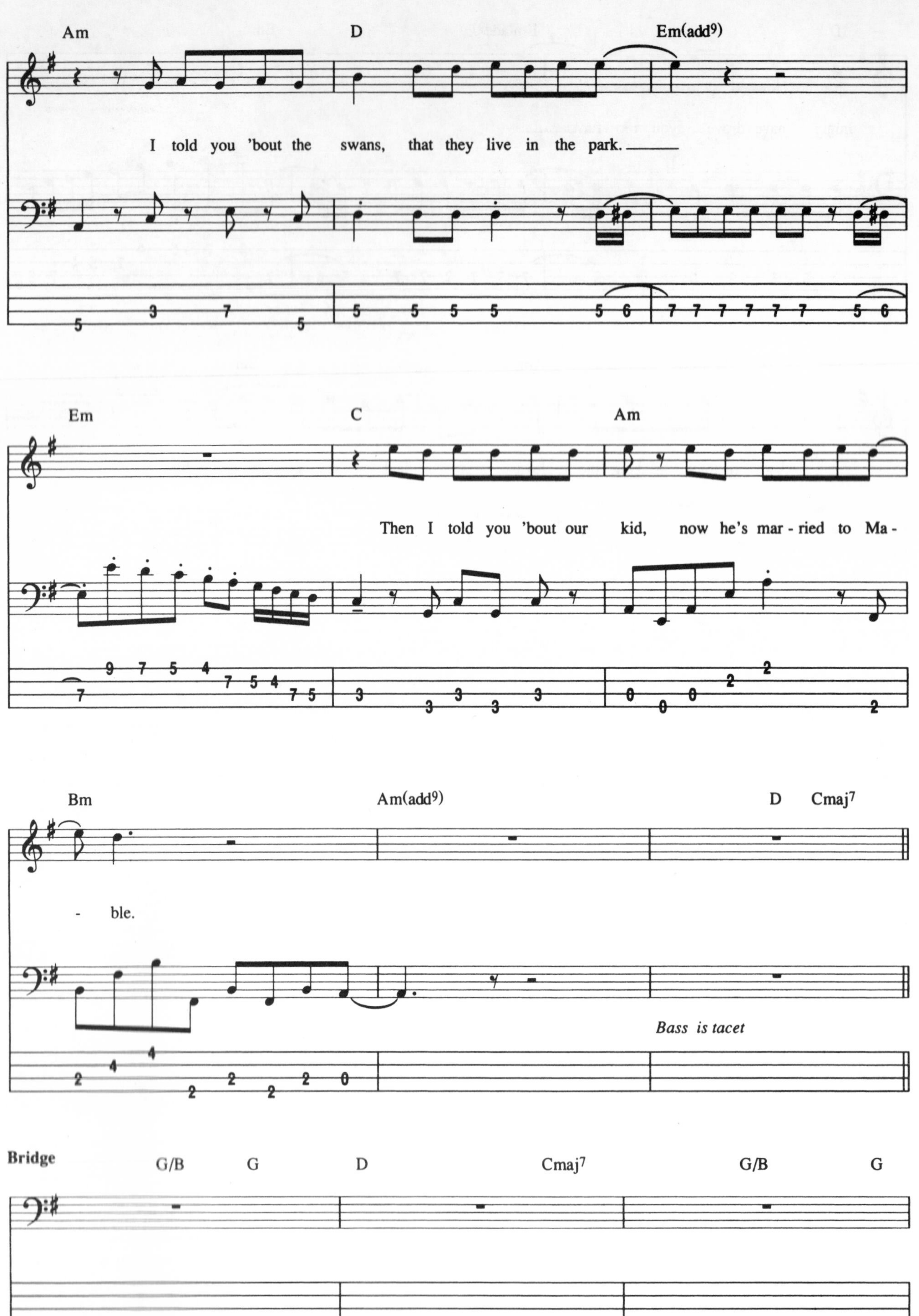
Am
D
Em(add9)
I told you 'bout the swans, that they live in the park.
Em
C
Am
Then I told you 'bout our kid, now he's mar - ried to Ma -
Bm
Am(add9)
D
Cmaj7
- ble.
Bass is tacet
Bridge
G/B
G
D
Cmaj7
G/B
G

D Cmaj7 G/B G D Cmaj7
Yes, I told you that the light goes up and down. Don't you no-
G/B G D Cmaj7 G/B G
- tice how the wheel goes 'round. And you bet - ter pick your - self up
D Cmaj7 G/B G D Cmaj7
from the ground be - fore they bring the cur - tain down. Yes, be - fore
G/B G D C Guitar Solo G/B G
they bring the cur - tain down.

D
Cmaj7
G/B
G
D
Cmaj7

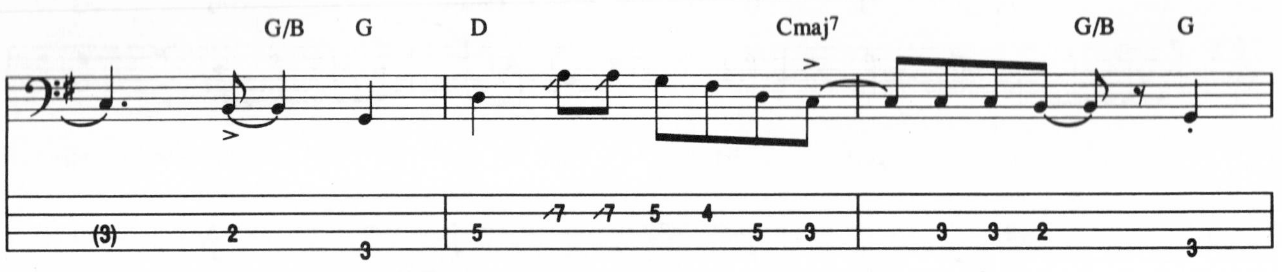
G/B
G
D
Cmaj7
G/B
G

D
Cmaj7
G/B
G
D
Cmaj7

G/B
G
D
Cmaj7

Third Verse
D
Am
D
Talk - in' 'bout a girl that looks quite like
Em(add9)
Am
you.
She did - n't have the
D
Em
time to wait in the queue.
C
Am
Bm
Am(add9)
Fine
She cried a - way her life since she fell off the cra - dle.

Barracuda

Words and Music by Roger Fisher, Nancy Wilson, Ann Wilson and Michael Derosier

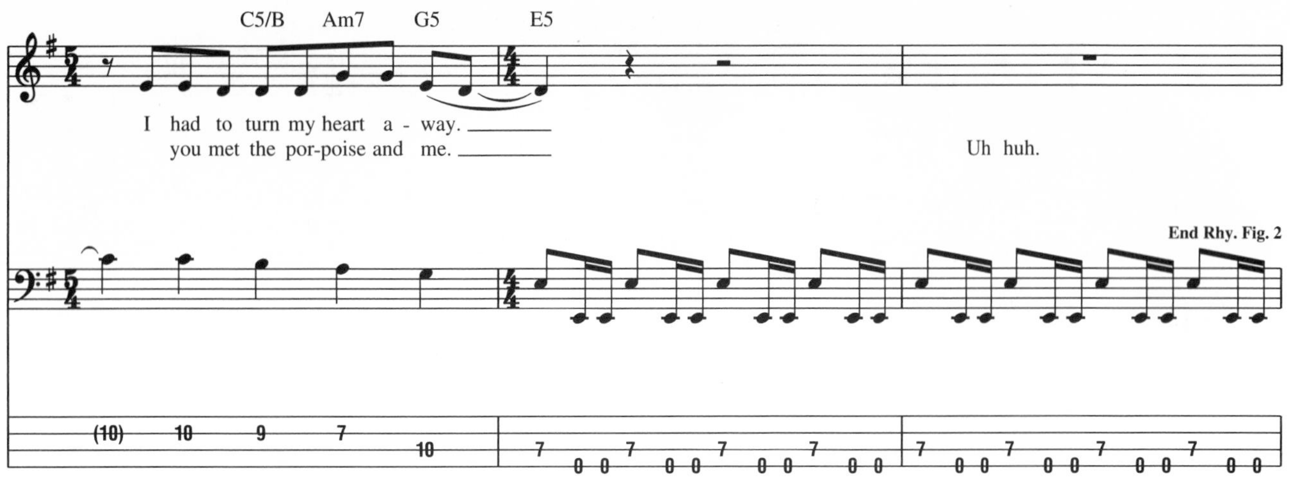
C5/B Am7 G5 E5
I had to turn my heart a - way.
you met the por-poise and me.
Uh huh.
End Rhy. Fig. 2
(10) 10 9 7 10
7 0 0 7 0 0 7 0 0 7 0 0
7 0 0 7 0 0 7 0 0 7 0 0

w/ Bass Fig. 2
E5
Csus2
Smile like the sun, kiss - es for ev - 'ry - one,
No right, no wrong; sell - ing a song, a name.

C5/B Am7 G5 E5
and tales that nev - er fail.
Whis - per game.
You ly - ing
And if the

Chorus
2nd time, w/ Bass Fill 1
To Coda
C5 C5/B N.C.(A5) E5 N.C.(C) (Am) E5
so low in - to the weeds. I bet you gon-na am - bush me. You'd have me
real thing don't do the trick, you bet-ter make up some-thing quick. You gon-na
10 9 7
7 7 7
8 10 7 10 8 7 5
7 7 7

Bass Fill 1
8 7 5
7 7 7

Dsus2
Asus2
down, down, down, down on my knees, now would-n't you, Bar-ra-cu-
12
(12) 14 12 14
12 14 14 12 14
12

w/ Bass Fig. 1
E5
F#5 G5
da?
Oh.

D.S. al Coda
E5
F#5 G5
G6
Coda
Dsus2
Asus2
burn, burn, burn, burn, burn it to the wick.

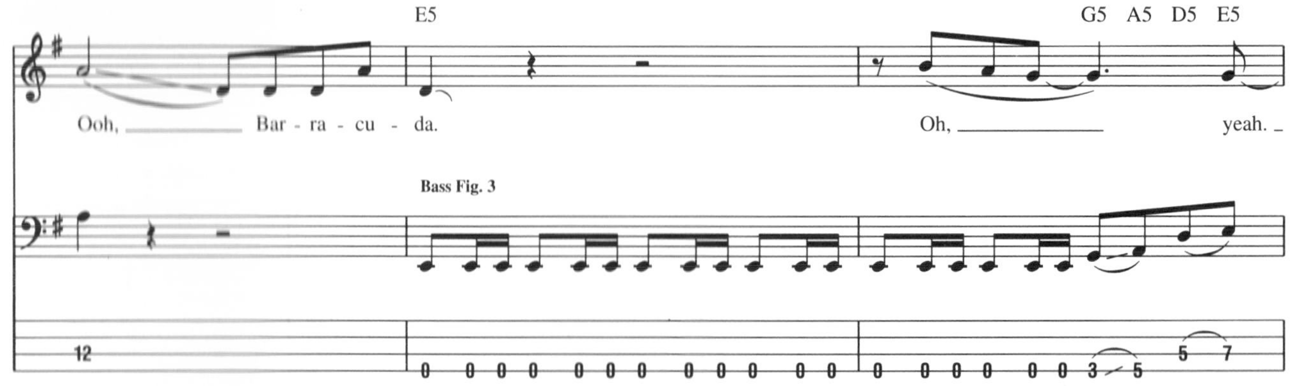
E5
G5 A5 D5 E5
Ooh, Bar-ra-cu-da. Oh, yeah.
Bass Fig. 3

Bridge
G5 A5 D5 E5 C
"Sell me, sell
End Bass Fig. 3
Bass Fig. 4
A
you," the por - poise said. Dive down, deep down, save my head. You,
End Bass Fig. 4
w/ Bass Fig. 3
E5
G5 A5 D5 E5
I think that you had the blues too.
G5 A5 D5 E5 C
w/ Bass Fig. 4
All that night
A
and all the next, swam with - out look - ing back, made for , the west - ern
E5
F#5 G5 A5 E5
F#5 G5 A5
pools. Sil-ly, sil-ly fools.

Guitar Solo
C
A
10 9 7
10 8 10 8 7 8
5 7 9
7 9 10 9 7 9

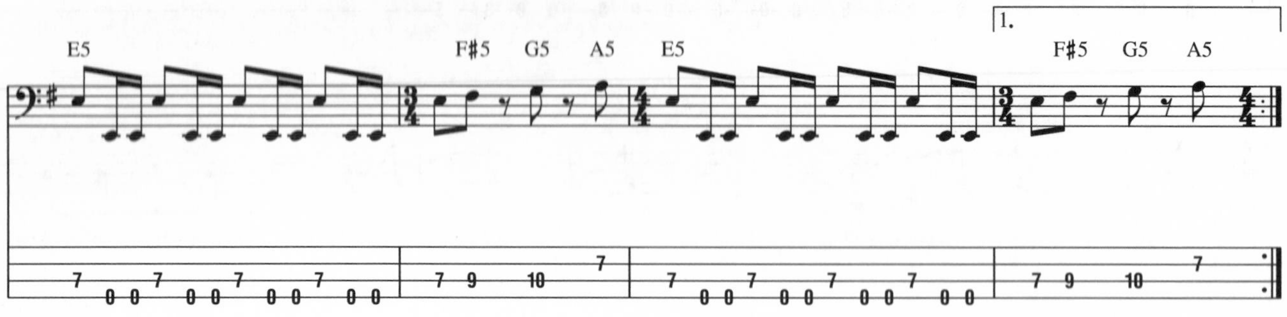
E5
F#5 G5 A5
E5
1.
F#5 G5 A5

2.
Chorus
F#5 G5 A5
C5 C5/B N.C.(A5) E5
The real thing don't do the trick, no, you bet - ter

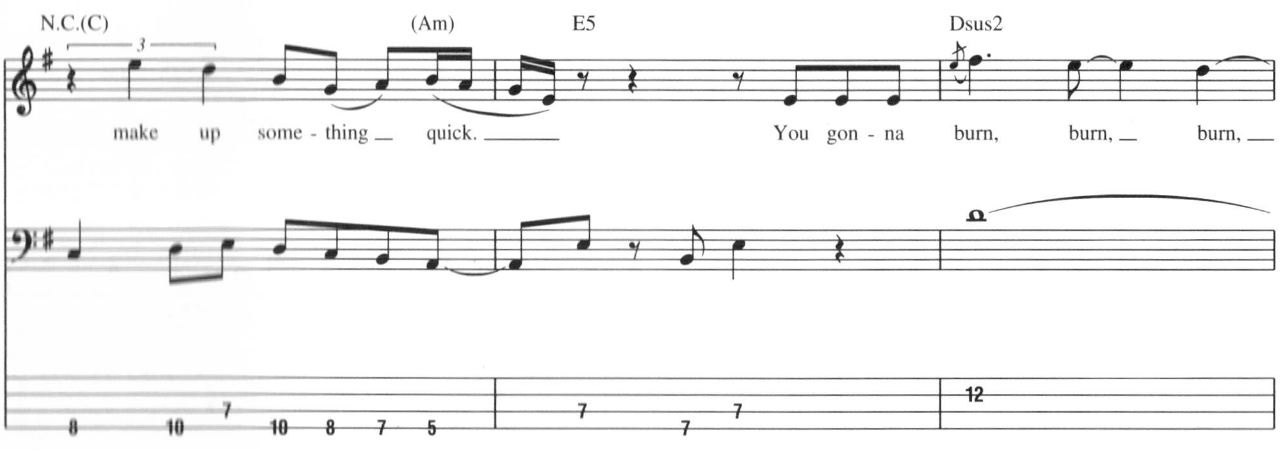
N.C.(C) (Am) E5 Dsus2
make up some - thing quick. You gon - na burn, burn, burn,

Asus2
burn, burn it to the wick.
E5
Oh, Bar - ra - bar - ra - cu - da. Yeah.
Outro
N.C.(Em)
Play 3 times

1.
2.
E5
1.-4.
F#5 G5 A5
5.
F#5 G5 A5

Birdland

Music by Josef Zawinul

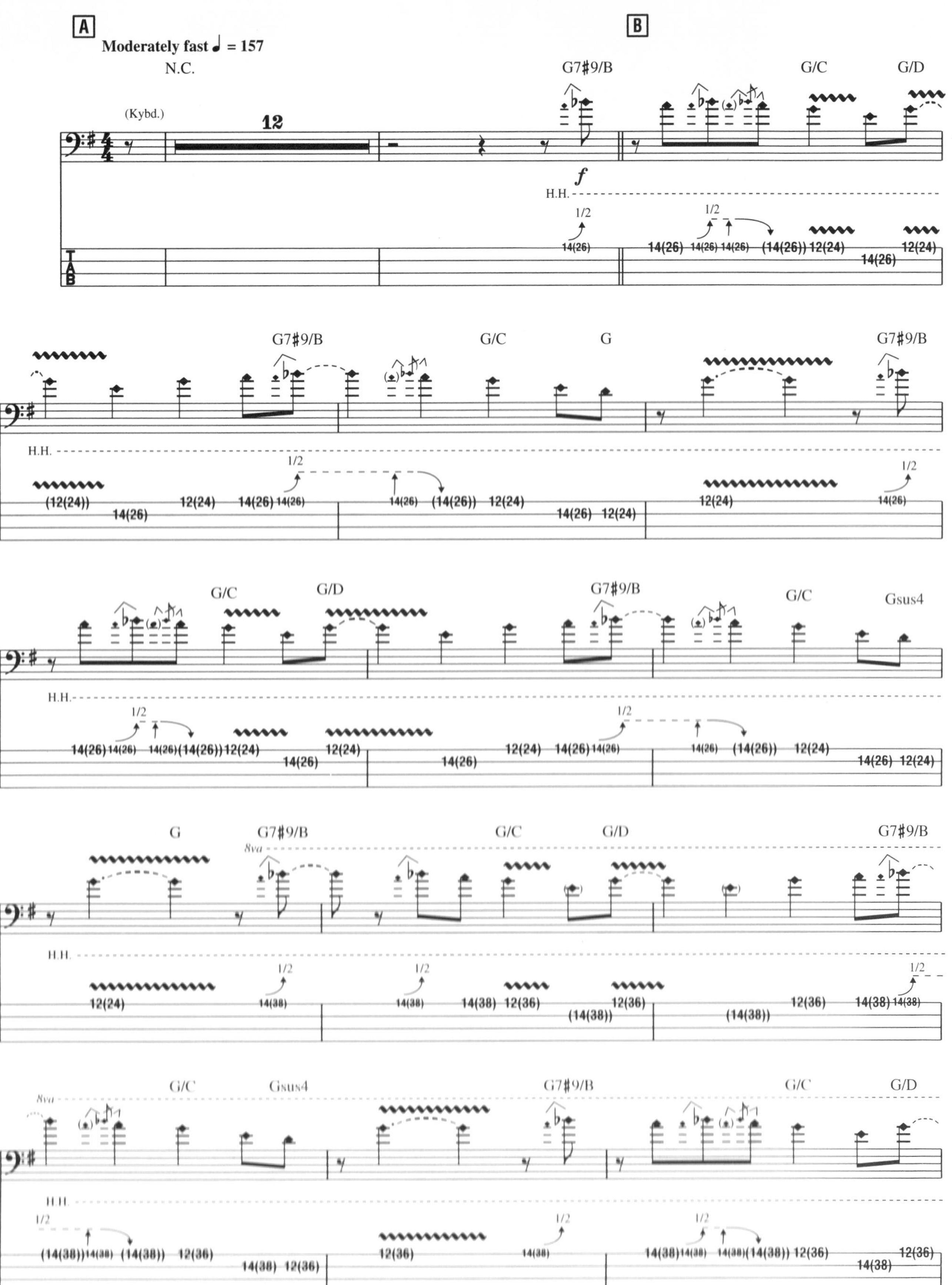

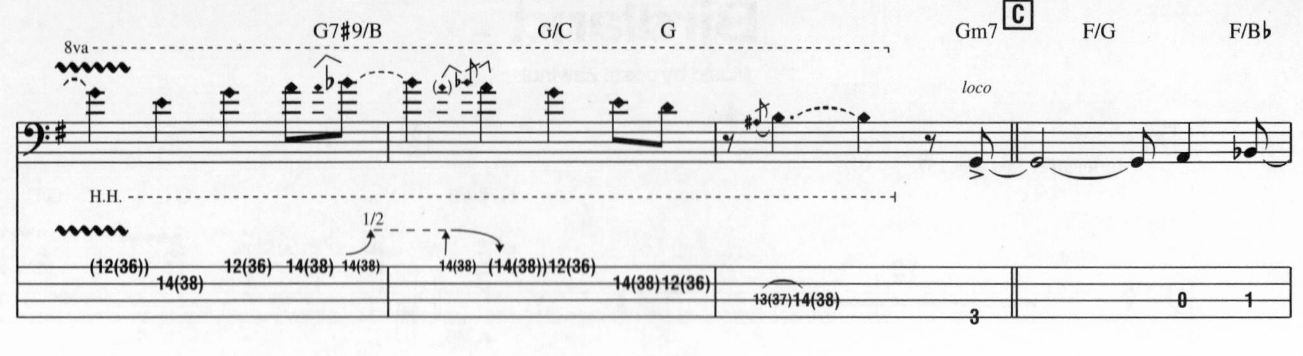
G7♯9/B
G/C
G
C
Gm7
F/G
F/B♭
8va
loco
H.H.
1/2
(12(36))
14(38)
12(36)
14(38)
14(38)
14(38)
(14(38))
12(36)
14(38)
12(36)
13(37)
14(38)
3
0
1

E♭/B♭
Dm7
Dm/G
F/C
Cm7
F/B
G6
Gm/C
F/E♭
(1)
1
3
0
3
0
3
0
1
2
0
2
0
3
0
1

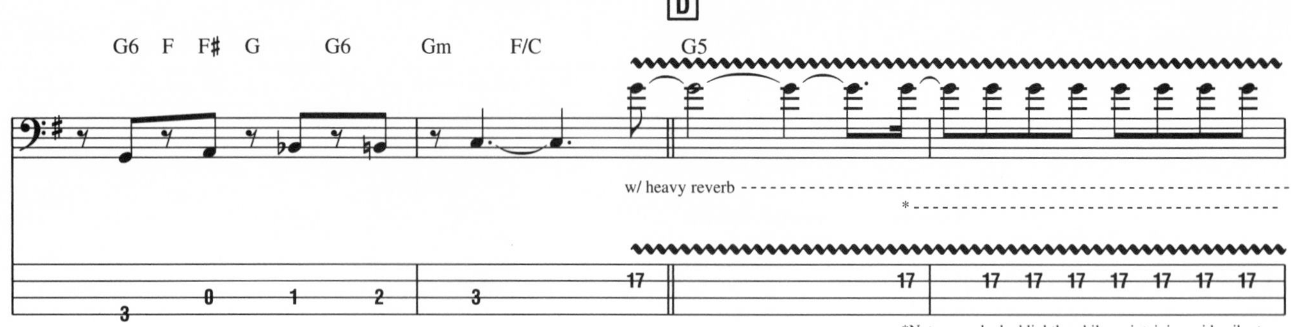
D
G6
F
F♯
G
G6
Gm
F/C
G5
w/ heavy reverb
3
0
1
2
3
17
17
17
17
17
17
17
17
17
*Notes are plucked lightly while maintaining wide vibrato.

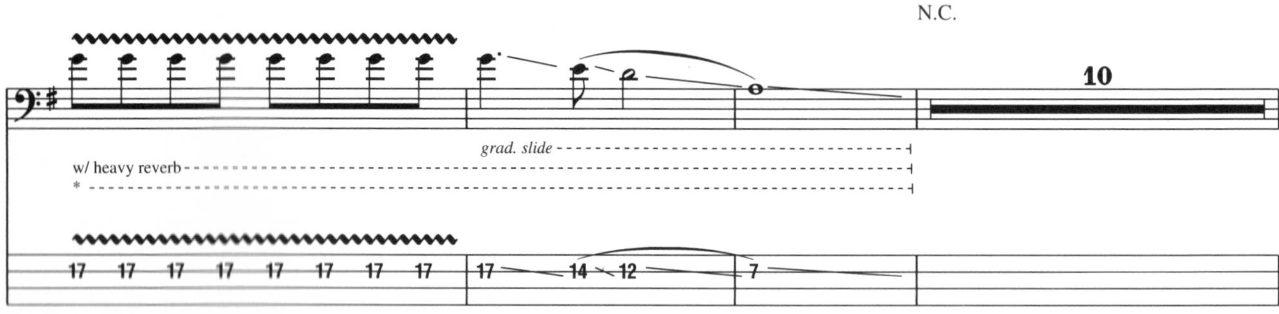
N.C.
10
grad. slide
w/ heavy reverb
17
17
17
17
17
17
17
17
17
14
12
7

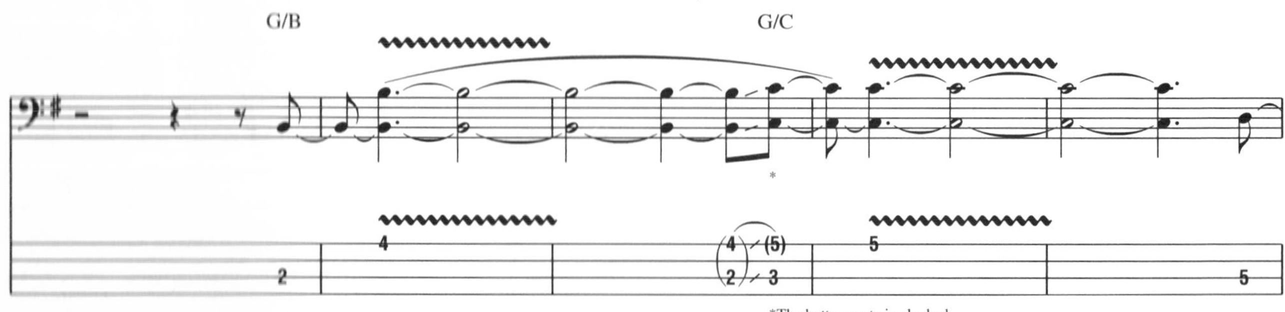
G/B
G/C
2
4
4
(5)
2
3
5
5
*The bottom note is plucked.

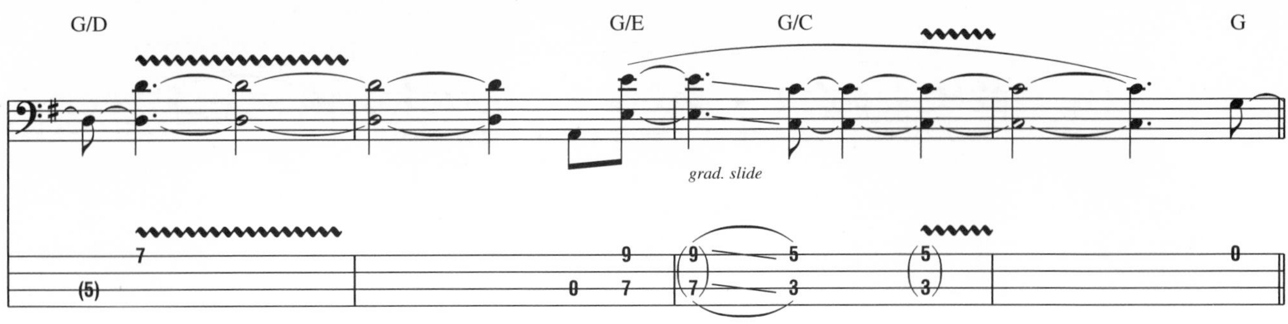
G/D
G/E
G/C
G
grad. slide

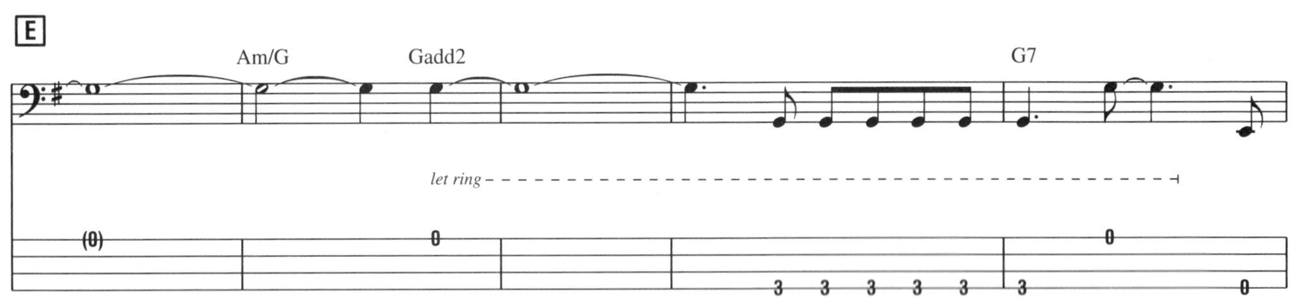
E
Am/G
Gadd2
G7
let ring

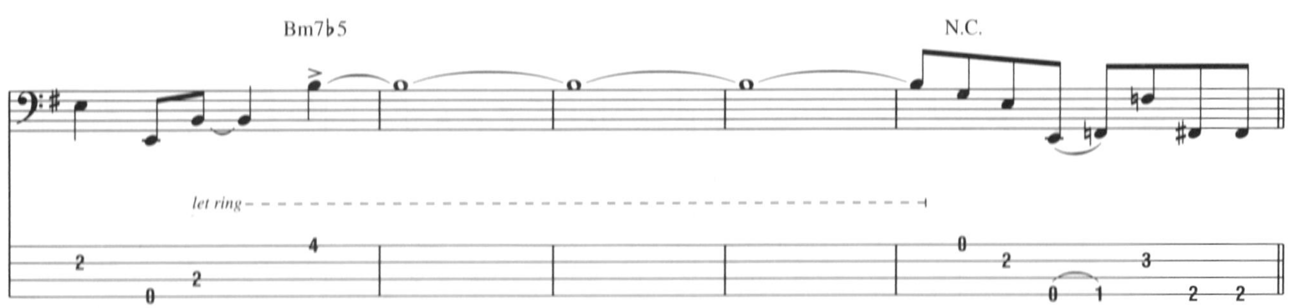
Bm7♭5
N.C.
let ring

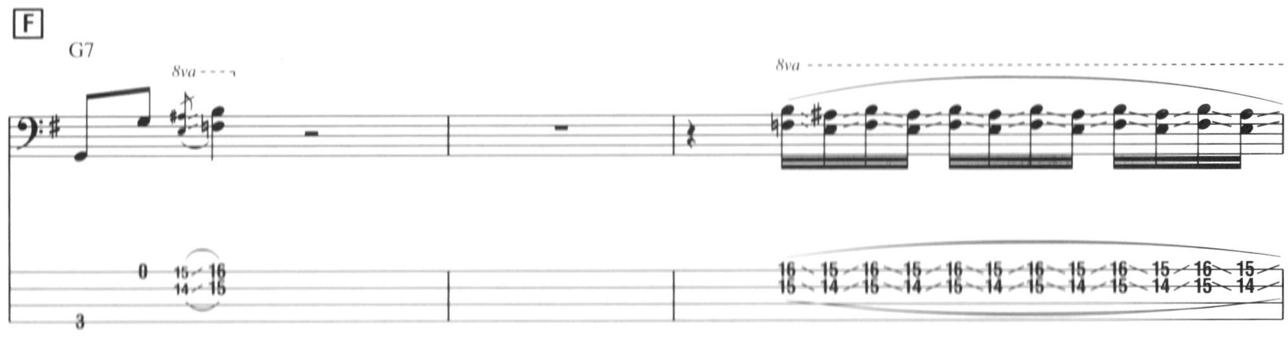
F
G7
8va

8va
loco

8va
G
loco
G
Bm Em G/B Cmaj7 C#m7b5 Bm7 Bm7/E Am7 C6 C/C# G
Bm Em C6 C#m7b5 C/D G/C C/D G
Bm Em G/B Cmaj7 C#m7b5 Bm7 E7b9 Am7 C6 C/C# G
Bm Em C6 C#m7b5 C/D G/C Em C/D G

Bm7 Em7 Em/D C♯m7♭5 C7 Bm7 E7♭9 Am7 C6 C/D G

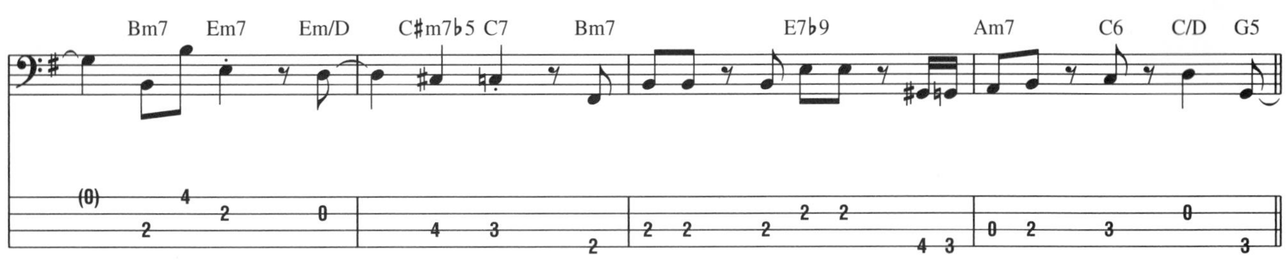
Bm7 Em7 Em/D C♯m7♭5 C7 Bm7 E7♭9 Am7 C6 C/D G5

H
Play 9 times
G7

I
F♯7 F7 E7 E♭7 D7 C♯7 G7 F♯7 F7 E7 E♭7 D7 C♯7 G7 F♯7 F7 E7

1., 2., 3.
4.
E♭7 D7 C♯7 G7 F♯7 F7 E7 E♭7 D7 C♯7 G7 E♭7 D7 C♯7 C7 G7
let ring

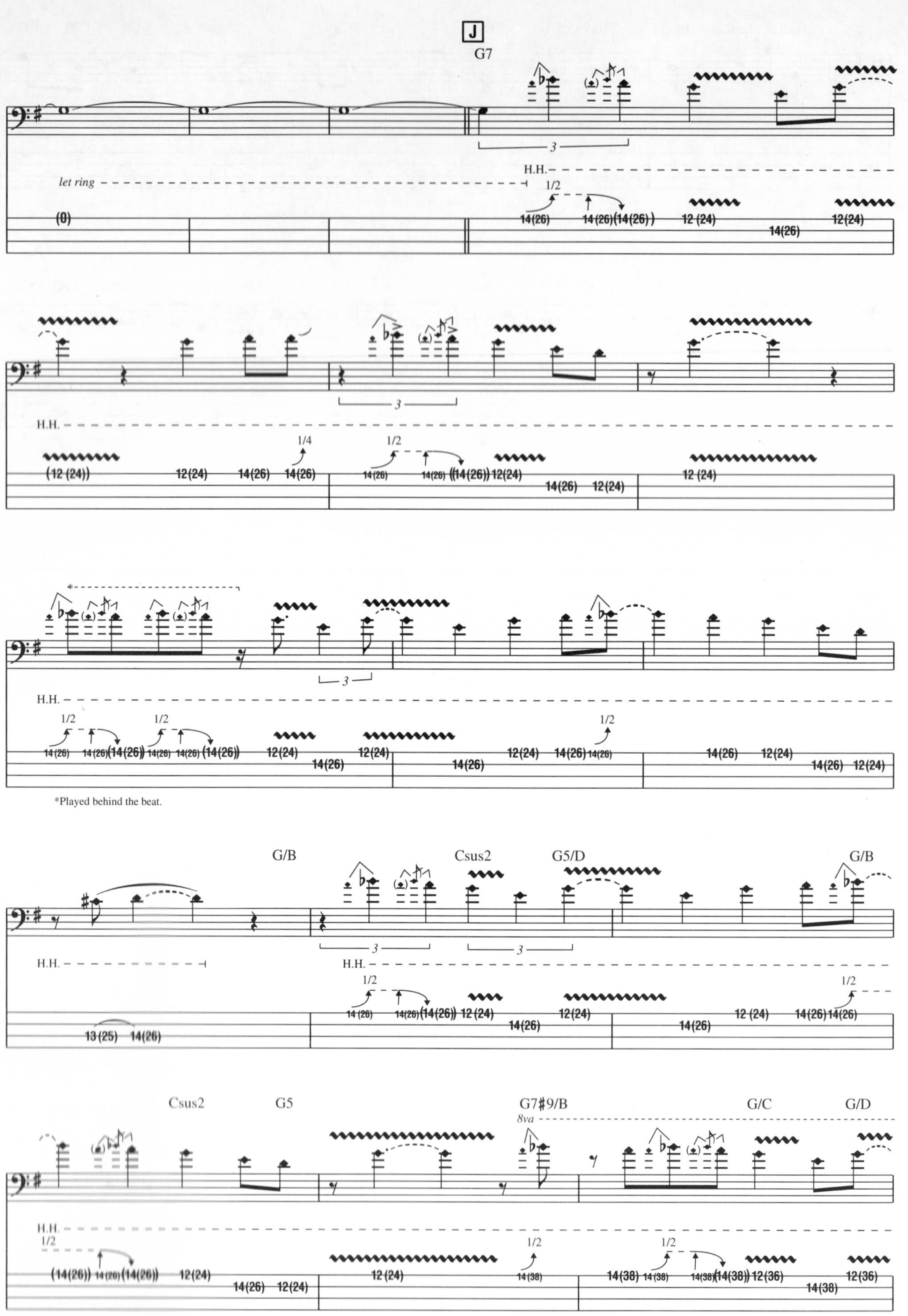

*Played behind the beat.

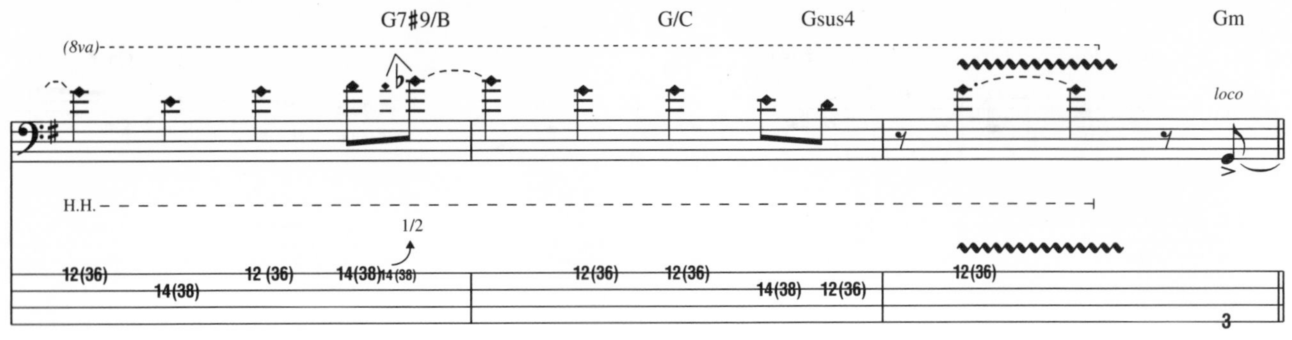
G7#9/B
G/C
Gsus4
Gm
(8va)
loco
H.H.
1/2
12(36)
14(38)
12 (36)
14(38)14(38)
12(36)
12(36)
14(38)
12(36)
12(36)
3

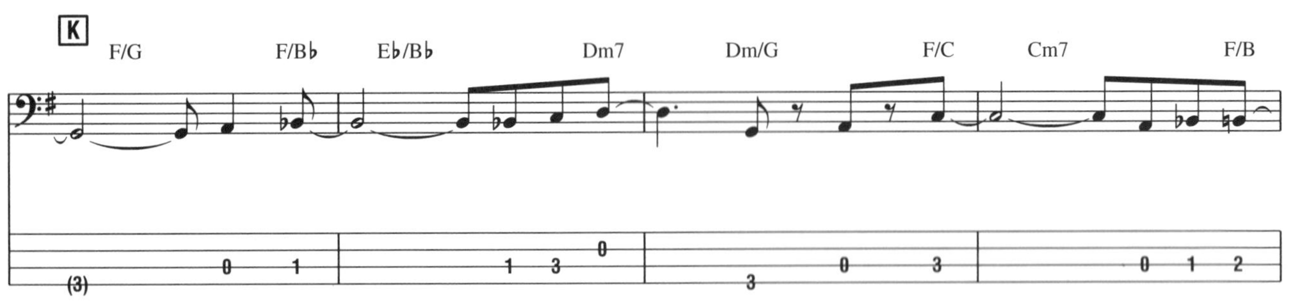
K
F/G
F/B♭
E♭/B♭
Dm7
Dm/G
F/C
Cm7
F/B
(3)
0 1
1 3 0
3 0 3
0 1 2

G6
Gm/C
F/E♭
G6
F
F♯
G
G6
Gm
F/C
G
(2) 0 2 0 3
0 1
3 0 1 2
3 3

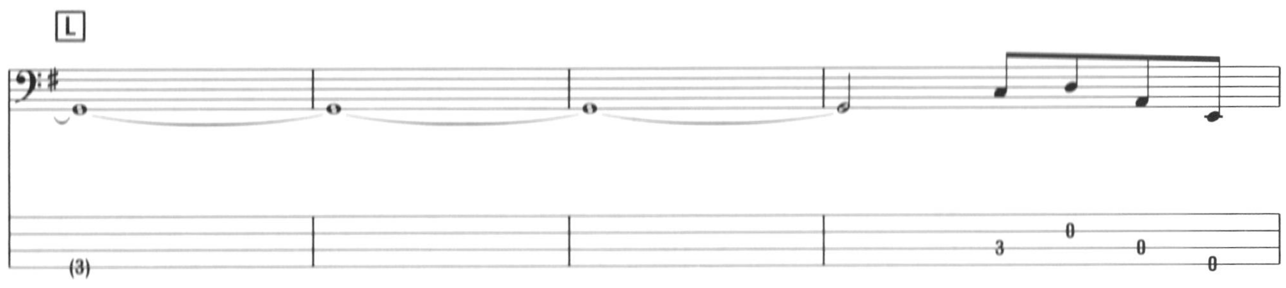
L
(3)
3 0 0 0

G/B
C5
G
let ring
let ring
2 4
0 5 5 3
5
3 0 0 0

M
Bm Em G/B Cmaj7 C♯m7♭5 Bm7 Em7 Am7 C6 C/C♯ G

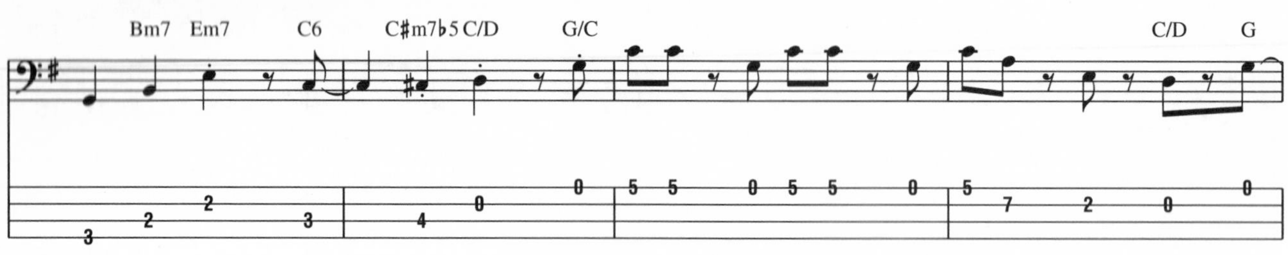
Bm7 Em7 C6 C♯m7♭5 C/D G/C C/D G

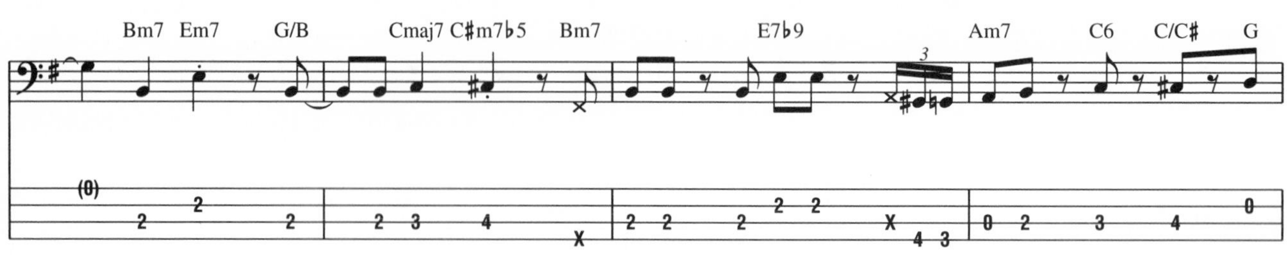
Bm7 Em7 G/B Cmaj7 C♯m7♭5 Bm7 E7♭9 Am7 C6 C/C♯ G

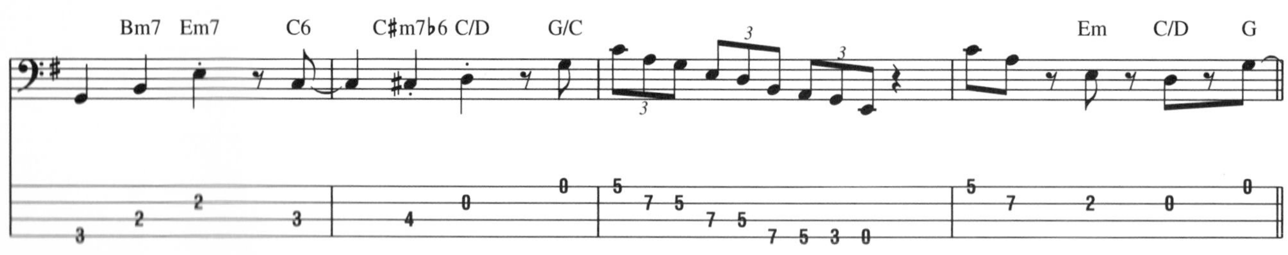
Bm7 Em7 C6 C♯m7♭6 C/D G/C Em C/D G

Bm7 Em7 Em/D C♯m7♭5 C7 B7 E7♯9 Am7 C6 C/D G

Bm7 Em7 Em/D C#m7#5 C7 Bm7 E7b9 Am7 C6 C/D G

Bm7 Em7 Em/D C#m7b5 C7 Bm7 E7b9 Am7 C6 C/D G

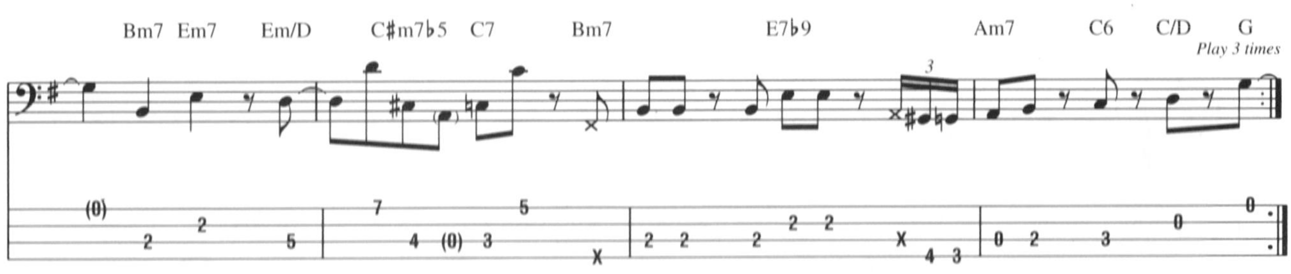
Bm7 Em7 Em/D C#m7b5 C7 Bm7 E7b9 Am7 C6 C/D G
Play 3 times

Bm7 Em7 Em/D C#m7b5 C7 Bm7 E7b9 Am7 C6 C/D G

Begin fade
Fade out
Bm7 Em7 Em/D C#m7b5 C7 Bm7 E7b9 Am7 C6 C/D G

Blue on Black

Words and Music by Tia Sillers, Mark Selby and Kenny Wayne Shepherd

Bass: w/ Bass Fig. 2, 4 times
D5 Csus2 D5 Csus2 D5 N.C. Cadd9 G/B G D5 Csus2 D5 Csus2 D5 N.C. Cadd9 G/B G
You turned and you ran, oh, yeah, oh,
Wrong can't be un - done. Oh,
D5 Csus2 D5 Csus2 D5 N.C. Cadd9 G/B G D5 Csus2 D5 Csus2 D5 N.C. Cadd9 G/B G
slipped right from my hand.
slipped from the tip of your tongue.
Hey,
Chorus
D5 Csus2 D5 Csus2 D5 N.C. Cadd9 G/B G
blue on black, tears on a riv - er, push on a shove, it don't mean much.
Bass
Jok - er on Jack, match on a fire, cold on ice, a dead man's touch.
N.C.
Whis - per on a scream does - n't change a thing. 1., 3. don't 2., 4. does - n't bring you

1.
To Coda 1
To Coda 2
A5
G
D5
Csus2
D5
Csus2
D5
N.C.
back.
Blue on
black.
Oh,

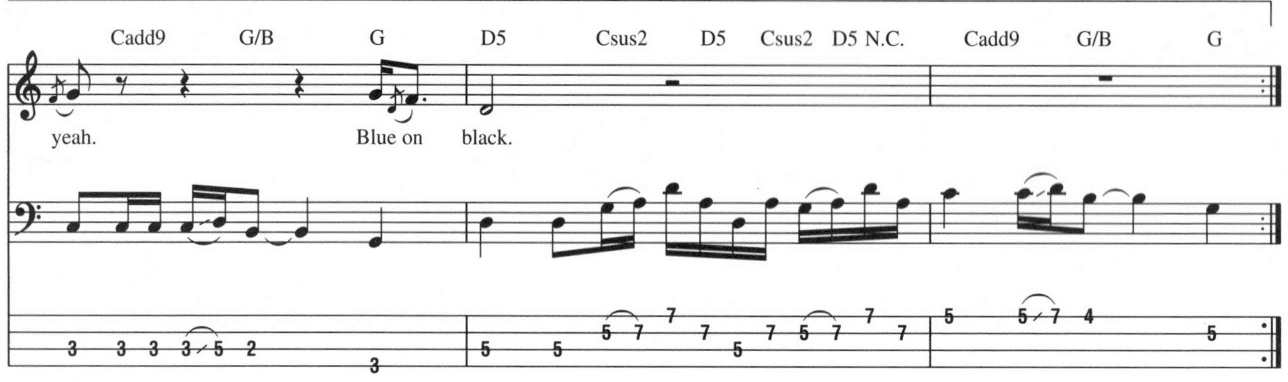
Cadd9
G/B
G
D5
Csus2
D5
Csus2
D5 N.C.
Cadd9
G/B
G
yeah.
Blue on
black.

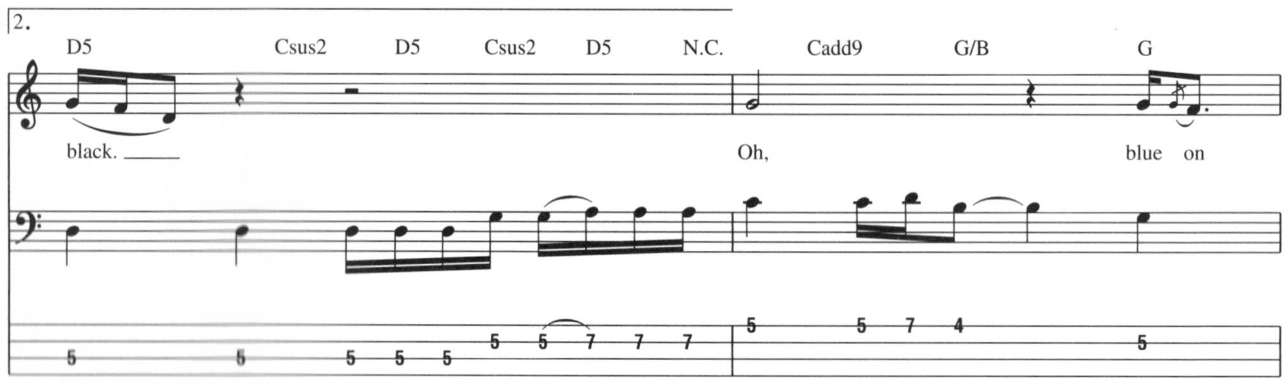
2.
D5
Csus2
D5
Csus2
D5
N.C.
Cadd9
G/B
G
black.
Oh,
blue on

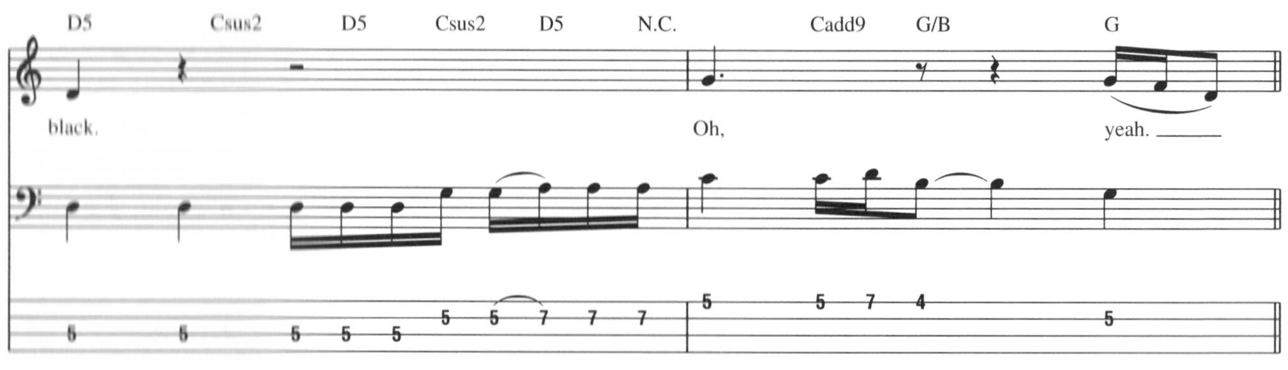
D5
Csus2
D5
Csus2
D5
N.C.
Cadd9
G/B
G
black.
Oh,
yeah.

Guitar Solo
D5
Csus2
D5
Csus2
D5
N.C.
Cadd9
G/B
G
play 6 times
F
G
F
G
D.S. al Coda 1
Coda 1
D5
Csus2
D5
Csus2
D5
N.C.
Cadd9
G/B
G
black.
Oh,
yeah.
Blue on
D.S. al Coda 2
D5
Csus2
D5
Csus2 D5
N.C.
Cadd9
G/B
G
black.
Hey,
1., 2., 3.
4.
Coda 2
D5
Csus2
D5
Csus2 D5
N.C.
Cadd9
G/B
G
black.
Oh,
blue on

Blue Suede Shoes

Words and Music by Carl Lee Perkins

To Coda
A
Tacet
A
Tacet
A
Well you can 2. knock me down
Well it's 3. burn my house
Step on my face
Steal my car
Tacet
A
Tacet
A
Tacet
A
Slan-der my name all
Drink my li-qour from an
o-ver the place
old fruit jar
And do an-y-thing that you
Tacet
A
Tacet
A
wan-na do
But uh uh ho-ney lay off
of my shoes And don't
(them)
D7
A
you step on my Blue Suede Shoes
You can

E9
A
do an-y-thing_ but lay off__ of my Blue__ Suede Shoes
1.
A
D9
A
E7
A
Well you can

2.
A

D9

A
E7

A

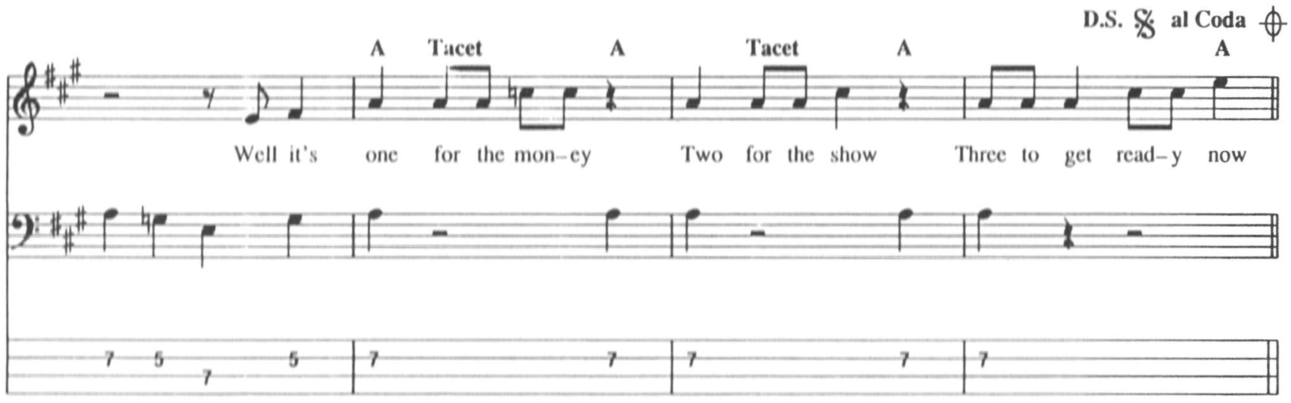
D.S. % al Coda ⊕
A Tacet A Tacet A A
Well it's one for the mon–ey Two for the show Three to get read–y now

Coda
A
Blue Blue Blue Suede Shoes Blue Blue
7 6 9 6 7 5 7 5 7 6 9 6
D7
Blue Suede Shoes Yeah Blue Blue Blue Suede Shoes Ba - by
7 5 4 7 5 4 7 4 5 4 5 6
A
E7
3
Blue Blue Blue Suede Shoes You could do an - y - thing but lay off
7 6 9 6 7 5 4 8 7 6 7 6
A
A6
of my Blue Suede Shoes
7 6 9 6 7 6 9 6 7 7

Bodhisattva

Words and Music by Walter Becker and Donald Fagen

2nd time to Coda I;
3rd time to Coda II
F♯maj7
F6
G
...Bo-dhi - satt - va, Bo-dhi - satt - va?
(2nd, 4th Verses)
I'm gon-na sell my house in town...
C
G
E♭maj7
A7♯5
Dm7
F6
E♭maj7
F6
4th time to Coda III
G
D.S. al Coda I
Coda I

C
G
Ebmaj7
A7♯5
Dm7
F6/Bb
Ebmaj7
F6
G
D.S. al Coda II
Coda II
G
C
G
Ebmaj7
A7♯5
Dm7
F6/Bb
Ebmaj7
F6

Play 12 times
D.S. al Coda III
G5 F5 G5 F5 G5 F5 G5
Bo-dhi-
Coda III
G
Ebmaj7
A7#5 Dm7 Bbmaj7 Ebmaj7 A7#5
Dm7 Bbmaj7
Play 3 times
Ebmaj7 A7#5
Dm7 Bbmaj7
Play 8 times
Eb5 F5
Free time
G5
sl.

Bombtrack

Written and Arranged by Rage Against The Machine

Verse
N.C.(F#5)
bomb - track. And suck-as be think-in' that they can fake this. But I'm - a drop it at a high-er lev - el. 'Cause I'm in -
Bass Fig. 2
1/4
clined to stoop down, hand out some beat - downs. Cold run - na train on punk ho's that think they run the game.
1/4
But I learned to burn that bridge and de-lete those who com-pete at a le-vel that's ob - so-lete. In -
1/4
stead I warm my hands up - on the flames of the flag, as I re - call our down-fall and the bus'-ness-es that burned us all.
End Bass Fig. 2
1/4

2. See through the news and the views . that twist re - al - i - ty. E-nough, I call the bluff for man-i-fest des - ti - ny.
bomb-track start - ed as a sketch in my note - book. And now dope hooks make punks take an-oth - er look. My

Land-lords and pow - er whores, on my peo-ple they took turns. Dis-pute the suits I ig - nite and then watch 'em burn
thoughts ya hear, _ and ya be - gin to fear that ya cord will get pulled if you in-ter - fere with the

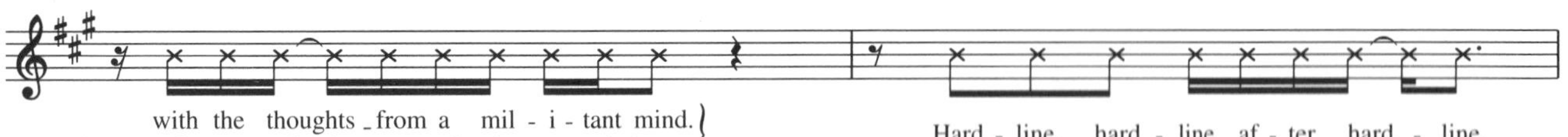

with the thoughts _ from a mil - i - tant mind.
thoughts from a mil - i - tant, mil - i - tant mind.
Hard - line, hard - line af - ter hard - line.

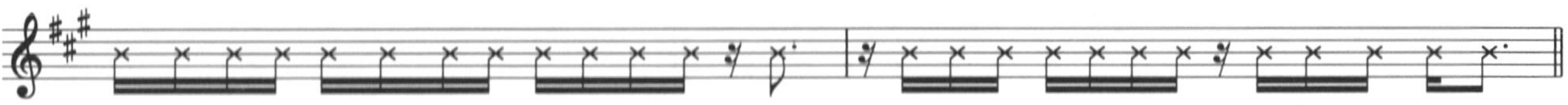

Land-lords and pow - er whores, on my peo-ple they took turns. Dis-pute the suits I ig - nite and then watch 'em burn.

Burn, burn, _ yes, you're gon-na burn. Burn, burn, _ yes, you're gon-na burn. Burn, burn, _ yes, you're gon-na burn.

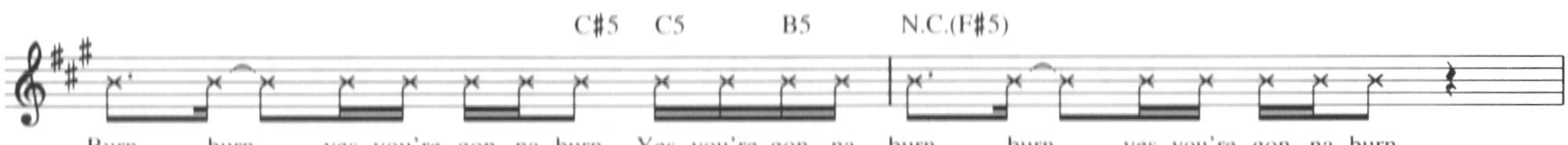

Burn, burn, _ yes, you're gon - na burn. Yes, you're gon - na burn, burn, _ yes, you're gon - na burn.

Burn, burn, _ yes, you're gon - na burn. Burn, burn, _ yes, you're gon - na burn.

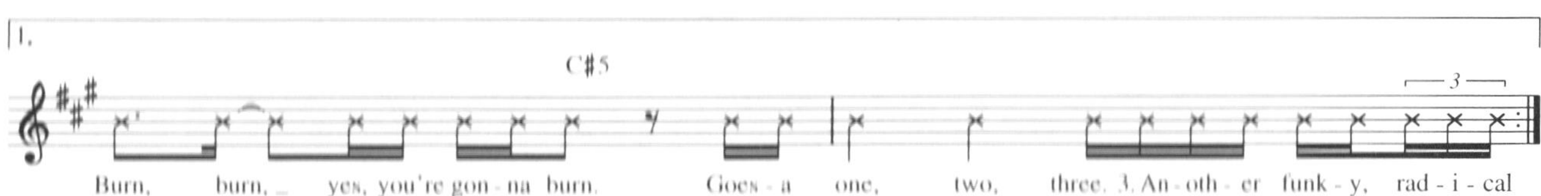

Burn, burn, _ yes, you're gon - na burn. Goes - a one, two, three. 3. An - oth - er funk - y, rad - i - cal

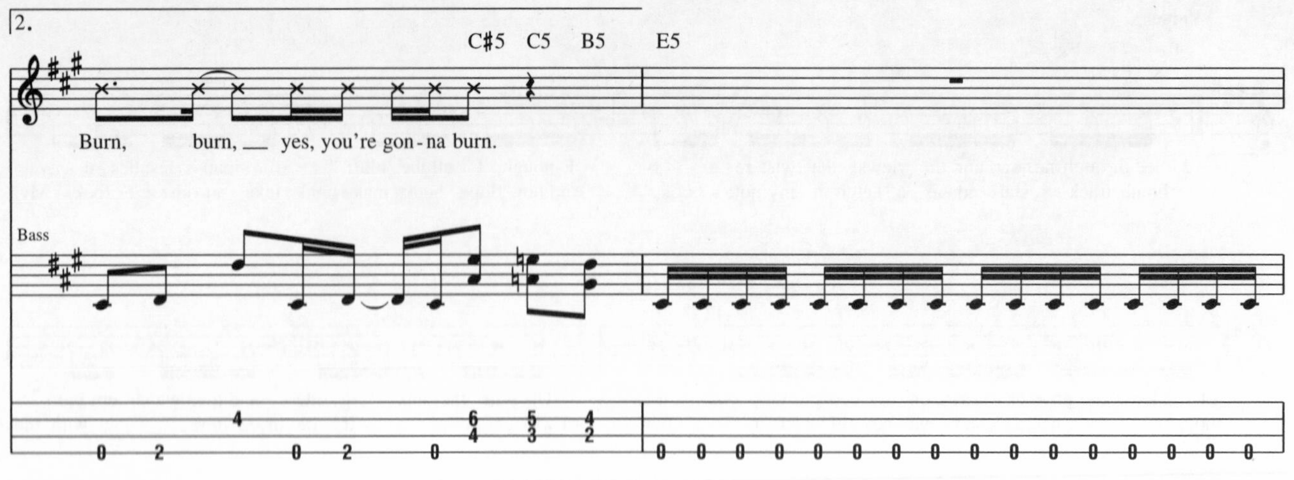
2.
C♯5 C5 B5 E5
Burn, burn, __ yes, you're gon - na burn.
Bass

w/ ad lib. Lead Voc.
N.C.(F♯5)
1/4

1., 2., 3.
4.
D.S. al Coda
1/4
1/4

Coda
C♯5 C5 B5 B5 B♭5 A5
Burn, burn, __ yes, you're gon - na burn. Burn.
Bass

Boom Boom (Out Go the Lights)

Words and Music by Stan Lewis

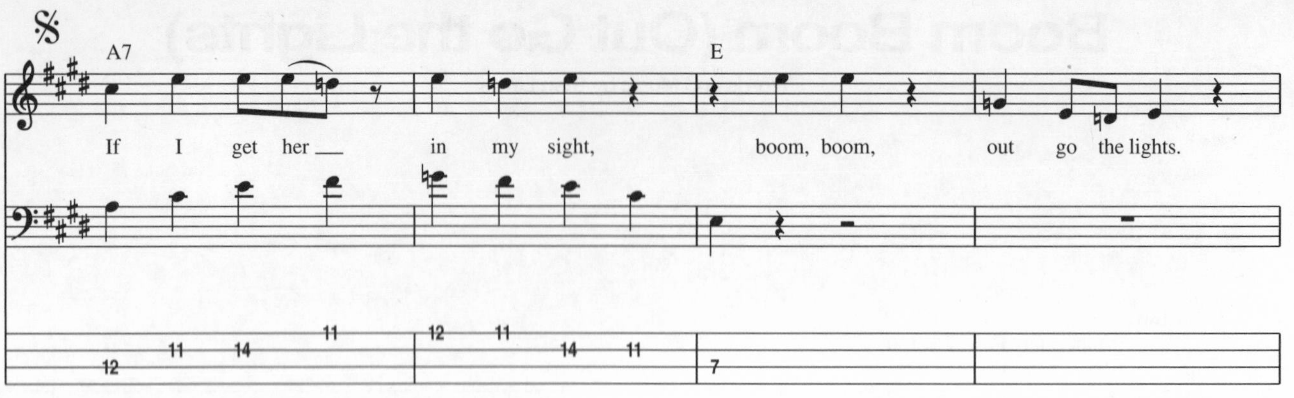
A7
E
If I get her in my sight,
boom, boom, out go the lights.

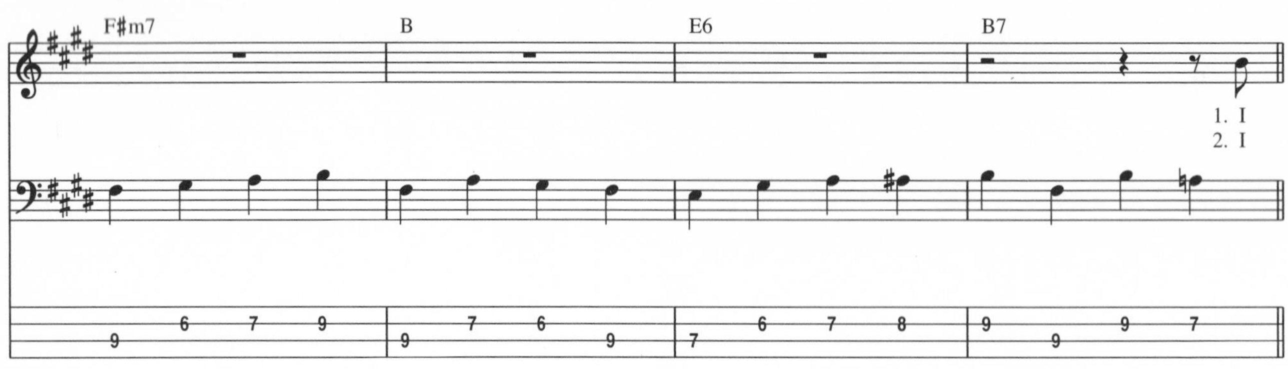
F#m7
B
E6
B7
1. I
2. I

Verse
E
thought I was treat-in' my ba - by fair, now she's get-ting all in my hair. And
nev - er been so mad be - fore, turned and found out she ain't mine no more.
simile on repeat

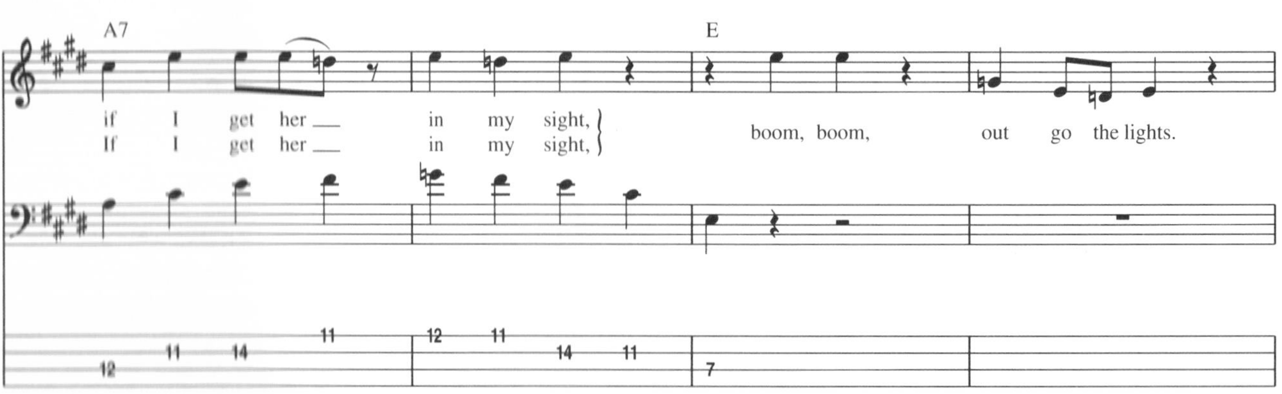
A7
E
if I get her in my sight,
If I get her in my sight,
boom, boom, out go the lights.

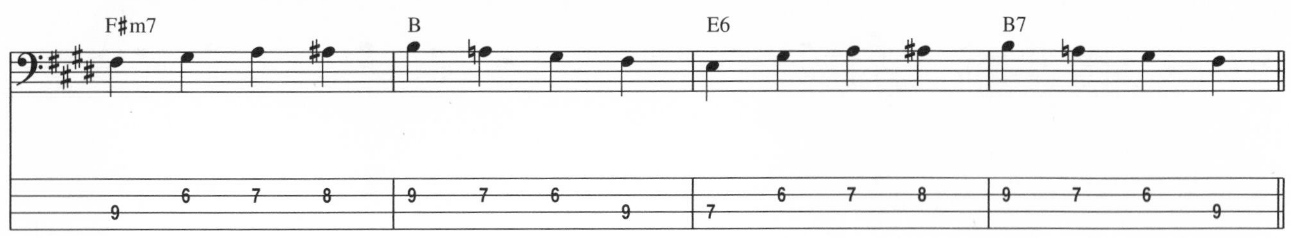
F#m7
B
E6
B7

Harmonica Solo
E
A7

To Coda
E
F#m7
B

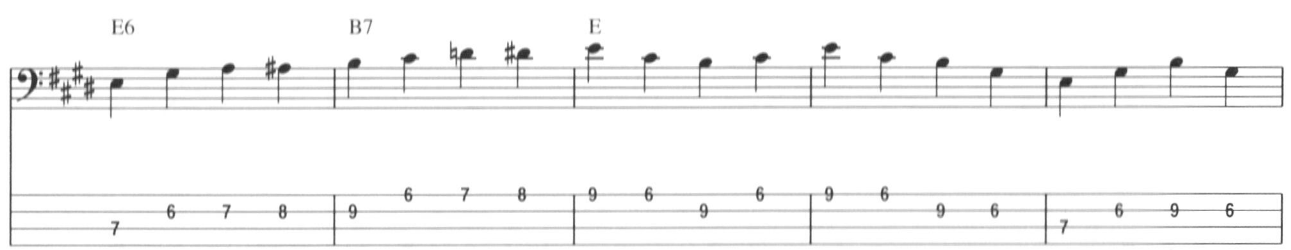
E6
B7
E

A7
E

F#m7
B
E6
B7

E
7
6
9
6
9
6
9
6
7
6
9
6
9
6
9
6

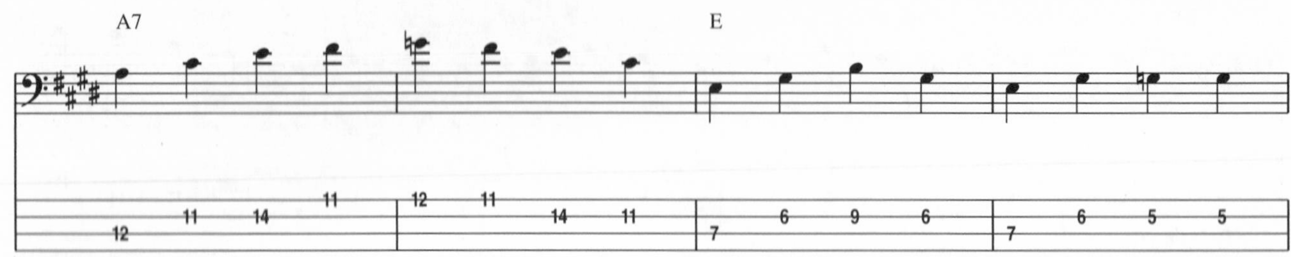
A7
E
12
11
14
11
12
11
14
11
7
6
9
6
7
6
5
5

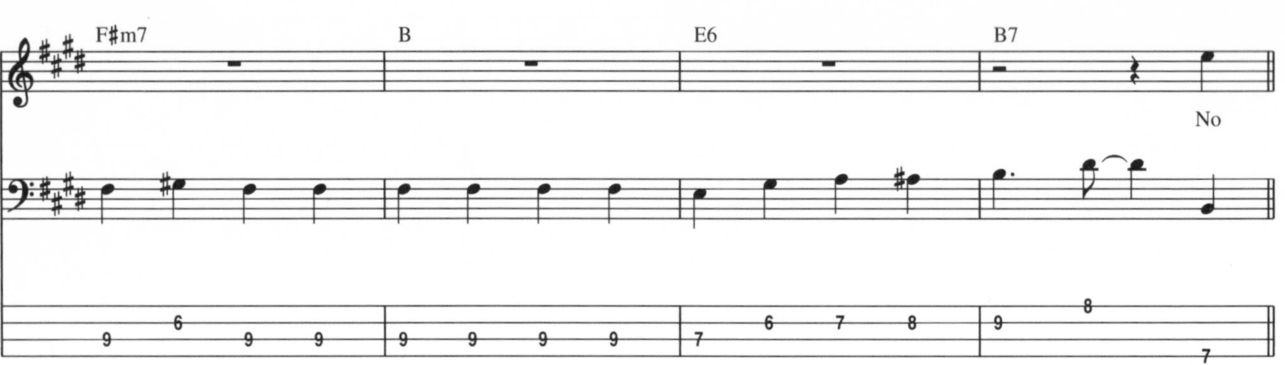
F♯m7
B
E6
B7
No

Chorus
E
D.S. al Coda
kid-ding, I'm read - y to go. And when I find her, boy don't you know.

Coda
Begin Fade
E
Fade Out

Breadfan

Words and Music by Anthony Bourge, John Burke Shelley and Raymond Phillips

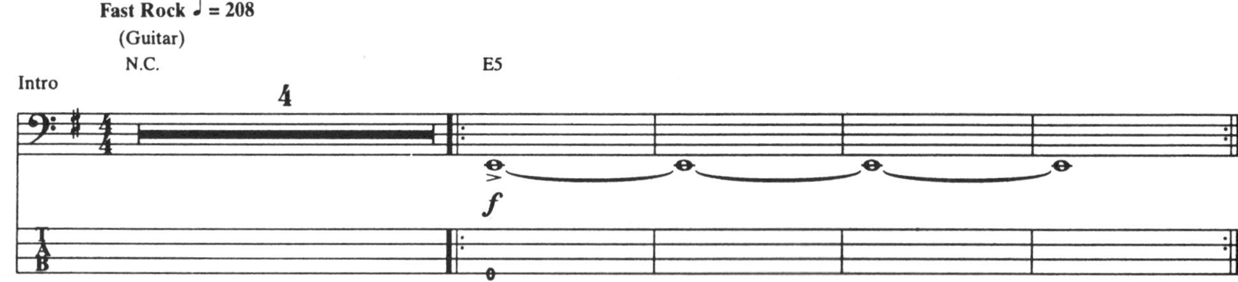

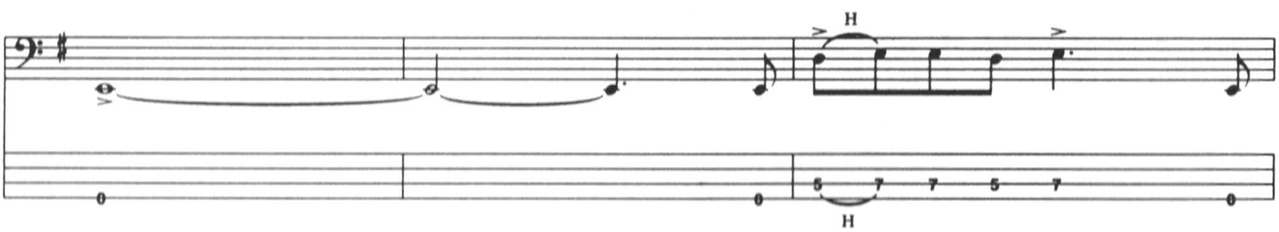

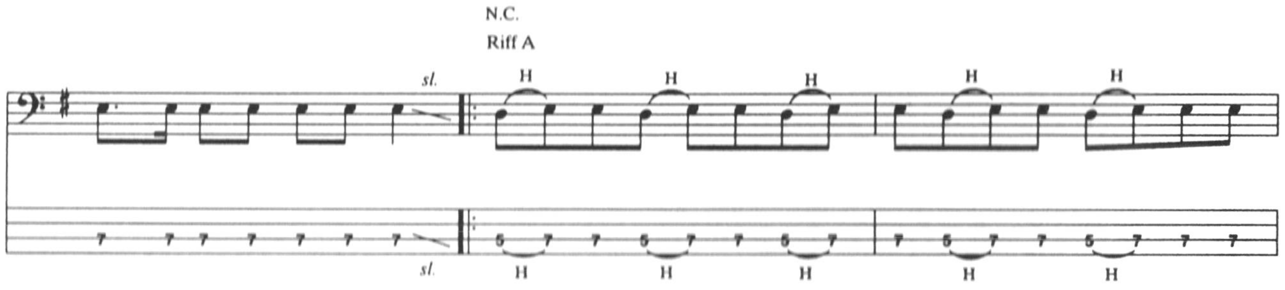

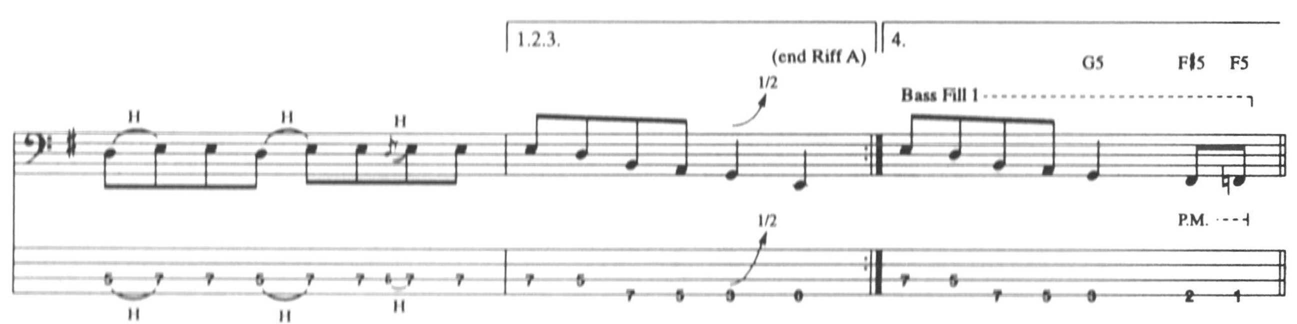

1st, 2nd, 3rd Verses
N.C.
1.3. Bread - fan, o - pen up your mind, o - pen up your purse, o - pen up your
2. Los - er, give it all a - way, nev - er stay with a win - ner, with the
Bass Fig. 1
P.M.
D5
D♯5
vault, nev - er, nev - er gon - na lose it.
man with all the crook - ed mon - ey.
(end Bass Fig. 1)
H
P.M.
w/Bass Fig. 1
N.C.
Bread - fan, take it all a - way, nev - er give an inch, got - ta make a
Come on, keep it all a - side with a ride on a rec - ord on the
D5
D♯5
mint, got - ta make me a mil - lion.
top, if you're gon - na be a bad boy.
N.C.
Bread - fan, you got it wrong, it's your long time friend, gon - na
P.M.
P.M.
P.M.

D5 

lose it in the end. Who's a fool?

H
P.M.
H

N.C.

Sea - gull, give it all a - way, stay a bird, stay a man, stay a

P.M. P.M. P.M.

To Coda

D5 D♯5

ghost, stay what you wan - na be.

H P
P.M.
H P

1.
E5 N.C. 3 E5 N.C.

H H H
H H H

w/Riff A (1¾ times) 7 w/Bass Fill 1

G5 F♯5 F5

sl.
sl.

2.
Guitar solo
E5 3 D♯5
E5 D5 D♯5 E5 D♯5 E5 D♯5
E5 D♯5 E5 F♯5 E5 F♯5 G5
P.M.
H
F♯5 G5 F♯5 G5 F♯5 G5
G♯5 A5 G♯5 A5 G♯5 A5
G♯5 A5 G5 A5 G5 A5 G5

Half time feel
N.C.
H
sl.
H
sl.
H
sl.
P.M. - - -
2nd time substitute Bass Fill 2
Play 4 times
A5
G5
A5
G5
A5
G5
Slower ♩ = 124
(end half time feel)
(Guitar)
E5
Em
Dm add9 add4
1.
2.
sl.
mf
*Sustain and fade over next 2 bars.
Half time feel
Em
Dm add9 add4
Em
Dm add9 add4
Bass Fill 2
P.M.

Cadd9
N.C.
Em7
N.C.
Em7
N.C.
Em
Dm add9 add4
Em
Dm add9 add4
Cadd9
N.C.
Em7
N.C.
Em7
N.C.
Em7
N.C.
Em7
sl.

N.C.
E5
(end half time feel)
sl.
f
P.M.
sl.
Tempo I ♩ = 208
A5
G5
A5
G5
A5
G5
E5
N.C.
3
E5
E5
P.M.
D.S. al Coda
E7(no3rd)
Outro
w/Riff A (4 times)
Coda
N.C.
16
E5
P.M.
N.C.
E5
(Spoken:) Mommy, where's Fluffy?

Brown Eyed Girl

Words and Music by Van Morrison

G C G D7
Laugh-ing and a run-ning, hey, hey, skip-ping and a jump-ing,
G C G D7
in the mis - ty morn - ing fog with our, our hearts a thump-in'. And you
C D7 G Em
my brown - eyed girl.
C D7 G D7
Yeah, you, my brown-eyed girl.

Verse
G
C
G
D7
2. Now, what-ev-er hap-pened to Tues-day and so slow?
Go-ing down the old mine with a tran-sis-tor ra-di-o.
Stand-ing in the sun-light laugh-ing, hid-ing be-hind a rain-bow's wall.
Slip-ping and a slid-ing all a-long the wa-ter-fall with you,

C
D7
G
Em
my brown - eyed girl.
C
D7
G
D7
You, my brown-eyed girl.
Do you re-mem -
Chorus
G
C
ber when we used to sing? Sha, la, la, la, la, la, la, la,
G
D7
G
la, la, la, te, da. Just like that. Sha, la, la, la,

C
G
D7
la, la, la, la, la, la, la, te, da. La, te, da.

G

Bass Interlude
N.C.(G)
(C)
(G)
(D7)

Verse
G
C
G
3. So hard to find my way now that I'm all

D7
G
C
on my own.
I saw you just the oth-er day;
G
D7
G
C
my, how you have grown.
Cast my mem-'ry back there, Lord.
G
D7
G
C
Some-times I'm o-ver-come think-in' 'bout it.
Laugh-ing and a run-ning, hey, hey,
G
D7
C
D7
be-hind the sta-di-um with you,
my brown-eyed girl.

G
Em
C
D7
A you, my brown-eyed girl.
G
D7
Do you re-mem-ber when a we used to sing?
Chorus
w/ Lead Voc. ad lib., till fade
G
C
G
D7
Sha, la, la, la, la, la, la, la, la, la, la, te, da.
Play 3 Times and Fade
G
C
G
D7
Sha, la, la, la, la, la, la, la, la, la, la, te, da.

Bulls on Parade

Written and Arranged by Rage Against The Machine

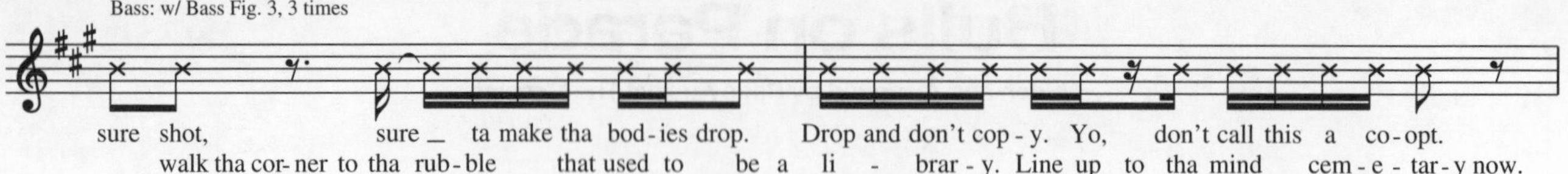
Bass: w/ Bass Fig. 3, 3 times
sure shot, sure ta make tha bod-ies drop. Drop and don't cop-y. Yo, don't call this a co-opt.
walk tha cor-ner to tha rub-ble that used to be a li - brar-y. Line up to tha mind cem-e-tar-y now.

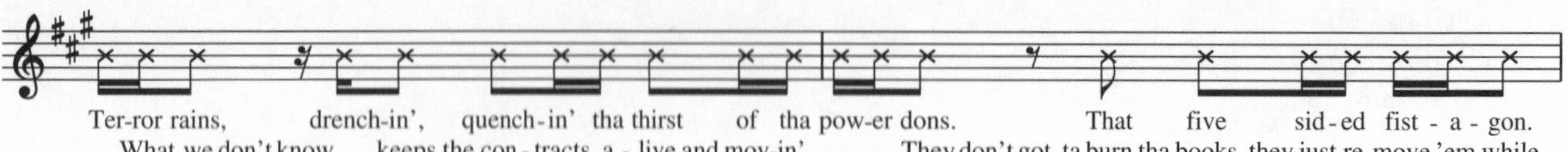
Ter-ror rains, drench-in', quench-in' tha thirst of tha pow-er dons. That five sid-ed fist-a-gon.
What we don't know keeps the con-tracts a-live and mov-in'. They don't got-ta burn tha books, they just re-move 'em while

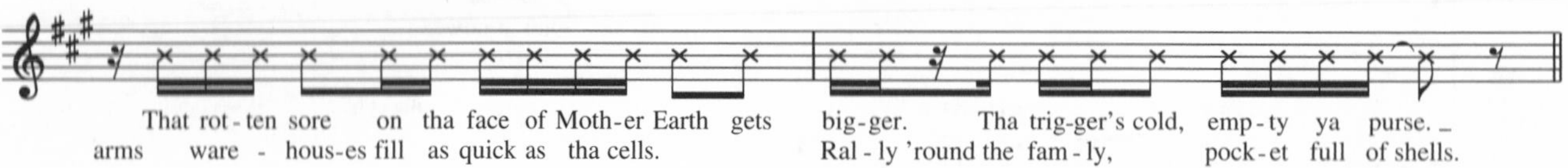
That rot-ten sore on tha face of Moth-er Earth gets big-ger. Tha trig-ger's cold, emp-ty ya purse.
arms ware-hous-es fill as quick as tha cells. Ral-ly 'round the fam-ly, pock-et full of shells.

Chorus

N.C.
Ral-ly 'round tha fam-'ly with a pock-et full of shells. They
Bass
Bass Fig. 4
End Bass Fig. 4

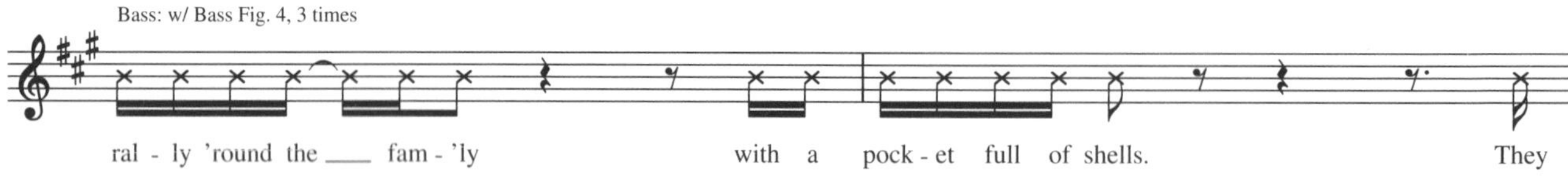
Bass: w/ Bass Fig. 4, 3 times
ral-ly 'round the fam-'ly with a pock-et full of shells. They

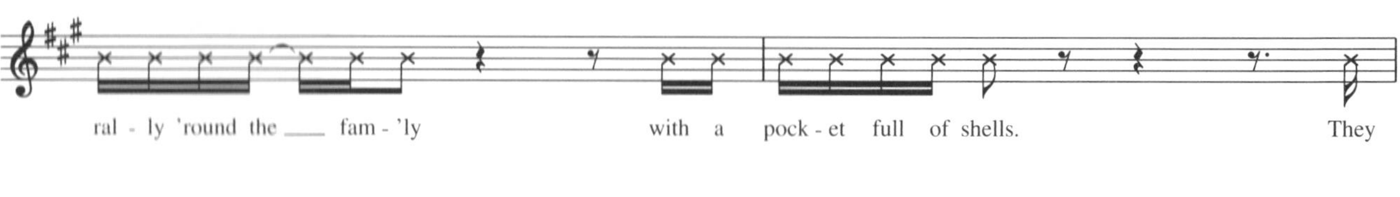
ral-ly 'round the fam-'ly with a pock-et full of shells. They

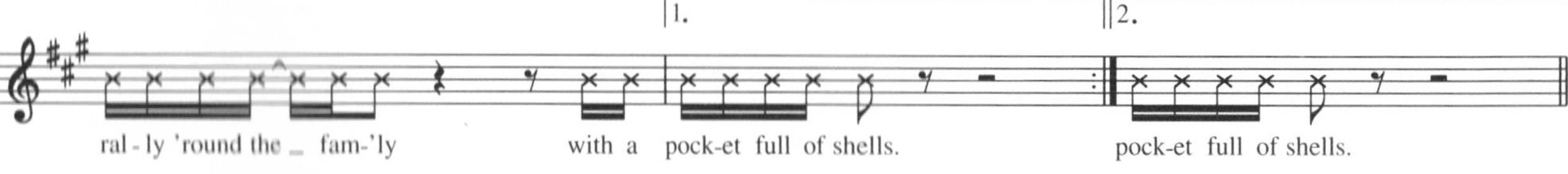
1.
2.
ral-ly 'round the fam-'ly with a pock-et full of shells. pock-et full of shells.

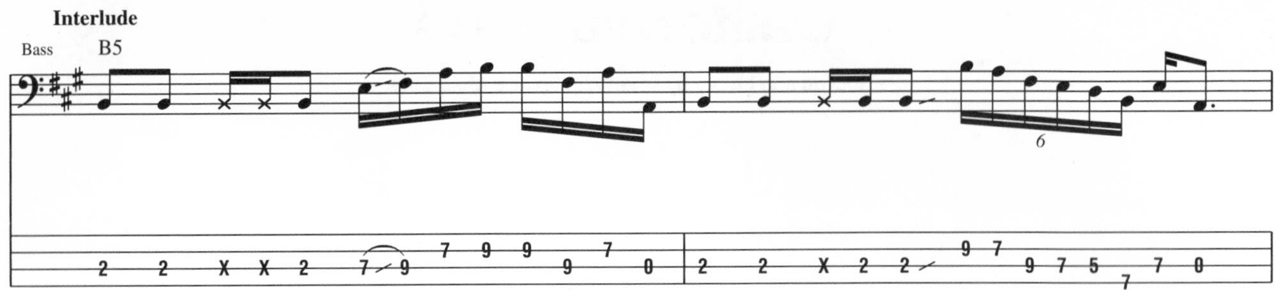
Interlude
Bass
B5
6
2 2 X X 2 7 9 7 9 9 9 7 0
2 2 X 2 2 9 7 9 7 5 7 7 0

Bulls on pa - rade!
2 2 X 2 2 7 9 9 7 9 9 9 9
2 2 X 2 2 14 16 16 16 12 14 14 14

Guitar Solo
* N.C.
play 4 times
Uh.
0 2 0 2 0 0 2
2 0 0 1
*Sing 1st time only.

Outro
Bass tacet
F#5
3
Bass: w/ Bass Fig. 2, 2 times
Quit it now!
Quit it now!
Bulls on pa-rade!

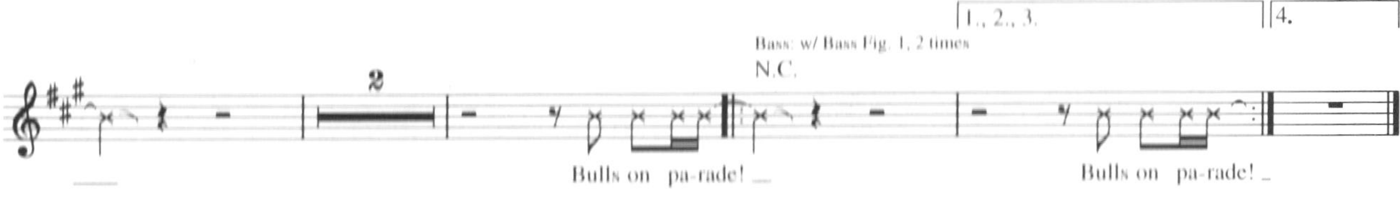
1., 2., 3.
4.
Bass: w/ Bass Fig. 1, 2 times
N.C.
2
Bulls on pa-rade!
Bulls on pa-rade!

California Girls

Words and Music by Brian Wilson and Mike Love

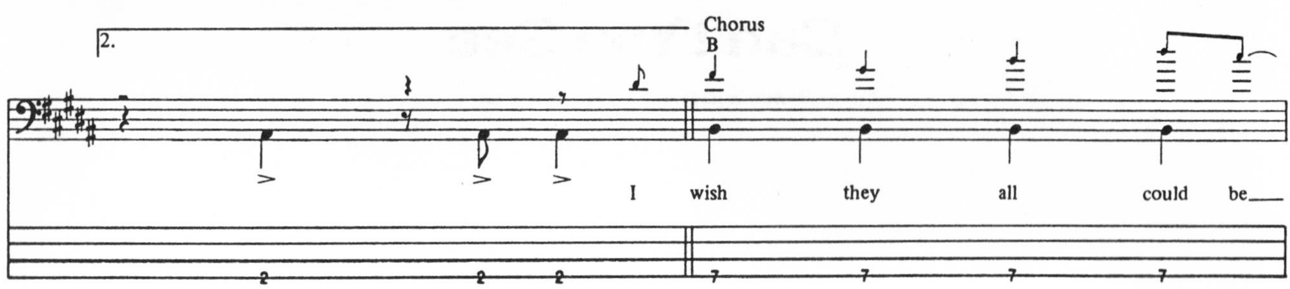
2.
Chorus
B
I wish they all could be

C♯m7
A
Bm7
Cal - i - for - nia girls.

G
Am7
2nd time to Coda
B
D.S. al Coda
2. The

Coda
B
N.C.

Chorus
B
C♯m7
Play 3 times and fade

Can't You See

Words and Music by Toy Caldwell

Chorus
D
Dsus4 D
Dsus2/G
G
1.
D
Dsus4
Dsus2
2.
D
Dsus4 D
2nd Verse
D
I'm gon- na find me...
D7/C
G
1.
D
Dsus4 D
Dsus2
2.
D
Can't you see...
Chorus
D
Dsus4
D
D5/C
*Play w/slight variations ad lib on D.S.
G
1.
D
Dsus4 D
2.
D
Dsus4
D
Dsus2
Guitar solos I & II
D
D5/C
G
H
H
4th time to Coda
1.
D
Dsus4
D
2.
D
Dsus4
D
H
H
H

3rd Verse
D
*H
D7/C
I'm gon - na buy a tick - et, now...
H
*Omit grace note on repeat.
1.
2.
D.S. (w/repeats) al Coda
G
D
Dsus4
D
Dsus4
Can't you see...
Coda
Chorus
(Drums tacet)
D
Dsus4
D
D
Dsus4
D
D5/C
H
mp
Can't you see...
G
D
Dsus4 D Dsus2
D
D5/C
G
D
Chorus
(Drums in)
D
Dsus4 D
Dsus2/C
1.
G
mf
Oh, she's such a cra - zy la - dy...
2.3.
D
G
D
Dsus4 D

4.
G
D
Dsus4
D
Guitar solo III
Dsus4
D
Dsus4
D
D5/C
G
H
H
D
Dsus4
D
Dsus4
D
Dsus4
D
D5/C
sl.
sl.
G
H
H
D
Dsus4
D
Outro
(Flute enters)
D
H
mp
D5/C
Csus2
G
rit.
Freely
D
Dsus2
D
trem. pick
mf

Change It

By Doyle Bramhall

C
To Coda
C
Get a-way from the blind side of life,
2nd time
B♭
Hon-ey I want ya ta be by my side.
F
Me and my back
3rd time
1st
2nd time
3rd time D.S. al Coda
1, 3.
Am
door moves ain't no more.
No more!
3rd time
2.
No more!
F

Am
F
Am

G
F
Am

F

Am
F
Am

G
F
Am

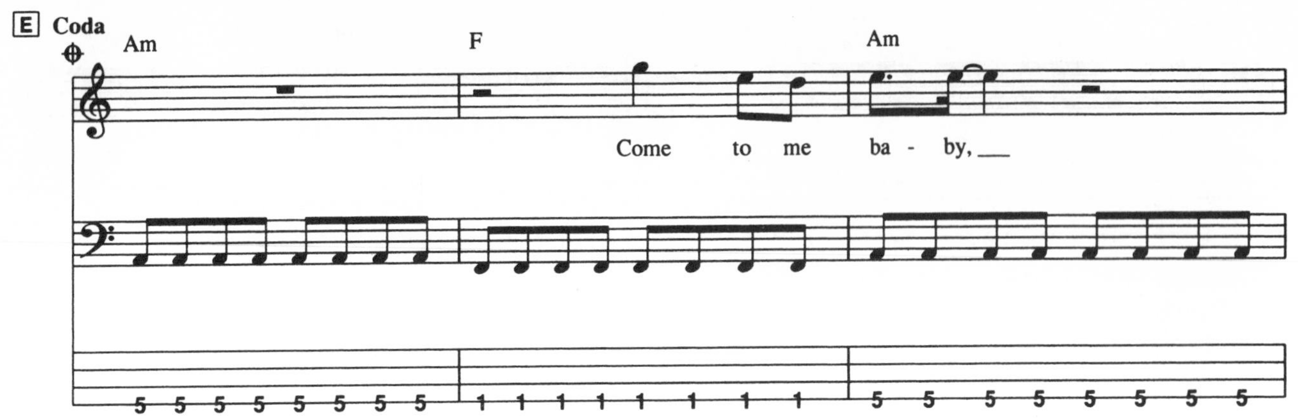
E Coda
Am
F
Am
Come to me ba - by, ___
5 5 5 5 5 5 5 5
1 1 1 1 1 1 1 1
5 5 5 5 5 5 5 5

F
Am
F
cone to me one more time. ___________
It's time we got
3
1 1 1 1 1 1 1 1
5 5 5 5 5 5 5 5 5
1 1 1 1 1 1 1 1

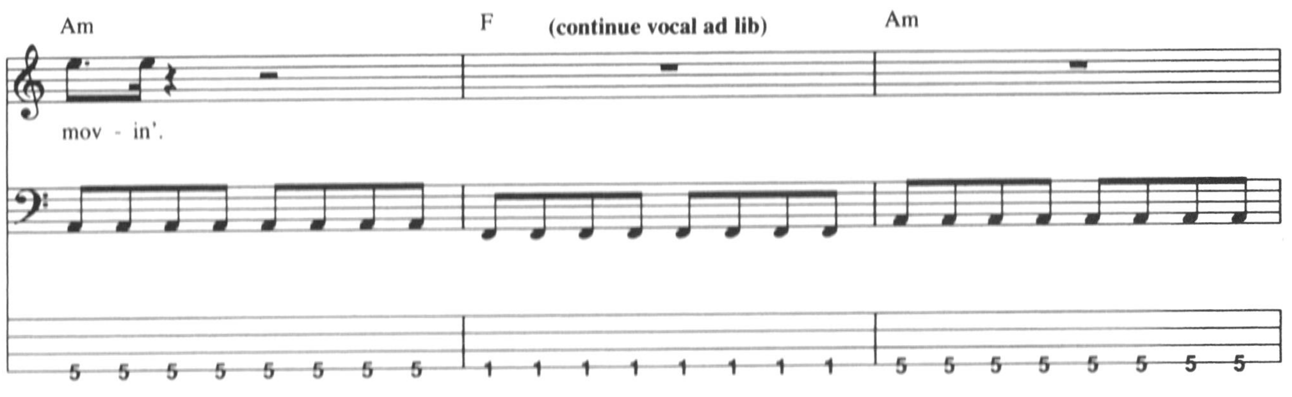
Am
F
(continue vocal ad lib)
Am
mov - in'.
5 5 5 5 5 5 5 5
1 1 1 1 1 1 1 1
5 5 5 5 5 5 5 5

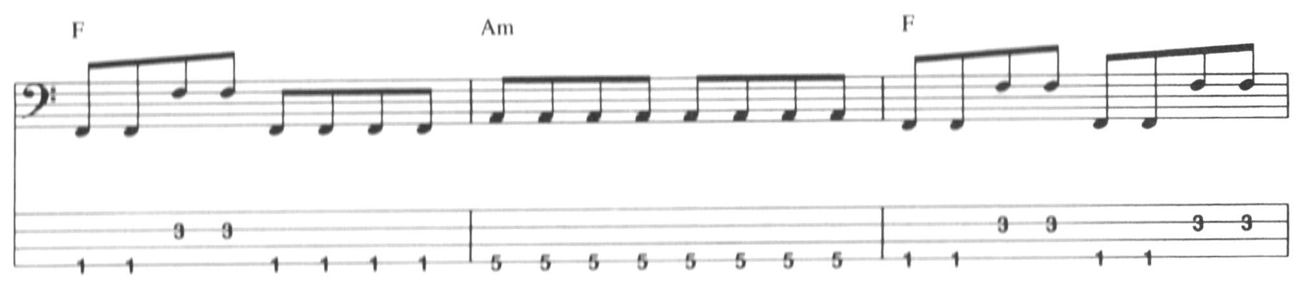
F
Am
F
3 3
1 1 1 1 1 1
5 5 5 5 5 5 5 5
3 3 3 3
1 1 1 1

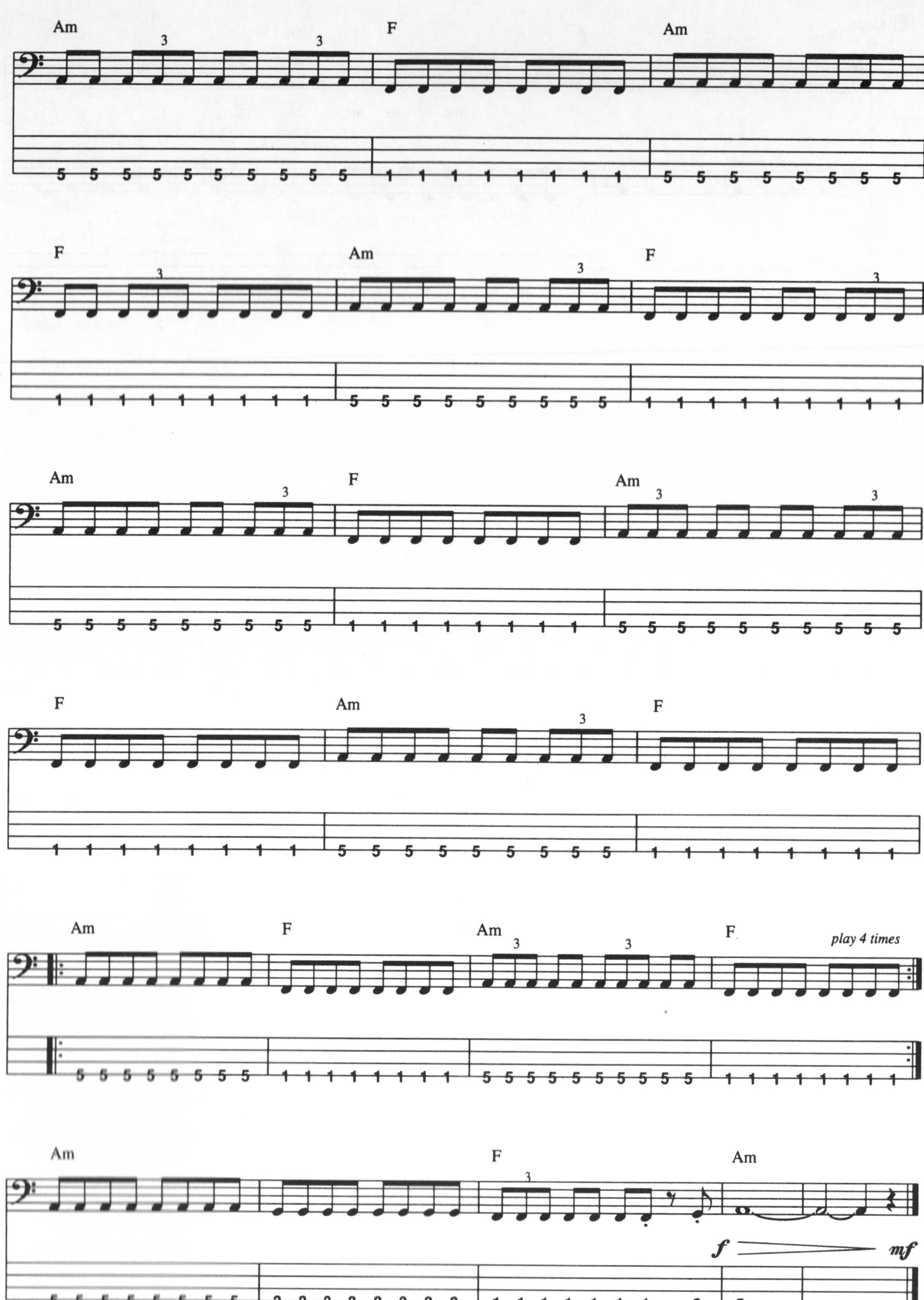
Am F Am
F Am F
Am F Am
F Am F
Am F Am F
play 4 times
Am F Am
f mf

Chop Suey!

Words and Music by Daron Malakian and Serj Tankian

Drop D tuning, down 1 step:
(low to high) C-G-C-F

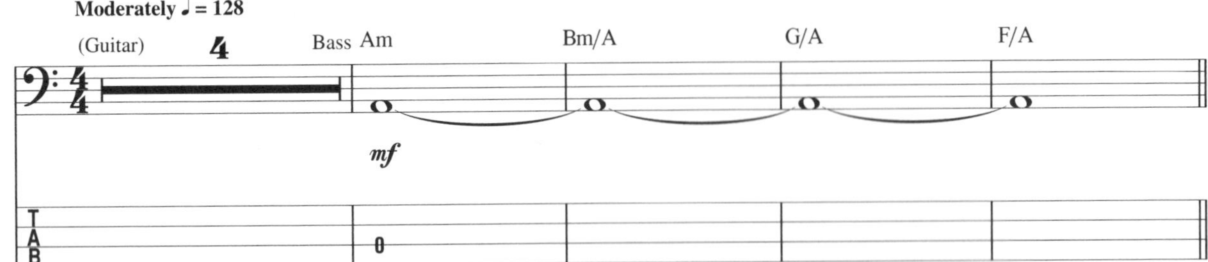

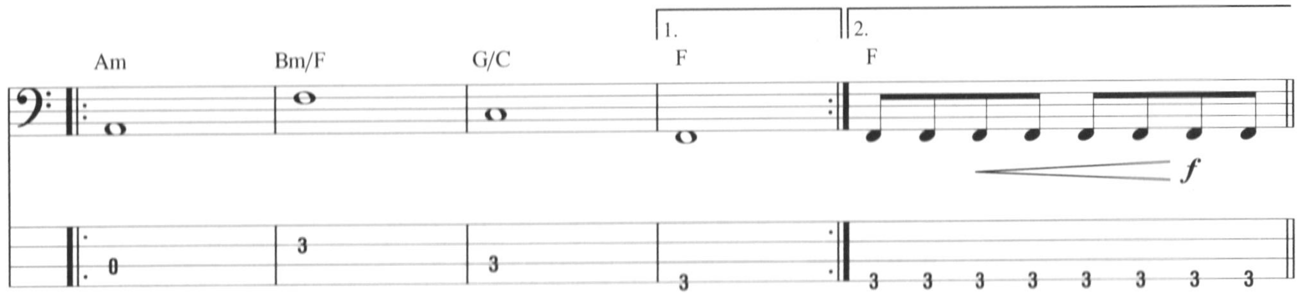

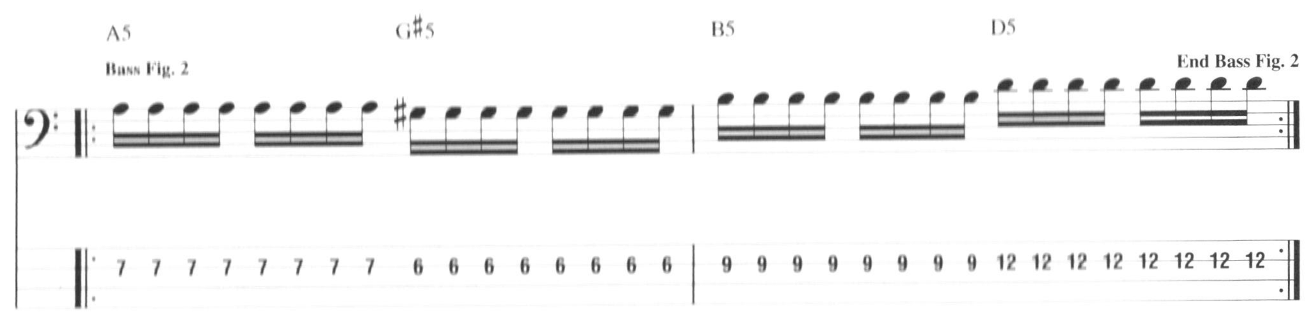

Verse
Ab5 A5 N.C.
Bb5 A5 Bb5 A5 Bb5 A5 Bb5 A5
G#5 N.C.
A5 G#5 A5 G#5 A5 G#5 A5 G#5
1., 2. Wake up, grab a brush and put a lit - tle make-up. Hide the scars to fade a - way the
Whispered: (Wake up.
Bass Fig. 3
End Bass Fig. 3
Bass: w/ Bass Fig. 3 (3 times)
Bb5 A5 N.C.
Bb5 A5 Bb5 A5 Bb5 A5 Bb5 A5
G#5 N.C.
A5 G#5 A5 G#5 A5 G#5 A5 G#5
shake-up. Why'd you leave the keys up - on the ta - ble? Here you go, cre - ate an - oth - er
Hide the scars to fade a - way the shake up.)
Bb5 A5 N.C.
Bb5 A5 Bb5 A5 Bb5 A5 Bb5 A5
G#5 N.C.
A5 G#5 A5 G#5 A5 G#5 A5 G#5
fa - ble, you want - ed to. Grab a brush and put a lit - tle make-up, you want - ed to. Hide the scars to fade a - way the
Bb5 A5 N.C.
Bb5 A5 Bb5 A5 Bb5 A5 Bb5 A5
G#5 N.C.
A5 G#5 A5 G#5 A5 G#5 A5 G#5
shake - up, you want - ed to. Why'd you leave the keys up - on the ta - ble? You want - ed to. I don't think you
Chorus
Half-time feel
Am
Bm/F
G/C
F
trust in my self - right - eous su - i -
Bass Fig. 4
End Bass Fig. 4

Bass: w/ Bass Fig. 4
End half-time feel
(1st time only)
Am
Bm/F
G/C
F
cide.
I
cry
when an - gels de - serve to

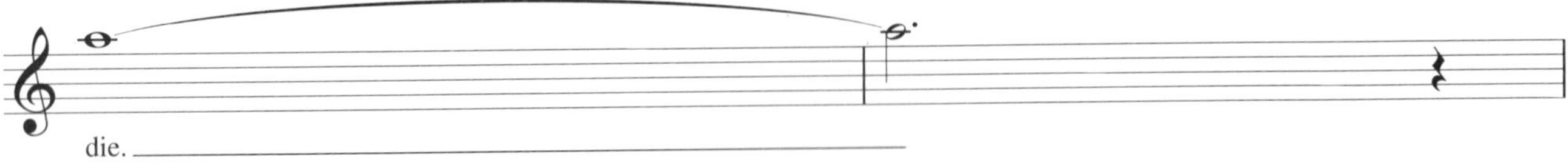

1.
Interlude
Bass: w/ Bass Fig. 1 (2 times)
Bb5 A5 Bb5 A5 Bb5 A5 Bb5 A5 G#5 A5 G#5 A5 G#5 A5 G#5 C5 B5 C5 B5 C5 B5 C5 B5 D5 C5 D5 C5 D5 C5 D5 C5
die.

Bb5 A5 Bb5 A5 Bb5 A5 Bb5 A5 G#5 A5 G#5 A5 G#5 A5 G#5 C5 B5 C5 B5 C5 B5 C5 B5 D5 C5 D5 C5 D5 C5 D5 C5

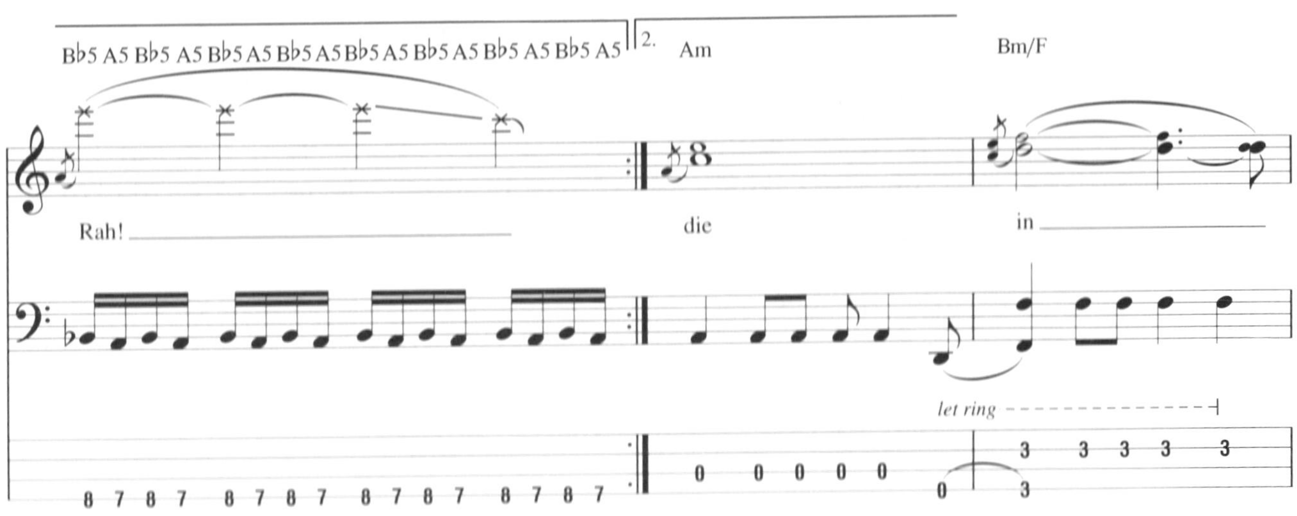

Bb5 A5 Bb5 A5 Bb5 A5 Bb5 A5 Bb5 A5 Bb5 A5 Bb5 A5 Bb5 A5
2.
Am
Bm/F
Rah!
die
in
let ring

G/C
F
Am
my
self - right - eous su - i - cide.

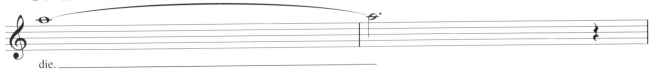

Bridge

Double-time feel

Bass: w/ Bass Fig. 1 (4 times)

2nd time, End double-time feel

B♭5 A5 B♭5 A5 B♭5 A5 B♭5 A5 G♯5 A5 G♯5 A5 G♯5 A5 G♯5

C5 B5 C5 B5 C5 B5 C5 B5 D5 C5 D5 C5 D5 C5 D5 C5

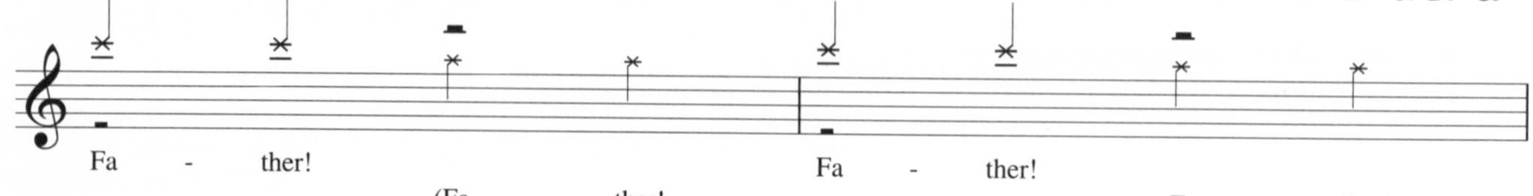

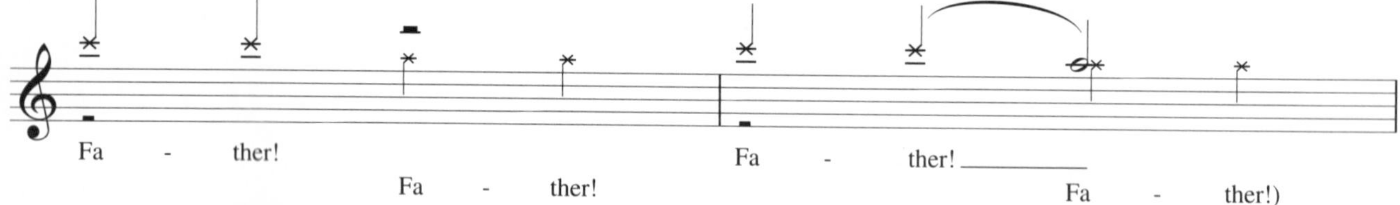

Bass: w/ Bass Fig. 2 (2 times)

Outro

Half-time feel

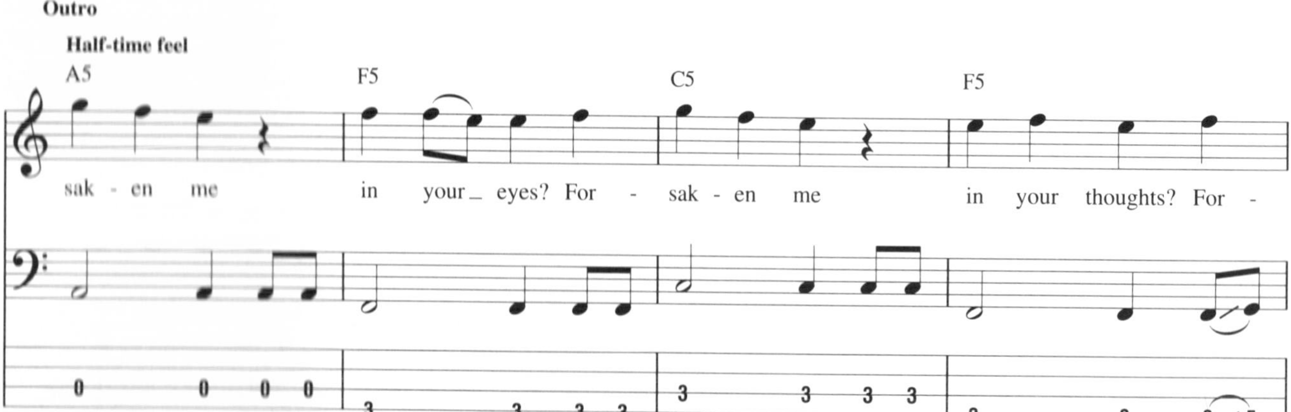

A5
F5
C5
F5
3
sak - en me in your heart? For - sak - en me. I'll
A5
F5
C5
F5
3
trust in my self - right - eous su - i - cide.
Bass Fig. 5
End Bass Fig. 5
Bass: w/ Bass Fig. 5 (2 1/2 times)
A5
F5
C5
F5
A5
I cry when an - gels de - serve to die
F5
C5
F5
3
A5
F5
in my self - right - eous su - i - cide. I
C5
F5
3
A5
cry when an - gels de - serve to die.

Come Original

Music by Nicholas Hexum and Aaron Wills
Lyrics by Nicholas Hexum and Doug Martinez

Bass: w/ Bass Fig. 1
G5
B5
A5
Ab5
come o - rig - i - nal, you got to come o - rig - i - nal.
All en - ter - tain - ers, hear why. 1. To
Verse
Bass: w/ Bass Fig. 1 (2 times)
come o - rig - i - nal, it ain't noth - in' strange. (You) got to rep - re - sent, you got to come full range. And
full range of e-mo-tion, full range of styles. When you come to town you'll have them com-in' for miles. And
Chorus
Bass: w/ Bass Fig. 1 (2 times)
come o - rig - i - nal, you got to come o - rig - i - nal. All en - ter-tain - ers, come o - rig - i - nal. You got to
come o - rig - i - nal, you got to come o - rig - i - nal. All en - ter-tain - ers, hear why.
Verse
2. Black Eyed Peas, they com-in' full range, and No - F - X, they com-in' full range and
3. Funk slap bass mixed with the dance hall and hip - hop beats and punk gui - tar. And
Ron - i Size, he com-in' full range. The one Mis - ter Ve - gas, know it ain't eas - y.
dead - ly on the mic is the one S A. The name is Three E - lev - en, and you know it ain't eas - y.
F#5

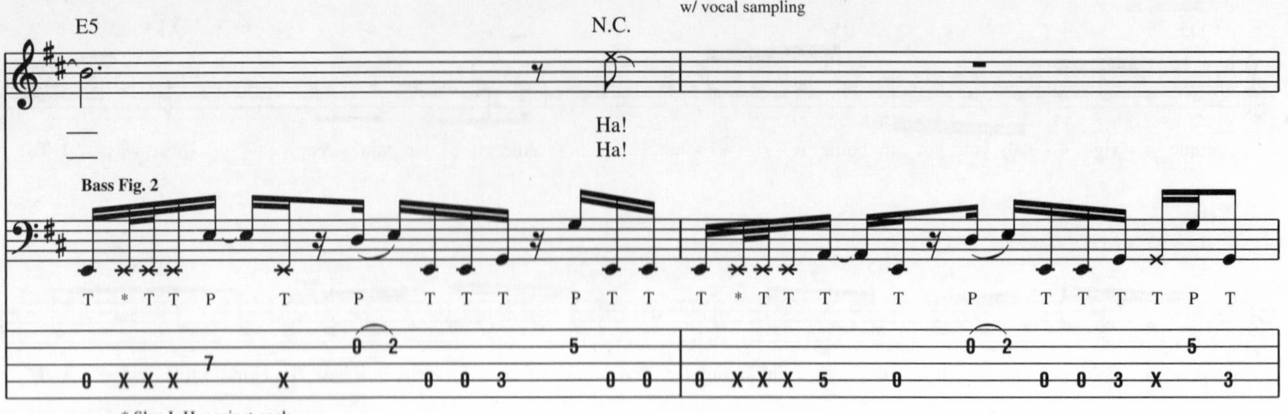
w/ vocal sampling
E5
N.C.
Ha!
Ha!
Bass Fig. 2
* Slap L.H. against neck.

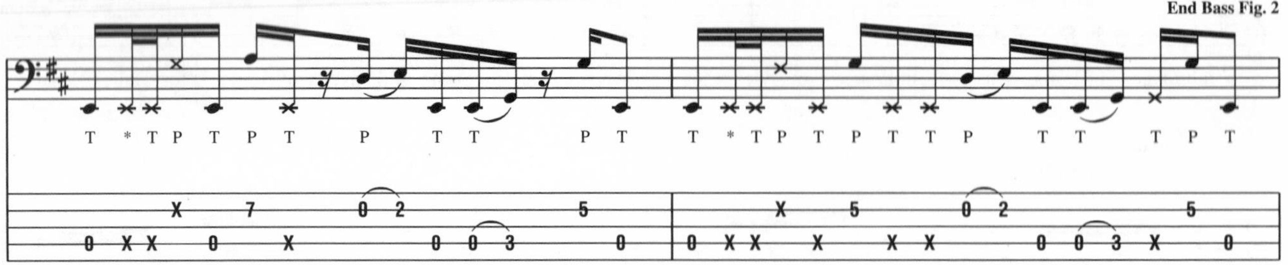
End Bass Fig. 2

Bass: w/ Bass Fig. 2 (1 3/4 times)
E5
warn-ing to the crews out there who think they're hot. (If) you're not o - rig - i - nal rock-ers, you will get shot down by the
This is not a test, there's no time to mope. . How you gon-na cope with ra - di - o - ac-tive i-so-tope and boss

kids ne-glect-in' your art, the stuff you did. Even-tu'-ally it gets so bad it puts you to bed. Cuz
d. - j. ill-ness u - pon you now quick - ly in-fect-ing you fast up on-the air - waves? This

when light-nin' flash-es sweet e - lec-tric - i - ty all the world then stands re-vealed with the clar - i - ty of raw
mes-sage brought to you by the so large sys-tem. Ac-ti - vate, at - tune your - self with med - i - ta - tion and green

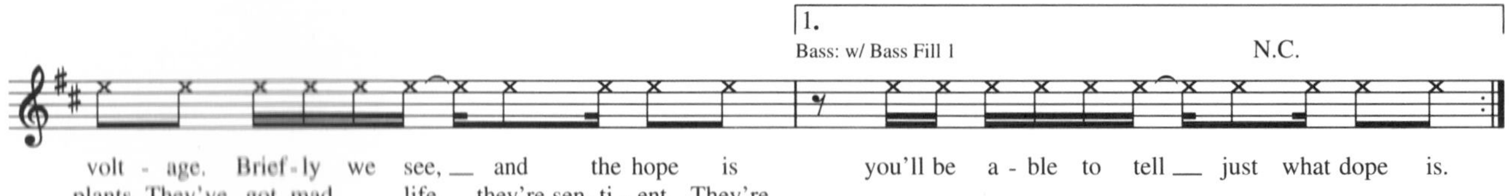
1.
Bass: w/ Bass Fill 1
N.C.
volt - age. Brief - ly we see, and the hope is you'll be a - ble to tell just what dope is.
plants. They've got mad life, they're sen - ti - ent. They're

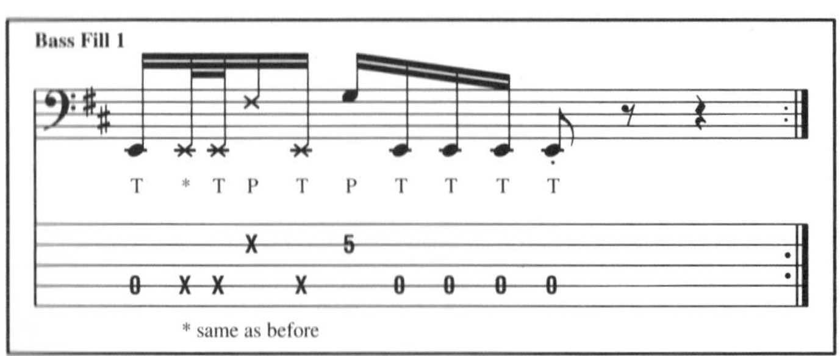
Bass Fill 1
* same as before

2.
Interlude
N.C.
N.C.
Play 4 times
beau-ti - ful as you and they like to dance.
(Last time: One, two, three, four.
Bass
Verse
Bass: w/ Bass Fig. 2 (1 3/4 times)
E5
4. Ev - 'ry-thing we do, we got - ta come o - rig - i - nal. Put your hand up in the air and pre - pare for bat - tle.
Sit u - pon the rhy-thm like a tire u - pon a rim. We do it non - stop and then we do it a - gain.
Some of them whine and some them bitch. They can - not do it, nev - er switch.
Com - in' up from the heart and de - liv - ered with a wild pitch.
Sit up on top of the rhy-thm like a wild stal - li - on. This is the rul-ing sys - tem.
Bass: w/ Bass Fill 1
Interlude
(Bass tacet)
Outro-Chorus
Bass: w/ Bass Fig. 1 (3 1/2 times)
1.,2.,3.
G
Bm
Am
Ab
Come o - rig - i - nal, you got to come o - rig - i - nal. All en - ter-tain - ers, come o - rig - i - nal. You got to
4.
Am
Ab
G
All en - ter - tain - ers, come o - rig - i - nal.
Bass

Come Together

Words and Music by John Lennon and Paul McCartney

1.
G5
to his knee.
you know me."
his knee.
is three."
Got to be a jok - er he just do what he please.
10
12
0 0
3

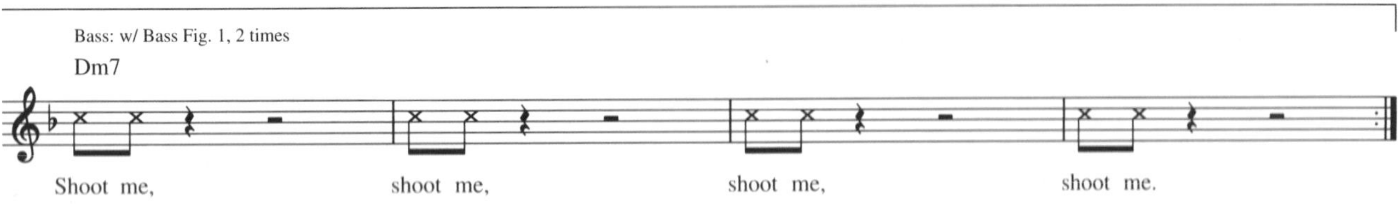
Bass: w/ Bass Fig. 1, 2 times
Dm7
Shoot me, shoot me, shoot me, shoot me.

2.
G5
One thing I can tell you is you got to be free.
Hold you in his arm - chair, you can feel his dis - ease.
Got to be good look - ing 'cause he so hard to see.
Come to - geth -
3

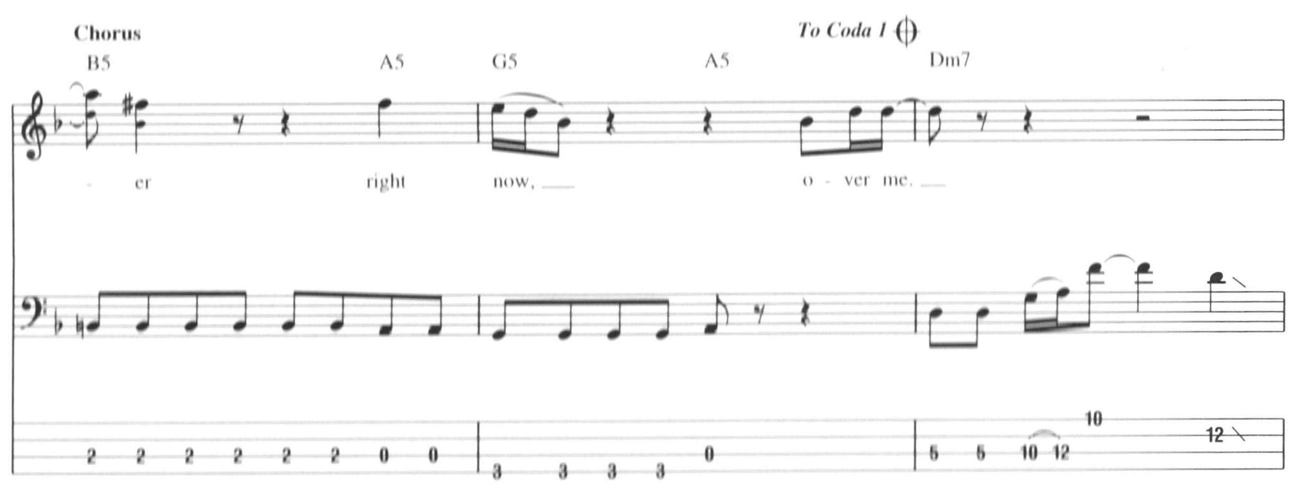
Chorus
To Coda 1
B5 A5 G5 A5 Dm7
- er right now, o - ver me.
2 2 2 2 2 2 0 0
3 3 3 3 0
5 5 10 12 10 12

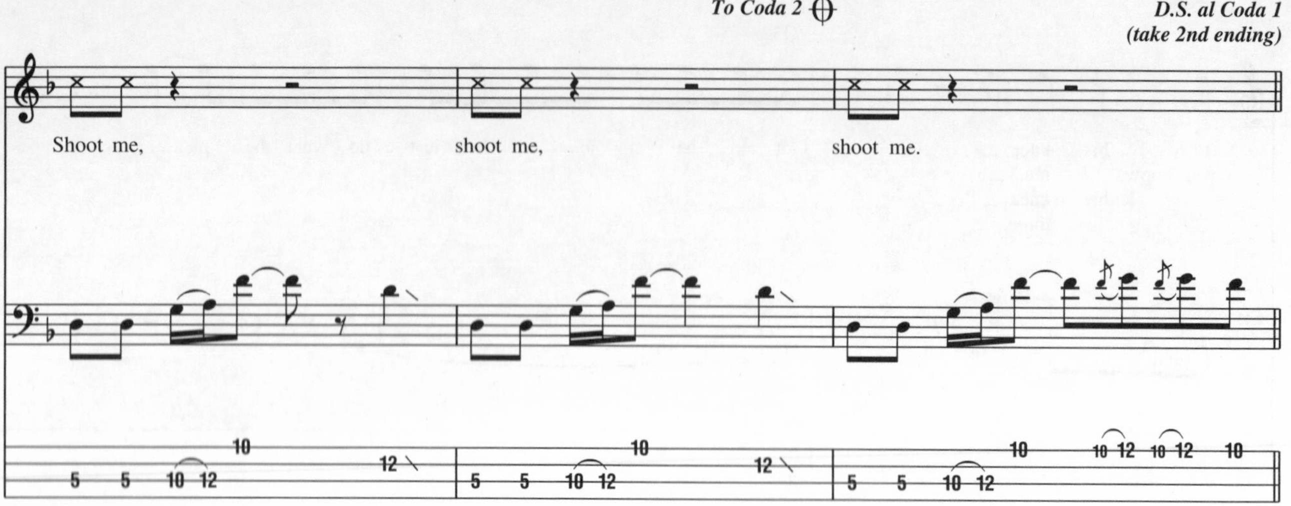
To Coda 2
D.S. al Coda 1
(take 2nd ending)
Shoot me,
shoot me,
shoot me.

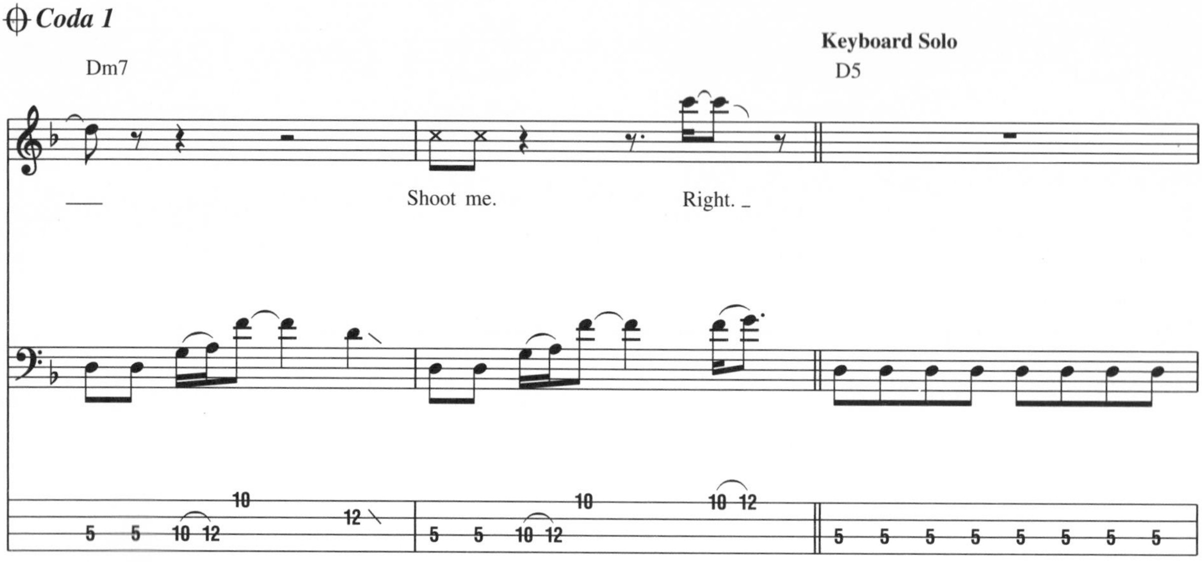
Coda 1
Keyboard Solo
Dm7
D5
Shoot me.
Right.

Come.

Guitar Solo

A5

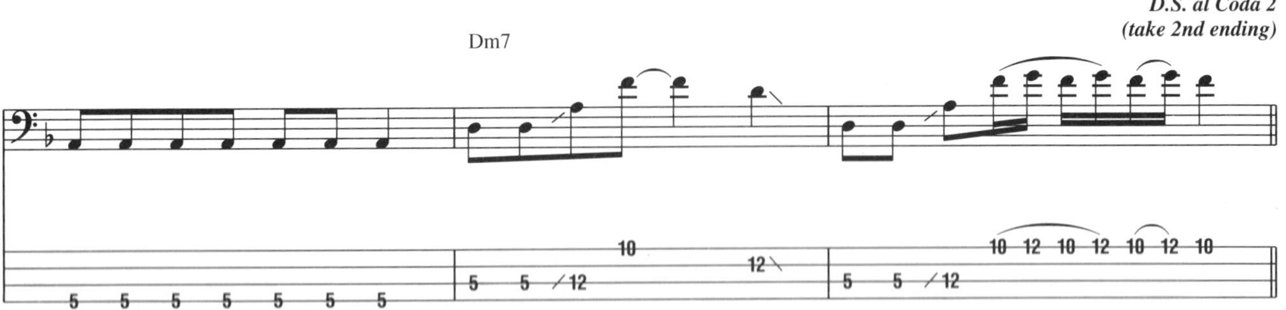
Dm7
D.S. al Coda 2
(take 2nd ending)

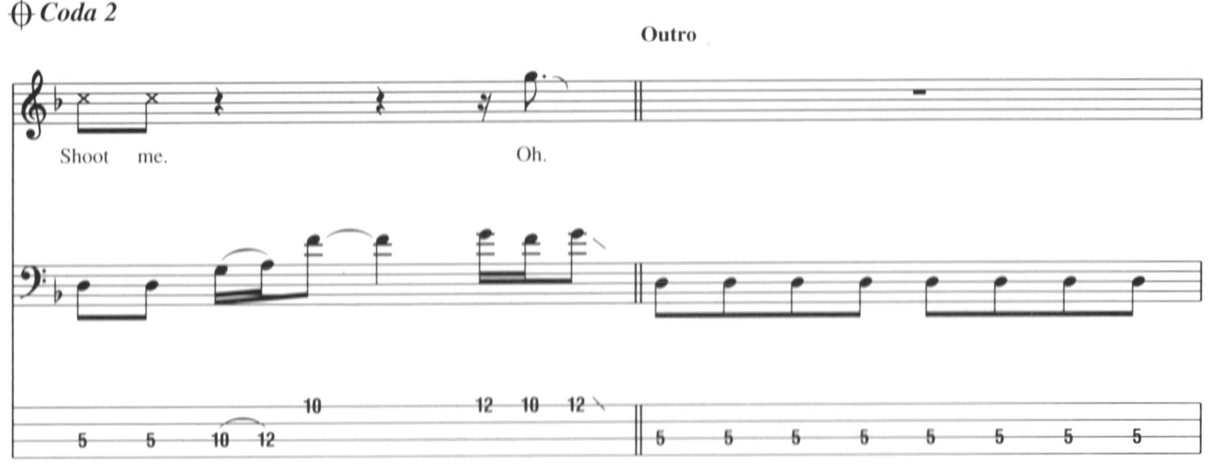
Coda 2
Outro
Shoot me.
Oh.

Play 10 Times and Fade
Come to - geth - er,
yeah.
simile on repeats

Comedown

Words and Music by Gavin Rossdale

Verse
Bass: w/ Bass Fig. 2, 2nd time
N.C.(Bm)
1. Love and hate, get it wrong. She cut me right back down to size.
2. There is no blame, on - ly shame. When you beg, you just com - plain.
Sleep the day, let it fade. Who was there to take your place?
The more I come, more I try. All po - lice are par - a - noid.
B5
A5/B
F♯5/B
G5/B
No one knows, nev - er will. Most - ly me but most - ly you.
So am I, so is the fu - ture. So are you, be a crea - ture.
Bass: w/ Bass Fill 1, 2nd time
B5
A5/B
F♯add4/B
G5/B
What do you say, do you do when it all comes down?
Bass Fill 1

Chorus
D
A
G
'Cause I don't wan-na come back down from this cloud. It's tak-en me all
Bass Fig. 3
f simile on repeat
this time to find out what I need, yeah.
End Bass Fig. 3
I don't wan-na come back down from this cloud. It's tak-en me all
this, all this time.
1.

Badd4
Aadd2/B
F#7add4/B
G5/B
N.C.(Bm)
2.
Guitar Solo
G
N.C.(Bm)
Shoot up,
shoot up,
shoot up.
You're
high.
Bmsus2
N.C.

E/B
N.C.
(2)

Verse

Bass: w/ Bass Fig. 1, 1 1/2 times
N.C.(Bm)
3. Love and hate, get it wrong, She cut me right back down to size.

Bass: w/ Bass Fill 2
Sleep the day, let it fade. Who was there to take your place?

Bass: w/ Bass Fig. 1, 1st meas.
B5
A5/B
Bass: w/ Bass Fig. 2
F♯/B
G5/B
No one knows, nev - er will. Most - ly me but most - ly you.

B5
A5/B
Bass: w/ Bass Fig. 1, 1st meas.
F♯5/B
G5/B
What do you say, do you do when it all comes down?

Bass Fill 2

Chorus

Outro

D
A
G
Come _ down?
D
A
G
I don't wan-na come back down _ from this _ cloud, this _ cloud, this _
D
A
G
_ cloud, this _ cloud, this _ cloud, this _ cloud, this _
D
A
G
A
Dmadd2
_ cloud, this _ cloud, this _ cloud.

Couldn't Stand the Weather

Written by Stevie Ray Vaughan

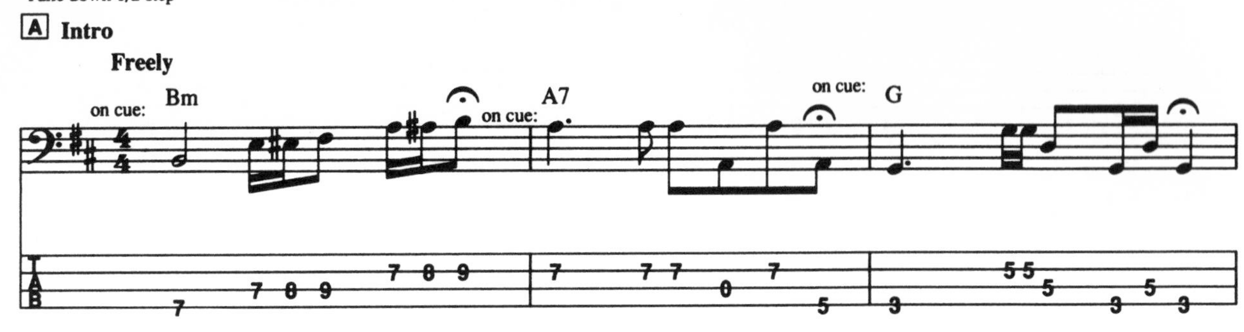

G5
D5

C Verse
D7#9
Com-in' through this - a bus- 'ness of life, ___ rais- in' sand if I'm
need - ed to. ____ Ain't so fun - ny when things ___ ain't feel- in' right;
dad - dy's hand _ helps to see me through. _
D Chorus
Bm
Sweet as sug- ar love
A
won't wash a - way. Rain or shine, it's al - ways here to stay.

G
F♯7
All these years you and I ___ spent to - geth - er. I guess we just
3 2 3 (4) 5 5 3 3 4 5 (x) 3 2 2 4 2 2 4

D5
G5
could-n't stand the weath - er. ___
2 2 4 2 2 4 5 3 5 1 3 4 5 3

D5
G5
5 3 5 5 5 2 3 3 3 4 4 5 5 5 3 5 1 3

(3) 4 5 3 5 3 5 5 2 3 4 4 5 5 5 5

E Verse
D7
Like a train that stops at ev- 'ry sta - tion, we all deal with trials
and trib- u- la - tions.
Fear hangs the fel-low that ties up his years,
F Chorus
Bm
en tan-gled in yel-low and cries all his years.
Chang- es come be - fore we
A
can grow.
Learn to see them be - fore we're too old.

G
F#7#9
Don't just take me for tryin' to be heav-y, un-der-stand ___ it's
time to get read-y for the storm.
G Guitar Solo
D#7#9

5 5 2 2 3 3 4 5 3 4
5 5 2 2 3 3 3 3 (4) 5 3
5 5 5 2 2 3 3 3 3 4⁄5 3

Bm
5 5 5 2 2 3 3 3 3 4⁄5 3
5 5 5 2 2 3 3 3 3 3 5 5
7 5 5 7 8 9

A7
(9) 7 8 9 9 7 5 7
5 5 4 5 6
7 5 6 7 5

G
F#7#9
3 3 3 2 3 4
5 3 4 5 3
2 2 4 4 2 2 4

Bm
2 2 4 2 2 4
2 (2) 5 7 8
9 7 8 9 9 7

A7
G
5 5 4 5 6
7 5 6 7 5
3 3 3 2 3 4

F♯7♯9
H Outro
D5
G5
D5
D5
G5
D7
play 3 times
G7
F
On cue:
Dm7
On cue:
Fade

Cowboy Song

Words and Music by Philip Parris Lynott and Brian Downey

Tune down 1/2 step:
④=E♭ ②=D♭
③=A♭ ①=G♭

Moderately slow ♩ = 92

1st Verse

A E5 F♯m7 E5 D

(Vocal:) 1. I am just a cow - boy...

mp

A C♯m7 F♯m7 E5 D

A E5 F♯m7 E5 D

Faster ♩ = 132

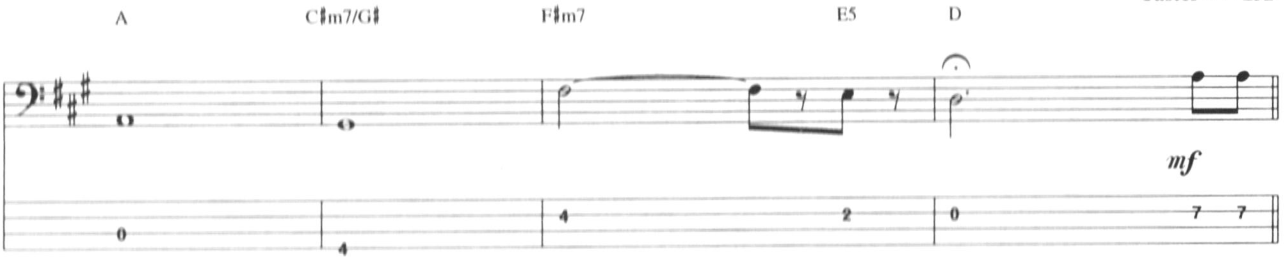

N.C.(D)
(A/C♯)
(Bm)
P
1.
A5
2.
A5
P
*2nd, 3rd Verses, Guitar solos I & II
A5
E5
F♯m7
E5
D
2. I am just a cow - boy...
3. I was took in Tex - as...
*Play w/variations ad lib on repeats.
A5
C♯m7/G♯
F♯m7
E5
D
A5
E5
F♯m7
E5
D

A5
C♯m7/G♯
F♯m7
E5
D
Chorus
N.C.(D)
(A/C♯)
*Roll me o - ver and turn me a - round...
*Vocal tacet 3rd time.
(Bm)
A5
N.C.(D)
(A/C♯)
P
(Bm)
4th time to Coda
1. 2.
3.
A5
A5
P
N.C.(D)
(A/C♯)
(Bm)
A5
Play 4 times
mp
Roll me o - ver...

N.C.(D)
(A/C♯)
(Bm)
(A)
(D)
mf
(A/C♯)
(Bm)
1.
(A)
(D)
mp
(A/C♯)
(Bm)
(A)
(D)
(A/C♯)
(Bm)
(A)
2.
(A)
D.S. al Coda
Coda
A5
N.C.(D)
(A/C♯)
(Bm)
(A/C♯)
(D)
(E)
A5

Crazy Train

Words and Music by Ozzy Osbourne, Randy Rhoads and Bob Daisley

Mil - lions of peo - ple, liv - ing as foes.
May - be,
it's not too late; To
learn how to love, and for - get how to hate.
0 7 6 4 2 0 7 0 7 0 0 7 6 4 2
0 0 0 0 0 7 6 4 2 0 0 0 0
0 7 6 4 2 0 7 0 7 0 0 7 6 4 2
0 0 0 0 0 7 6 4 2

F♯m E F♯m
D
Men - tal wounds not heal -
- ing,
F♯m E F♯m
D
life's a bit - ter shame.
I'm
A
E
F♯m
go - ing off the rails on a cra - zy train.
A
E
I'm go - ing off the rails on a cra - zy train.

F♯m E F♯m A E F♯m E F♯m D E
Let's go . . .
A
2. I've
A
lis - tened to preach - ers, I've lis - tened to fools.
(3rd verse see additional lyrics)
I've watched all the drop - outs, who make their own rules.

One per - son con - di - tioned,
to rule and con - trol.
The
me - di - a sells it
and you live the role.
F♯m E F♯m
D
Men - tal wounds still scream - ing.

F♯m E F♯m
D
A
E
Driv - ing me in - sane!
I'm go - ing off the rails
F♯m
on a cra - zy train.
I'm
A
E
F♯m E F♯m
A
go - ing off the rails on a cra - zy train.
To Coda
E
F♯m E F♯m
D
A

F♯m
A
E
F♯m
D
E
M8: I know that things are go - ing wrong for me.
F♯m
A
E
F♯
D
E
You got - ta lis - ten to my words, yeah,
F♯m
E
D
C♯
B
A
G♯
F♯m
yeah!
guitar solo
1.2.
F♯m
E
D
C♯
B
A
G♯
F♯m

Heirs of a cold war
That's what we've become
Inheriting troubles I'm mentally numb
Crazy, I just cannot bear
I'm living with something that just isn't fair

Mental wounds not healing
Who and what's to blame
I'm going off the rails on a crazy train

Crosscut Saw

Words and Music by R.G. Ford

Verse
A7
I'm a cross - cut saw, ba - by drag me a - cross
your log.
D7
I'm a cross - cut saw,
ba - by drag me a - cross your log.
A7
I'll cut your
E7
D7
A7
wood so eas - y for you, you can't help but say "Hot dog."

A7
2nd Verse
Some call me Wood_ Cut-tin' Sam, some call me Wood_ Cut-tin' Jim.
D7
Last girl _ I could work for she wants me_ back a-gain_ I'm a cross-cut saw,
A7
ba-by drag_ me a-cross___ your log. I'll cut your
E7
D7
A7
wood so eas-y for you,_ you can't help but say "Hot___ dog."_

A7
Guitar Solo
Spoken: All right!
D7
A7
E7
D7
A7
Guitar Solo

A7
D7
A7
E7
D7
A7
3rd Verse
I've got a double blade ax that really cuts 'em good, but I'm a
cross-cut saw, you can bur-y me in your wood. I'm a cross-cut saw,
D7

A7
ba - by drag me a - cross your log.
I'll cut your
E7
D7
A7
wood so eas - y for you, you can't help but say, "Hot dog!"
Guitar Solo
D7
A7

E7
D7
A7

D7

A7

Repeat 3 times and Fade
E7
D7
A7

Crossfire

Written by Bill Carter, Ruth Ellsworth, Reese Wynans, Tommy Shannon and Chris Layton

C Chorus
(E#7#9)
N.C.
– ed, ___ caught in ___ the cross – fire.
Strand-ed, ___ caught in the cross-fire. ___
D Verse
(E)
N.C.
2. Tooth for tooth, eye for an eye, _ sell your soul _ just to buy, buy, _ buy. ___
Beg - gin' a dol - lar, steal - in' a dime, _ come on can't cha see that I, I'm _ strand -

E Chorus
(E7#9)
N.C.
– ed? Caught in the cross - fire. I am strand-
– ed, caught in the cross – fire.
F Bridge
G A G A
I need some kind of kind-ness, some kind of sym-pa-thy, Oh no, we're
G Chorus
strand-ed, caught in the cross – fire.

H Guitar Solo

(E7#9)
N.C.
Play 4 times

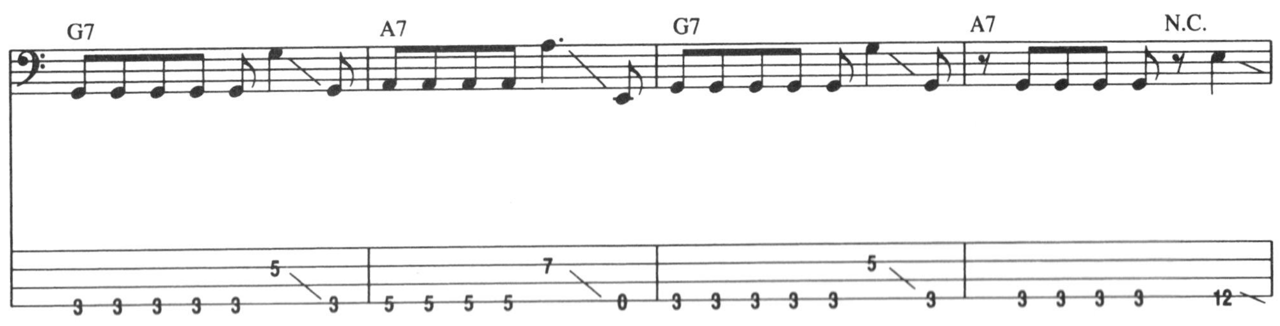
G7
A7
G7
A7
N.C.

(E)
N.C.

I Verse

3. Save the strong, lose the weak. never turn - ing the oth - er cheek.

Trust no-bod-y, don't be no fool. What-ev-er hap-pened to the gold- en rule? We got strand-

J Chorus
(E7#9)
N.C.
– ed, caught in the cross - fire. We got strand –

– ed, caught in the cross – fire. We got strand-

K Chorus
- ed,
caught in the cross - fire.

Strand - ed,
caught in the cross - fire.
Help me!

L Guitar Solo
(E7)
N.C.
Play 7 times

Day Tripper

Words and Music by John Lennon and Paul McCartney

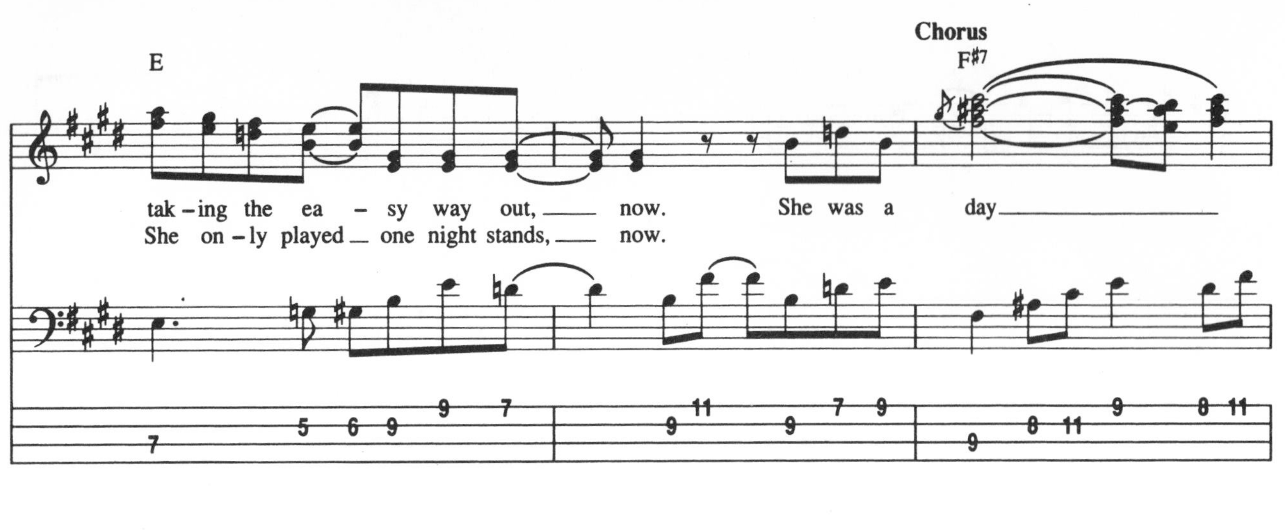
Chorus
E
F#7
tak – ing the ea – sy way out, now. She was a day
She on – ly played one night stands, now.
7 5 6 9 9 7 9 11 9 7 9 9 8 11 9 8 11

trip – per, one way tick – et, yeah; it took me
Sun – day driv – er yeah;
9 8 11 9 9 8 11 9 8 11 9 8 11 9 8 11 9 8 11

A
G#
C#
so long to find out and I found
5 4 7 5 4 7 4 3 6 4 3 6 4 3 6 6 4

B
To Coda
E
out.
2 1 4 4 1 2 7 5 6 9 9 7 9 11 9 7 9

2nd Verse
She's a big tea – ser,
she took me half the way there.
A
She's a big tea – ser,
E
she took me half the way there now.
She was a day
Chorus
F♯7
trip – per,
one way tick – et yeah;
it took me

A
G♯
so
long
to find out
C♯
B
Solo
(4 times)
and I found out.
(2 times)
Ah
Ah

D.S. al Coda

E
Ah.
9 9 9 9 9 9 9 9
7 5 6 9 9 7
9 11 9 7 9

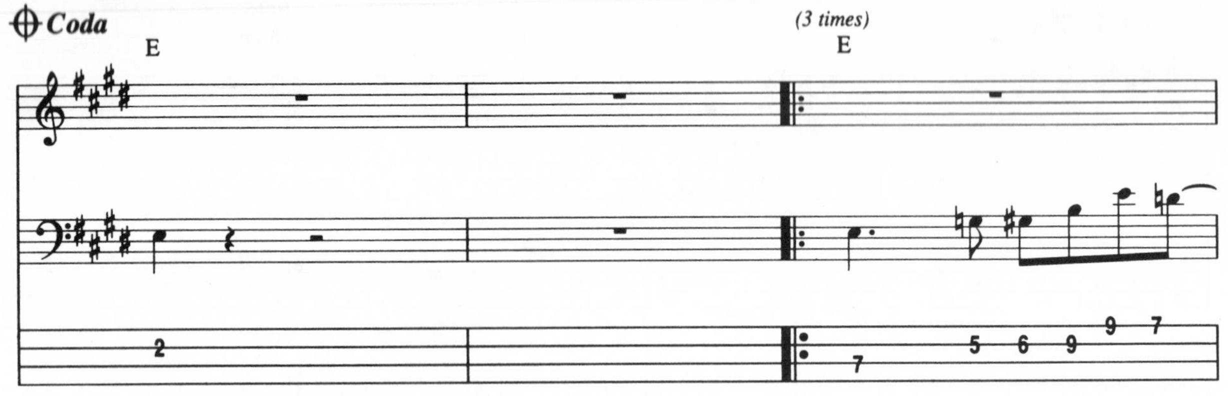
Coda
E
(3 times)
E
2
7 5 6 9 9 7

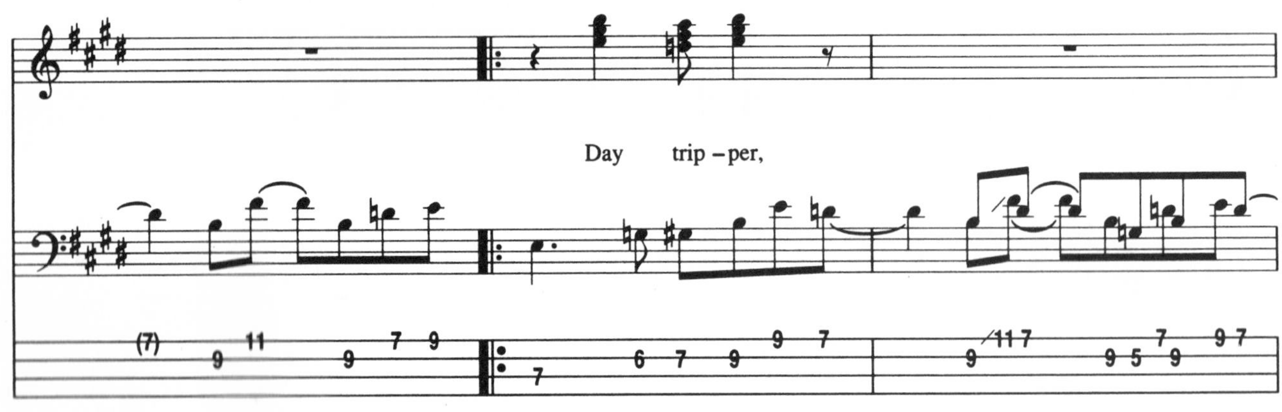
Day trip – per,
(7) 9 11 9 7 9
7 6 7 9 9 7
9 11 7 9 5 7 9 9 7

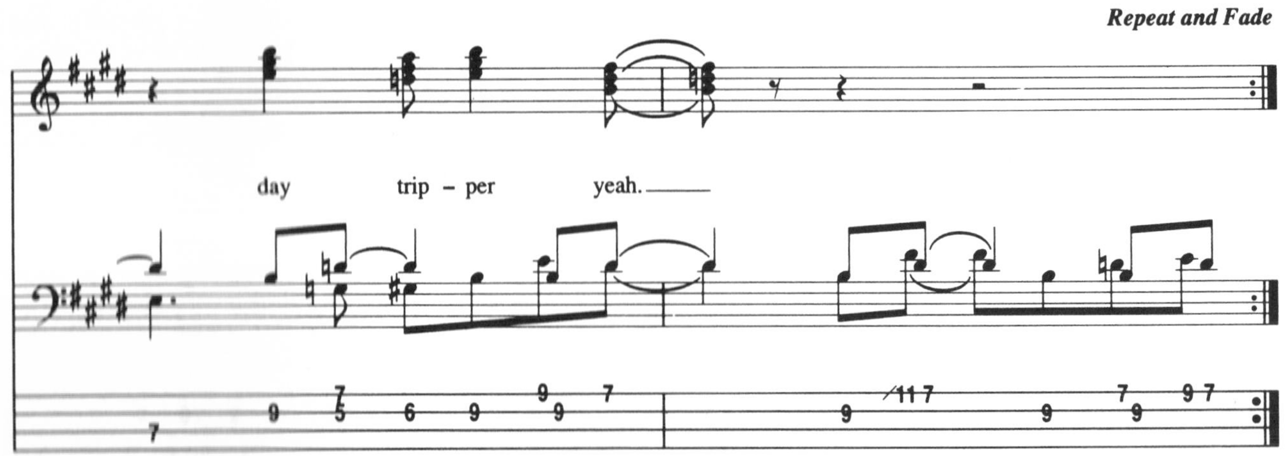
Repeat and Fade
day trip – per yeah.
7 9 7 5 6 9 9 9 7
9 11 7 9 7 9 9 7

Detroit Rock City

Words and Music by Paul Stanley and Bob Ezrin

Tune Down 1/2 Step:
①= G♭ ③= A♭
②= D♭ ④= E♭

* Chord symbols derived from gtr.

E5
hear my song and it pulls me through.
B F♯ A5
Comes on strong; tells me what I got - ta do. I got to... Get up!
Chorus
A5 B
Ev - 'ry - bod - y's gon - na move their feet. Get down! Ev - 'ry - bod - y's gon - na leave their seat.
N.C.(C♯m) A
You got - ta lose your mind in De - troit Rock Cit - y. Get up!
B
Ev - 'ry - bod - y's gon - na move their feet. Get down! Ev - 'ry - bod - y's gon - na leave their seat.

Verse
C♯5
E5
2. Get - ting late, I just can't wait.
B
F♯
C♯
Ten o' - clock, and I know I got - ta hit the road.
E5
First I drink, then I smoke.
B
F♯
A5
Start the car, and I try to make the mid - night show. Get up!
Chorus
A5
B
Ev - 'ry - bod - y's gon - na move their feet. Get down! Ev - 'ry - bod - y's gon - na leave their seat.

Interlude
N.C.(C♯m)
1.
2.
D♯5
C♯5
F♯
E5
A5
B
Verse
C♯5
E5
3. Mov-in' fast, __ do-in' nine - ty-five. __
4. Twelve o'-clock, __ I got - ta rock. __
There's a
Hit top speed, __ but I'm still mov-in' much too slow. ________
truck a - head, __ lights star-in' at my eyes. ________
B
F♯
C♯
I

E5
feel so good, I'm so a - live.
Oh my God! No time to turn.
I
3
3
6 4
6 2
4 2 2 4 2 4 2 4 2 4 2 4

To Coda
B
F#
A5
Hear my song play - in' on the ra - di - o. It goes:
got to laugh 'cause I know I'm gon-na die! Why?
Get up!
3
3
4 2 2 4 2 4 2 4 2 4 2 X
4 2 4 2 4 0 5

Chorus
A5
B
C#
Ev - 'ry-bod-y's gon-na move their feet. Get down! Ev - 'ry-bod-y's gon-na leave their seat.
(5)
0 7
4 4

Interlude
N.C.
A5
B
(drums)
4
15
6 6 6 6 6 6 6 6
0 5
17 0 7

N.C.(C#m)

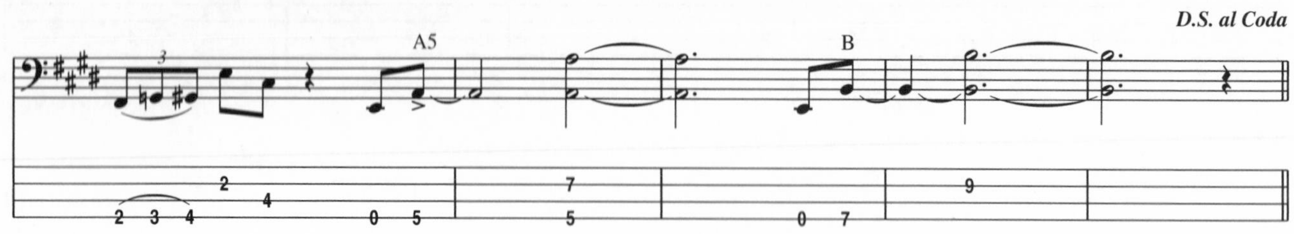
D.S. al Coda
A5
B

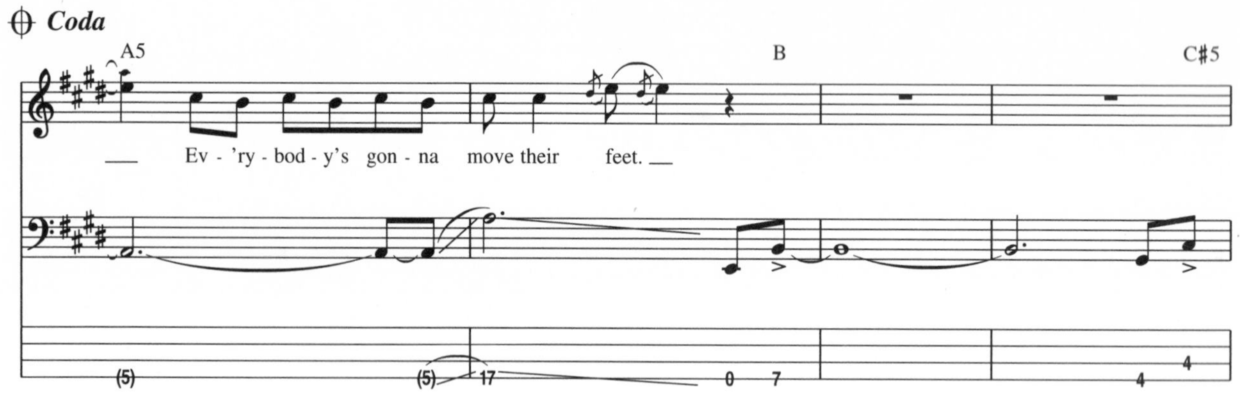
Coda
A5
B
C#5
Ev - 'ry - bod - y's gon - na move their feet.

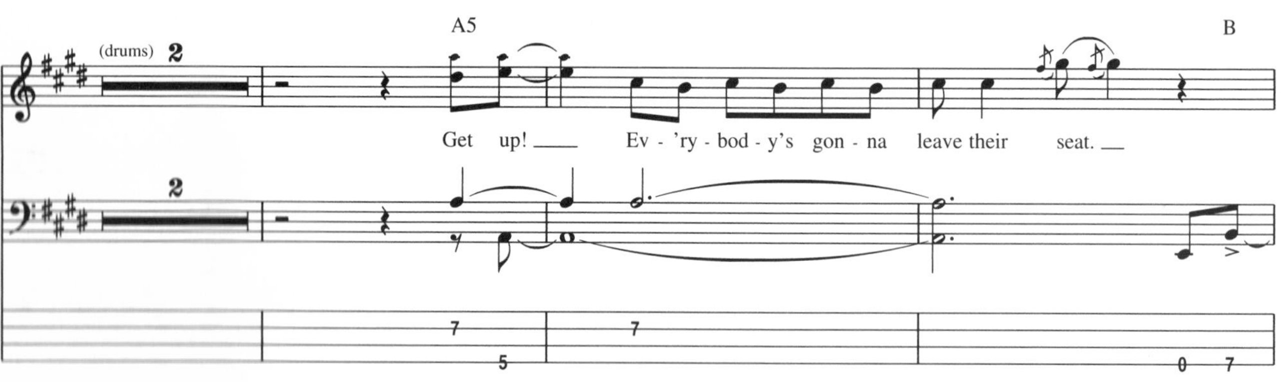
(drums)
A5
B
Get up! Ev - 'ry - bod - y's gon - na leave their seat.

w/ auto crash, explosion & gtr. siren effects
C#5

Don't Be Cruel

(To a Heart That's True)

Words and Music by Otis Blackwell and Elvis Presley

Moderately Fast (♩ = 174)

A7
1 D
2 D
D7
G
to a heart that's true.
to a heart that's true.
I don't want no oth - er
A7
G
A7
D
love, Ba - by, it's just you I'm think - ing of.
D
D7
G
Don't stop think - ing of me Don't make me feel this way, Come on o - ver here and
walk up to the preach - er and let us say, "I do." Then you'll know you
D
Em7
A7
love me, You know what I want you to say. Don't be cruel to a heart that's
have me, And I'll know that I'll have you. Don't be cruel to a heart that's
T
A
B

D
D7
G
A7
G
A7
true. Why should we be a - part, I real - ly love you ba - by cross my
true. I don't want no oth - er love, Ba - by, it's just you I'm think - ing
D
D
Em7
A7
heart. Let's of. Don't be cruel to a heart that's
D
Em7
A7
D
D7
true. Don't be cruel to a heart that's true. I don't
G
A7
G
A7
D
want no oth - er love, Ba - by, it's just you I'm think - ing of.

Don't Look Back in Anger

Words and Music by Noel Gallagher

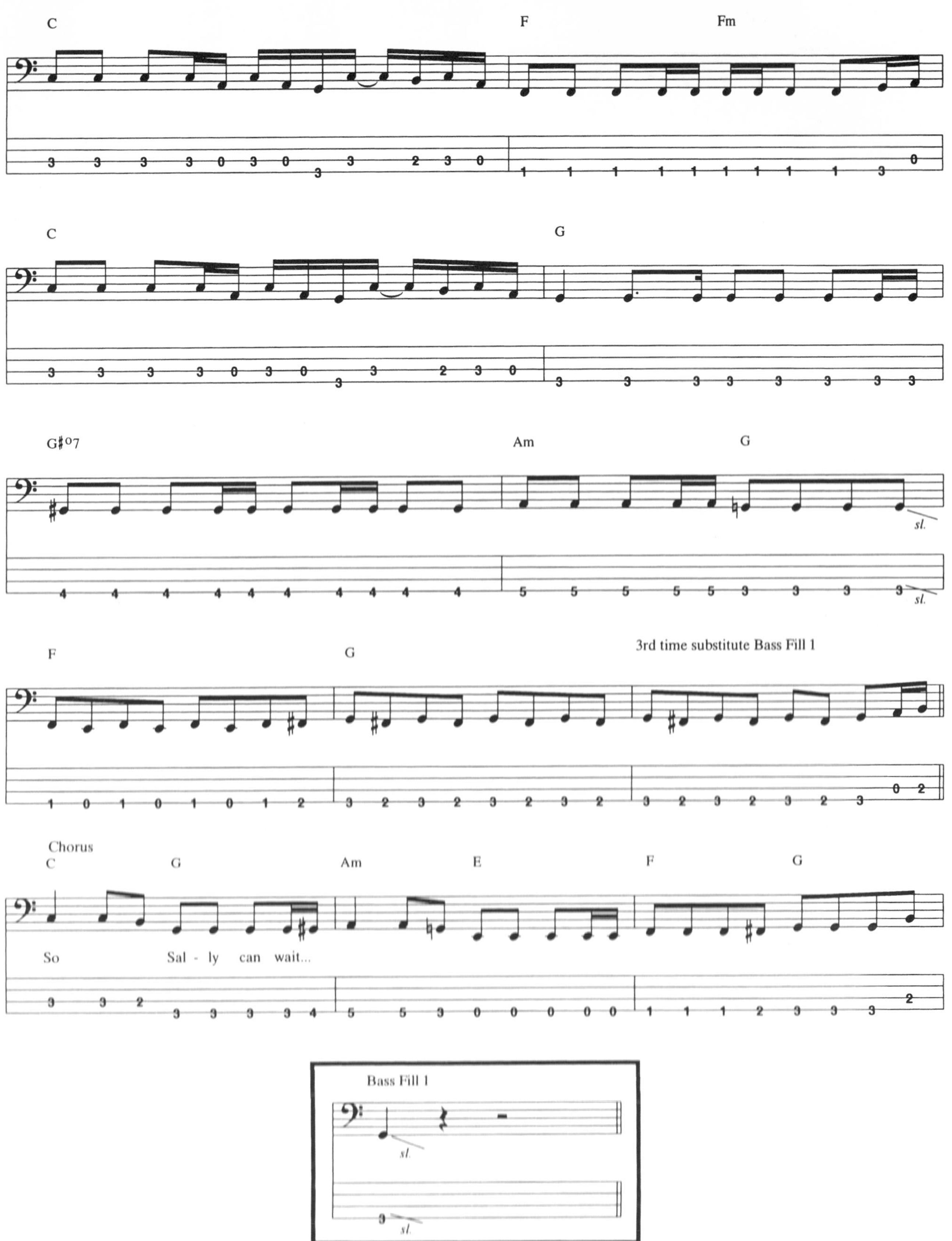
C
F
Fm
C
G
G♯°7
Am
G
sl.
F
G
3rd time substitute Bass Fill 1
Chorus
C
G
Am
E
F
G
So
Sal - ly can wait...
Bass Fill 1
sl.

C Am G C G Am E
To Coda
1.
F G C G Am E
2.
D.S. al Coda
F G C Am G C Am G
Coda
C Am G C G Am E
F G C Am G C G Am
F Fm C G Am E F Fm C
mp
rit.

Don't Speak

Words and Music by Eric Stefani and Gwen Stefani

Chorus
Eb
Bb
C
Fm
Bbm
Bbm7
N.C.(Fm)
Bridge
D
Ab/C
Cb
Gb/Bb
It's all end - ing...
A
A(b5)
Eb7sus4
Ab
Guitar solo
Cm
Gm
sl.

3rd Verse
Fm
F5
B♭5
3. You and me...
mf
Chorus
Fm
B♭m
E♭
C
B♭m7
C
Don't speak...
1.
2.
Fm7
B♭m7
C
Fm
B♭m
C
Outro
Fm
B♭m
E♭
C
B♭m7
C
Fm
B♭m7
C
Fm
B♭m
E♭
C
B♭m7
C
Repeat (ad lib) and fade
Fm
B♭m7
C

Dream On

Words and Music by Steven Tyler

D5 E5 F♯m C♯m D♯m7♭5 Dmaj7♭5 F♯m F♯sus4 F♯m
2nd Verse
F♯m C♯m/F♯ F♯m6 Dmaj7♭5/F♯ F♯m C♯m/F♯
1.
F♯m6 Dmaj7♭5/F♯
Half_ my life's___ in book's writ-ten pag - es,...
2.
F♯m6 Dmaj7♭5/F♯
Chorus
F♯5 E5 D5 E5 F♯5 E5
Sing with me, sing for the years,...
D♯m7♭5 D (C♯m)
Interlude
F♯m C♯+5/F♯ F♯m9 Badd2
E7/6 E♯o F♯m C♯+5/F♯ F♯m9 Badd2 E7/6 E♯o
Well,_
Chorus
F♯5 E5 etc. D5 E5 F♯5 E5 D♯m7♭5 D
_ sing with me,...

(C♯m)
B5
C♯5
etc.
D5
E5
F♯5
Dream on,_ . . .
B5
C♯5
D5
E5
F♯5
sl.
sl.
sl.
B5
C♯5
D5
E5
F♯5
G♯5
A5
B5
C♯5
Chorus
F♯5
E5
D5
E5
Play 3 times
F♯5
E5
D♯m7♭5
D5
C♯5
Fade out

Drive My Car

Words and Music by John Lennon and Paul McCartney

* Chord symbols reflect overall harmony.

Chorus
Bm
G
in be - tween." –
bet - ter time." –
that's a start."
"Ba - by, you can drive my car. ___
Bass Fig. 1
Bm
G
Bm
Yes, I'm gon - na be a star. ___
Ba - by, you can drive my car, _
E
A
To Coda
1.
D
G
A
___ and may - be I'll love ___ you."
End Bass Fig. 1
2.
D
G
A N.C.
Guitar Solo
D
___ you."
Beep, beep, mm, beep, beep, yeah! ___
* Sing 1st time

G
Play 3 times
A7#5#9
Chorus
w/ Bass Fig. 1
Bm G Bm G
"Ba-by, you can drive my car.
Yes, I'm gon-na be a star.
D.S. al Coda
Bm E A D G A
Ba-by, you can drive my car, and may-be I'll love you."
Coda
Outro
D G A N.C. D G
you."
Beep, beep, mm, beep, beep, yeah!
Repeat and fade
A N.C. D G A N.C.
Beep, beep, mm, beep, beep, yeah!
Beep, beep, mm, beep, beep, yeah!

Eight Days a Week

Words and Music by John Lennon and Paul McCartney

Bass: w/ Bass Fig. 1
3rd time, Voc.: w/ Voc. Fill 1
E
G
D
Hope you need my love, babe,
just like I need you.
One thing I can say,
girl,
love you all the time.

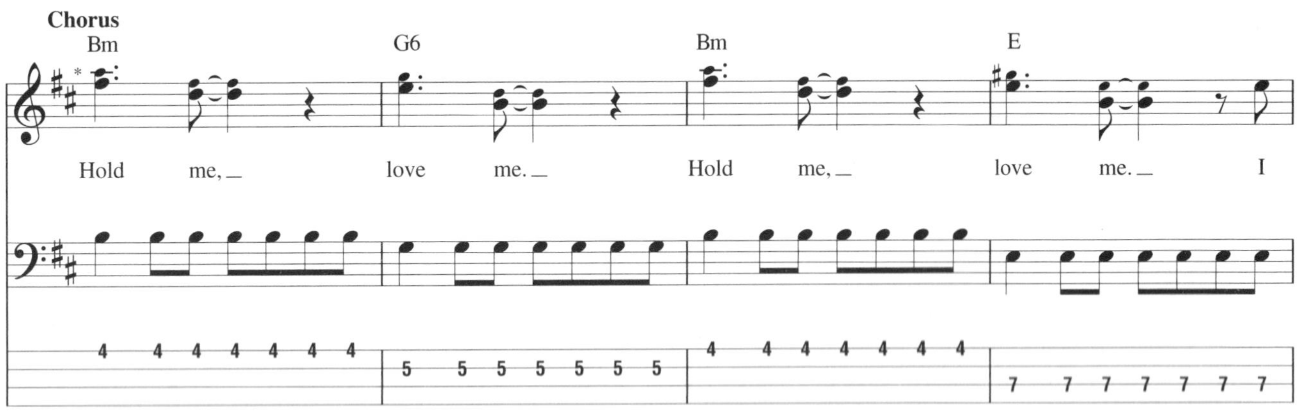
Chorus
Bm
G6
Bm
E
Hold me, love me. Hold me, love me. I
4 4 4 4 4 4 4
5 5 5 5 5 5 5
4 4 4 4 4 4 4
7 7 7 7 7 7 7
* Sing harmonies 2nd and 4th times only.

Bass: w/ Bass Fig. 1
To Coda 2
D
E
G
D
ain't got noth - in' but love,
1., 3., 4.babe,
2. girl,
eight days a week.
Bridge
A
Bm
Eight days a week, I love you.
7 7 7 7
7 7 7 7
4 4 4 4
4 4 4 4

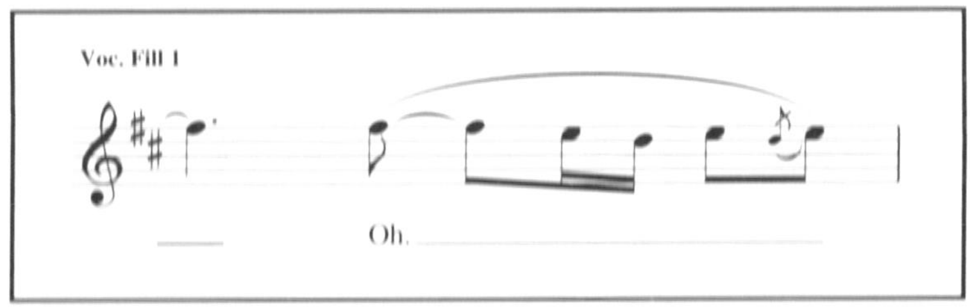
Voc. Fill 1
Oh.

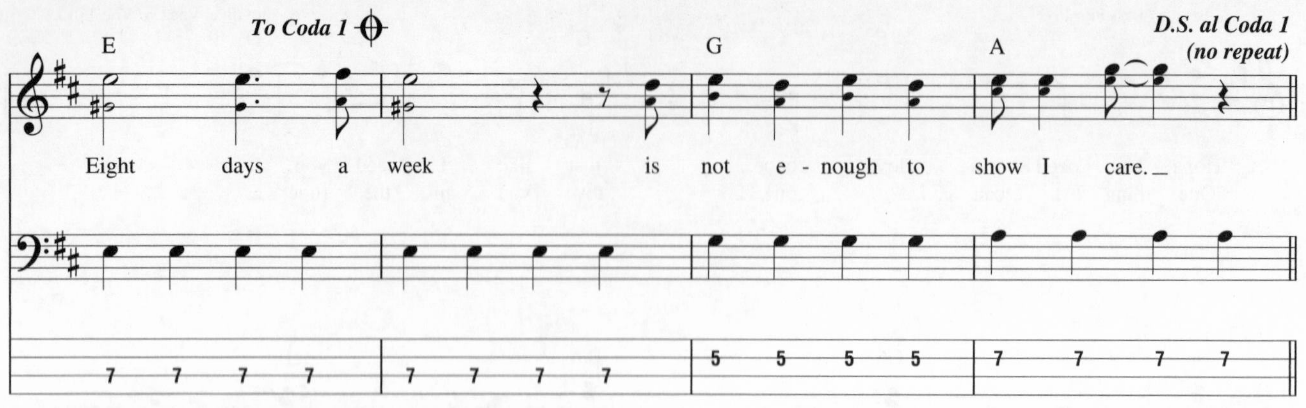
To Coda 1
E
G
A
D.S. al Coda 1
(no repeat)
Eight days a week is not e - nough to show I care.

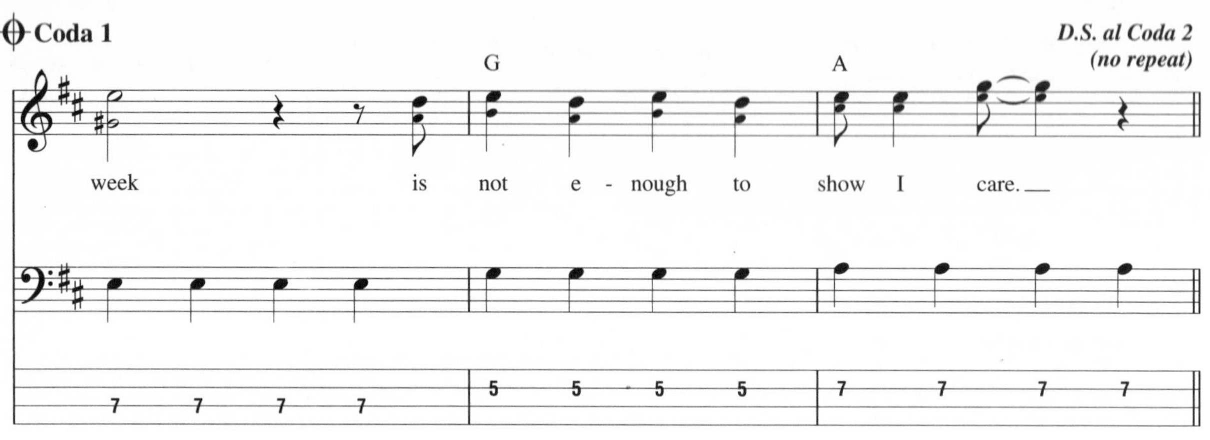
Coda 1
G
A
D.S. al Coda 2
(no repeat)
week is not e - nough to show I care.

Coda 2
G
D
Outro
Dadd9
Eight days a week.

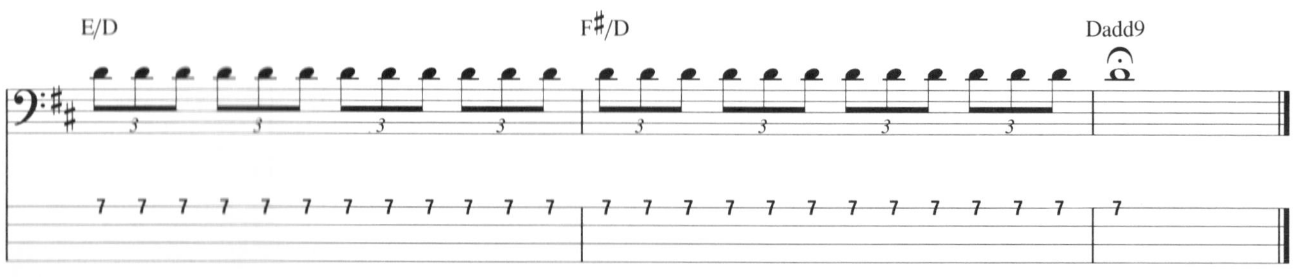
E/D
F♯/D
Dadd9

Even Flow

Music by Stone Gossard
Lyric by Eddie Vedder

Drop "D" Tuning:
④=D ②=D
③=A ①=G
(Recording sounds 1/4 step sharp.)

Intro
Moderate Rock ♩=108

Fretless Bass N.C.

Harm. (8va)

Harm.

Verse
N.C.

1. Freez - in', rest's his head on a pil - low made of con - crete a - gain.
2. Kneel - in', look-in' through the pa - per though he does-n't know to read. Ooh

yeah. Oh, feel - in' may - be he'll see a lit - tle bet - ter Sat - ur - days.
Whoa, pray - in' up to some-thing that has nev - er showed him an - y - thing.

Ooh yeah. Whoa, hey now,
Oh, deal - in',
fac-es that he sees come a-gain ain't. that fa-mil - iar. Ooh yeah. Whoa,
un-der-stands the weath - er or the win - ter's on its way. Oh,
no grin he can't have when his hap-py looks in - sane. Ooh
ceil - ings few and far be-tween all the le-gal hall of shame. Yeah.
To Coda 1
yeah.
Chorus
D5
B♭5
E - ven - flow,
Fill 1
Harm.
(8va)
End Fill 1
Bass Fig. 1
Harm.

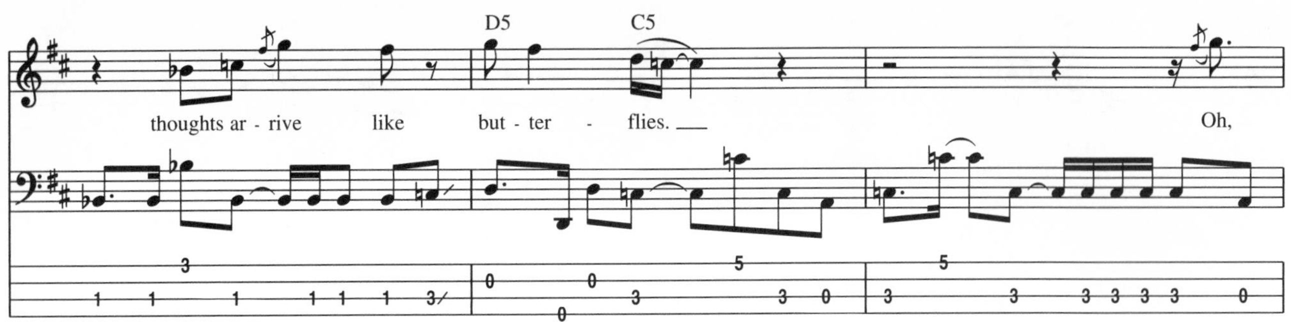
D5
C5
thoughts ar - rive like but - ter - flies.
Oh,

D5
Bb5
D5
C5
he don't know,
so he chas - es them a-way.

D5
Bb5
Oh, some-day yet
he'll be - gin his

D.S. al Coda 1
D5
C5
life a - gain,
life a - gain,
life a - gain.
End Bass Fig. 1

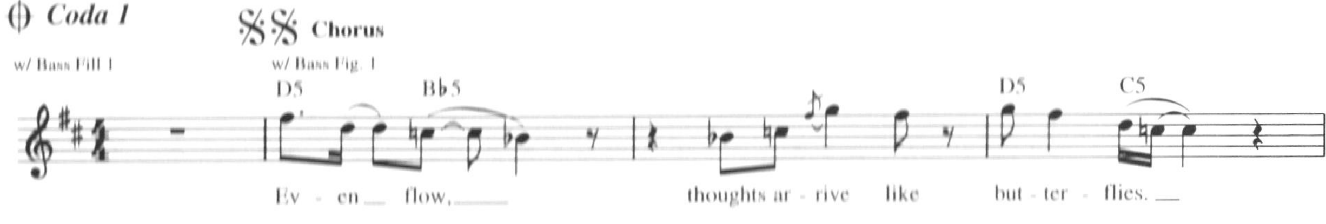
Coda 1
Chorus
w/ Bass Fill 1
w/ Bass Fig. 1
D5
Bb5
D5
C5
Ev - en flow,
thoughts ar - rive like
but - ter - flies.

D5
B♭5
D5
C5
Oh, he don't know,
so he chas - es them a-way.

D5
B♭5
D5
C5
Oh, some - day yet
he'll be - gin his life a - gain.

D5
B♭5
Ooh,
whis-p'ring hands
gent - ly
lead him a-way,

D5
C5
D5
C5
D5
C5
him a - way,
him a - way.

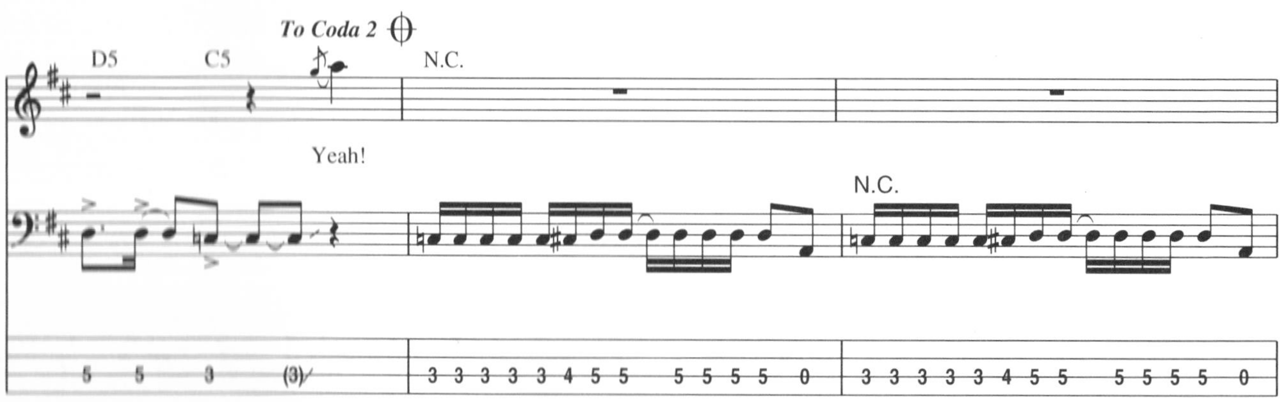
To Coda 2
D5
C5
N.C.
Yeah!
N.C.

Guitar Solo
N.C.
play 8 times

1., 2., 3.
4.
D.S. al Coda 2
N.C.
N.C.
mf (grad. cresc.)

Coda 2
N.C.

Everything to Everyone

Words by Art Alexakis
Music by Art Alexakis and Everclear

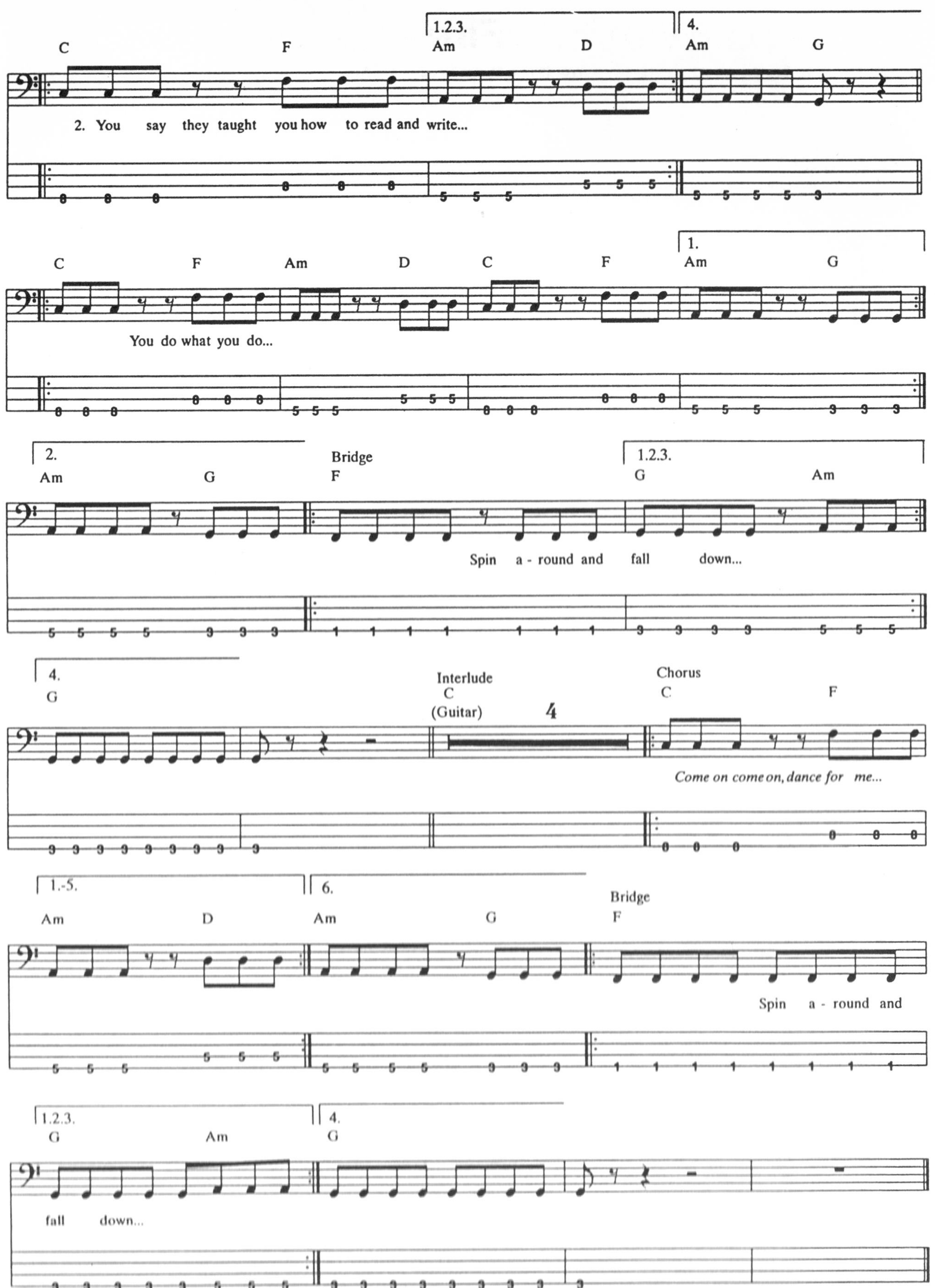
1.2.3.
4.
C F Am D Am G
2. You say they taught you how to read and write...
1.
C F Am D C F Am G
You do what you do...
2.
Am G
Bridge
F
1.2.3.
G Am
Spin a - round and fall down...
4.
G
Interlude
C
(Guitar)
4
Chorus
C F
Come on come on, dance for me...
1.-5.
6.
Am D Am G
Bridge
F
Spin a - round and
1.2.3.
4.
G Am G
fall down...

Fire

Words and Music by Jimi Hendrix

Dadd9
Cadd9
Dadd9
Cadd9
fire!
Whoa, let me stand, ba - by!
(Let me stand next to your fire!)
(Let me stand next to your

Dadd9
Cadd9
Let me stand.
Yeah, ba - by!
fire!)
(Let me stand next to your fire!)

D.S. al Coda
Bass: w/ Bass Fig. 1, 2 times
N.C.(D)
Lis - ten here, ba - by,
and stop act - in' so cra - zy.
2. You say your

Coda
Chorus
Dadd9
Cadd9
Dadd9
Cadd9
(Mss - sta!)
Yeah!
Let me stand, ba - by!
(Let me stand next to your fire!)
(Let me stand next to your
Bass

Dadd9
Cadd9
Let me stand!
fire!)
(Let me stand next to your fire!)
Oh, let me stand!

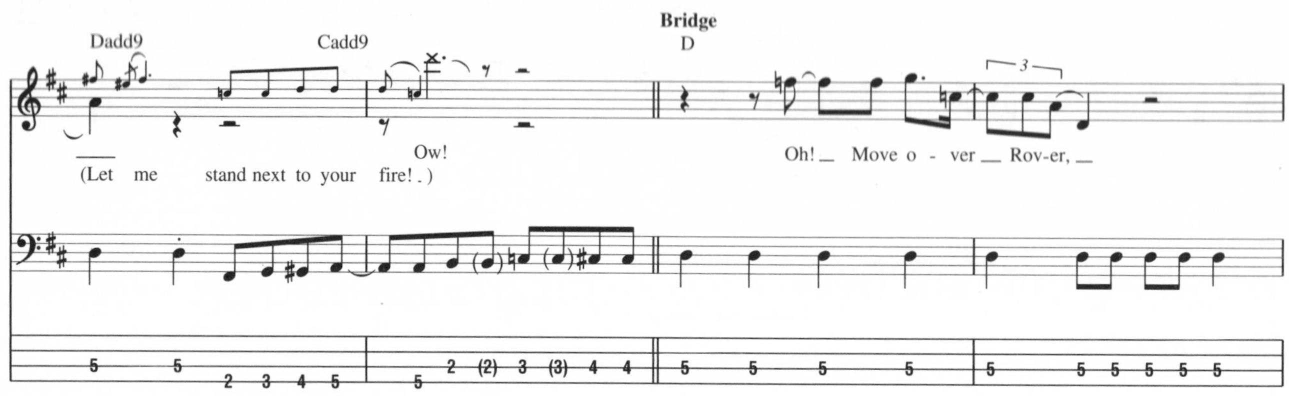
Dadd9
Cadd9
Bridge
D
(Let me stand next to your fire!)
Ow!
Oh! Move o - ver Rov-er,

Cadd9
A
and let Jim - i take o - ver!
Yeah, you know what I'm

C
8va
loco
Guitar Solo
N.C.(E)
talk-in'a-bout!
Yeah!
Get on withit ba - by!

Interlude

N.C.

Verse

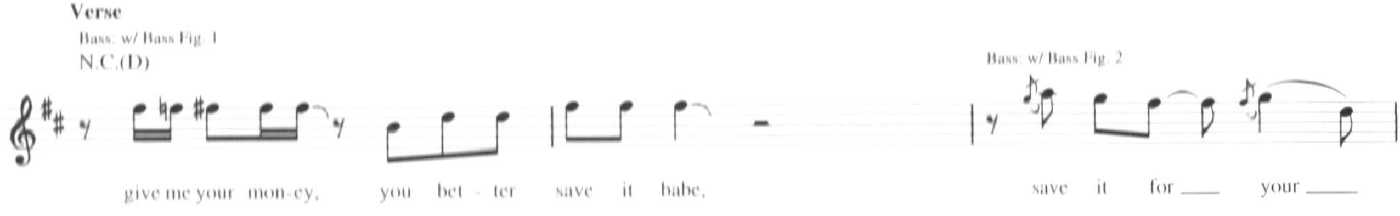

Chorus
Dadd9
Cadd9
fire, ha!
Ow!
Uh, let me stand!
(Let me stand next to your fire!)
Bass
Dadd9
Cadd9
Dadd9
Cadd9
Oh, let me stand, ba - by!
(Let me stand next to your fire!)
(Let me stand next to your
Dadd9
Cadd9
I ain't gon-na do you no harm.
Ow!
fire!)
(Let me stand next to your fire!)
Outro
Eadd9
N.C.(E)
Yeah!
You bet-ter move o-ver,
*Played behind the beat.

*(D)
ba-by!
I ain't gon-na hurt ya, ba-by!
Ah, _ I ain't talk with your
3
(E)
ol' la-dy.
Ow!
Ah, _ yes this is Jim-
Begin Fade
(D)
i talk-in' to you!
Yeah, _ ba-by!
(E)
8va
Do, do, do, do, do, do!
Fade Out
(D)

Foolin'

Words and Music by Steve Clark, Robert John "Mutt" Lange and Joe Elliott

Moderately (♩=100)

Guitar only
4
Am
La - dy Luck ___ ne - ver smiles, _ so lend your love ___ to

F
Am
F
Am
me a - while. ___ Do with me _ what you will, _ break the spell,

F
Am
F
Am
take your fill. _ On and on _ we rode the storm, ___ the flame has died and the
T
A
B
5 2 2
3 2
5 2 2

F
Am
F
Am
fire has gone.
Oh, this emp-ty bed is a night a - lone,
I re - al - ized that
long a - go.
is an - y - bod-y out there?
A5
An-y - bod-y there?
D5
C5
A5
Does an - y - bod-y won - der?
C5
G5
A5
E5
F5
An - y - bod-y care?

G5 A5 Bb5 C

Oh, I just got-ta know

Bb5/D C/E

if you're real-ly there and you real - ly care

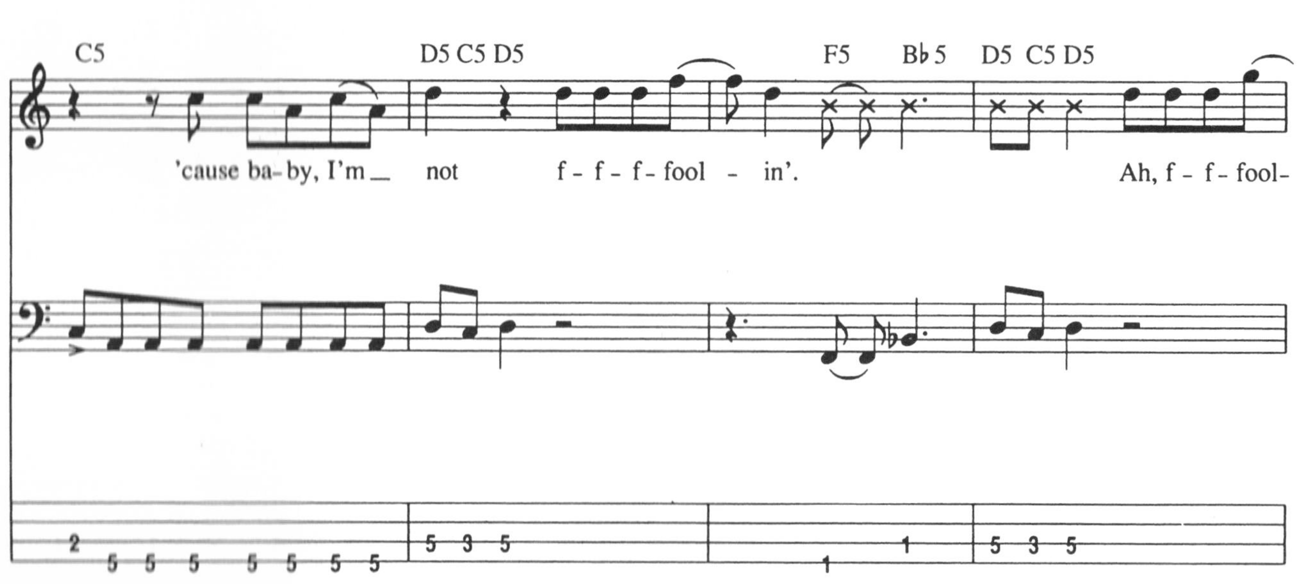

F5
G5
D5 C5 D5
F5
B♭5
D5 C5 D5
in'. __
F - f - f - fool - in'.
Ah, f - f - fool-
To Coda
F5
G5
D5
Am
in'.
Won't you stay with me __ a - while
F
Am
F
Am
F
Close your eyes, __ don't run and hide, __

Am
F
Am
Eas - y love. is no eas - y ride. Just wak - in' up to
Am
D.S. 𝄋 al Coda
what we had could stop good love from go - in' bad. Is
Coda
(Solo Guitar)
D5 C5 D5
F5
B♭5
D5 C5 D5
F5
B♭5
D5 C5 D5
F5
B♭5
D5 C5 D5
A5

C5 G5 A5
Dm C A5
C5 G5 A5 E5 F5 G5 A5 B♭
Oh,
C
B♭5/D
I just got-ta know
if you're real-ly there

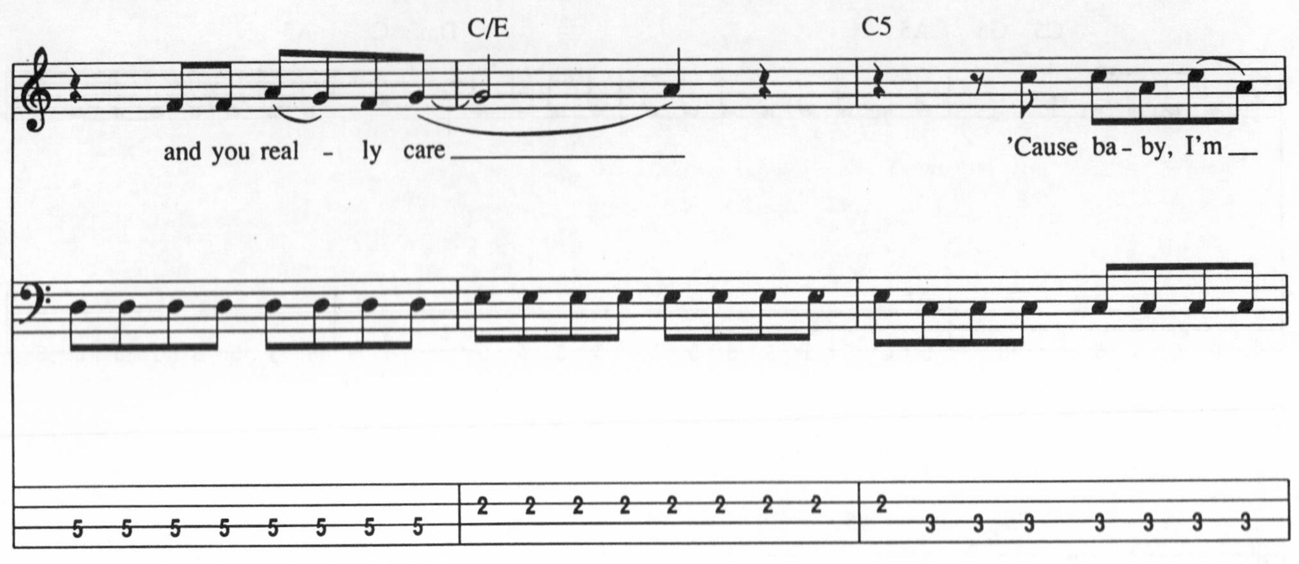
C/E
C5
and you real - ly care
'Cause ba - by, I'm

D5 C5 D5
F5
B♭5
D5 C5 D5
F5
G5
not f - f - f - fool - in',
Ah, f - f - fool - in'

D5 C5 D5
F5
B♭5
D5 C5 D5
F5
G5
Repeat and Fade
F - f - f - fool - in',
Ah, f - f - fool - in'
I'm

Free Bird

Words and Music by Allen Collins and Ronnie Van Zant

Slow Rock ♩ = 60
Intro
G
D/F♯
Em
F
C
D
8va
loco
D5
1st, 2nd Verses
1. If I leave here to - mor - row, (etc.)
2. Bye bye, ba - by, it's been sweet now, (etc.)

D
G
D/F♯
Em
F
C
D
G
D/F♯
Em
F
C
D
G
D/F♯
Em
F
C
D
On repeat, play these two bars twice.
F
C
D
F
C
D
F
C
1. D
sl.
H
8va
loco

Double-time feel (♩ = 120)
2.
D
G
B♭5
C
Guitar solo
B♭
Play 4 times
Play 4 times
Play 3 times

G
B♭5
C
Play 4 times
sl.
G
B♭
C
Play 4 times
G
B♭5
C
Play 4 times
P
G
B♭
C
Play 4 times
G
B♭
1. C
2. C
G

B♭
C
G
B♭
sl.
C
8va
sl.
8va
loco
sl.
P
G5
B♭5
C5
sl.
B♭5
Play 3 times
G5
B♭5
C5
sl.
B5
B♭5
A5
Begin fade
G
B♭
C
sl.
B♭
sl.
Play 3 times and fade
G
B♭
C
B♭

Funk #49

Words and Music by Joe Walsh, Dale Peters and James Fox

N.C.
A5
N.C.
B5
N.C.
B5
N.C.
E7#9
A7
D/A
A7
D/A G/B D/A
A7
2. A
Verse
Bass: w/ Fill 1, 2nd time
A7
D/A
A7
D/A G/B
D/A
A7
jump-in' up, fall - in' down, _ don't mis - un - der - stand me.
3. Out all night, sleep all day, _ I know what you're do - in'.
Fill 1

A7
D/A
A7
D/A G/B
D/A
A7
You don't think that I know your plan; what you try'n' to hand me?
If you're gon - na act this way, I think there's trou - ble brew - in'.
Interlude
N.C.
A5
N.C.
A5
N.C.
B5
N.C.
B5
N.C.
To Coda
E7#9
A7
D/A
A7
D/A G/B
D/A
A7

Percussion Solo
Bass tacet
16
Guitar Break
2
A7
D/A
A7
D/A
A7
D/A
A7
D/A
A7
D.S. al Coda
Coda
Outro
A7
D/A
A7
D/A G/B
D/A
A7
D/A
A7
D/A G/B
D/A
A7
D/A
A7
D/A G/B
D/A
A7
D/A
A7
D/A G/B
D/A
A7

D/A A7 D6/A A7
D/A A7 D/A A7
Begin Fade
D/A A7
D/A A7
Played behind the beat.
D/A A7 D/A A7
D/A A7 D/A A7
Fade Out

Get Back

Words and Music by John Lennon and Paul McCartney

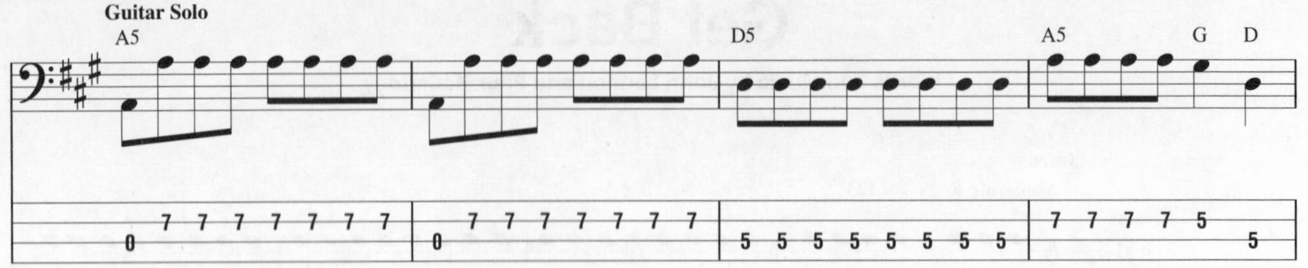
Guitar Solo
A5
D5
A5
G
D

A5
D5
A5
G
D5/A
Go home!
Get back, _

Chorus
A5
D5
A5
G
D5/A
_ get back, _ back _ to where you once be - longed. _ Get back, _

A5
C5
D5
_ get back, _ back _ to where you once be - longed. _ Here.

Piano Solo
A5
Uh, get back Jo!

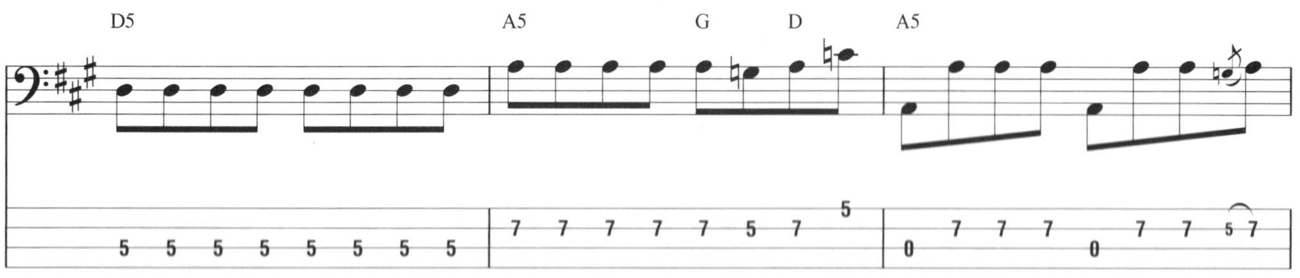
D5
A5
G
D
A5

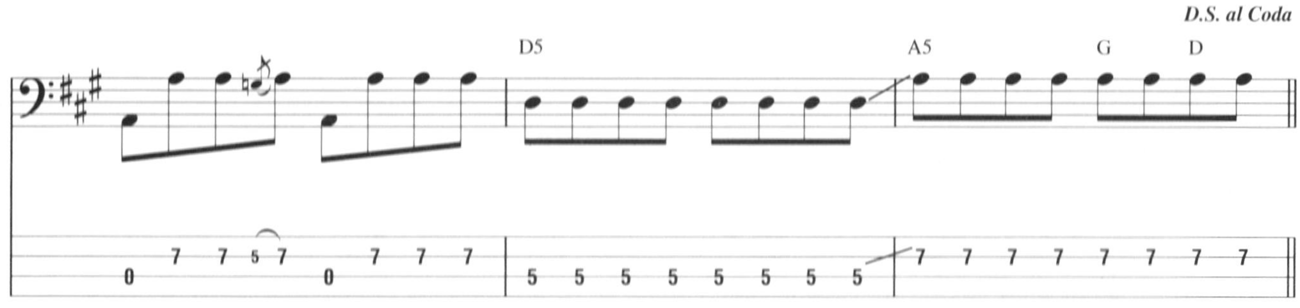
D.S. al Coda
D5
A5
G
D

Coda
Guitar Solo
A5
D5

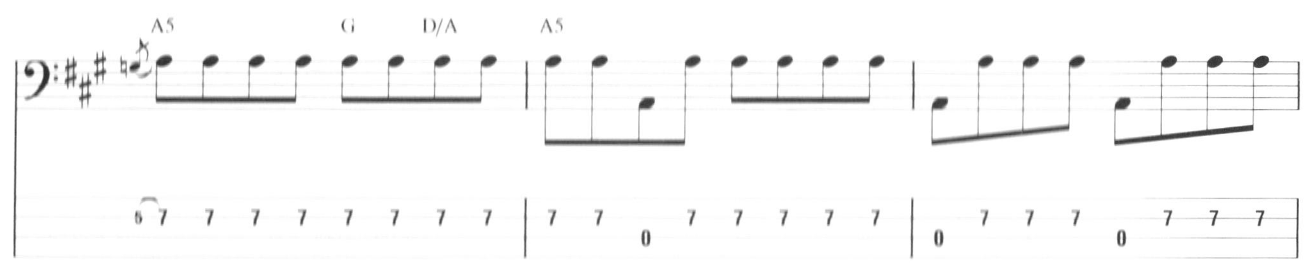
A5
G
D/A
A5

Chorus
D5
A5
G
D5/A
A5
Go home. Oh, get back, you get back, get back
D5
A5
G
D
A5
to where you once be - longed. Ya, get back, get back, get back
D5
to where you once be - longed. Oo.
Outro
Bass: w/ Bass Fig. 1 (till fade)
A5
D5
A
G/A D5/A
Spoken: Get back Lor - et - ta. Your mom-my's wait - in' for ya. Wear-in'
get back, get back to where you once be-longed. Oh, get back,
2nd time, Begin fade
Fade out
A5
D5
A
G/A D5/A
her high - heel shoes and her low-necked sweat - er. Get back home Lor - et - ta. Sung: Get back
get back, get back, oh yeah.

Gimme Three Steps

Words and Music by Allen Collins and Ronnie Van Zant

Verse

I was cut-ting the rug_ down at a place called The Jug_ with a

A7
D
girl named_ Lin - da Lu___ when_ in walked a man_ with a gun in his hand_ and he was

E7
A7
D
look-ing for you know who.__ He said, "Hey_ there fel-low with the hair col-ored yel - low,

G
E7
D
what you try-in' to prove?_ 'Cause that's my wom-an there_ and I'm a man who_ cares_ and this

A7
D
might be all
for you.

A
D

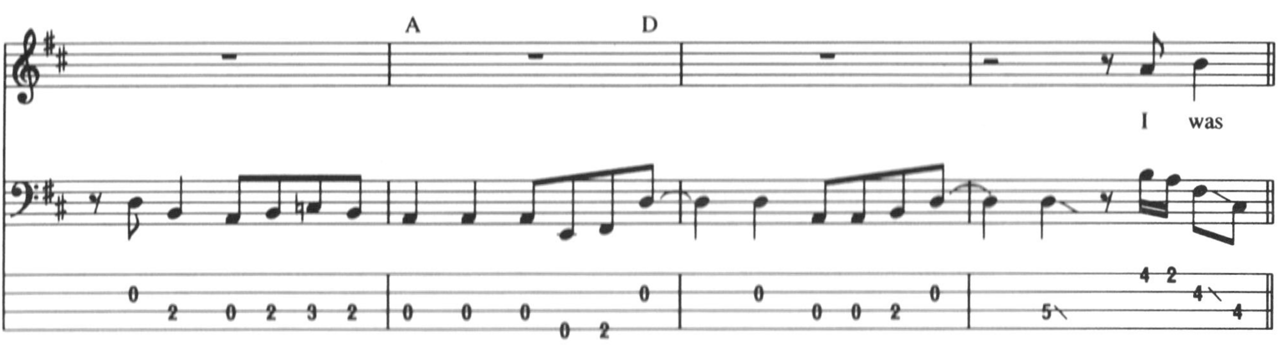
A
D
I was

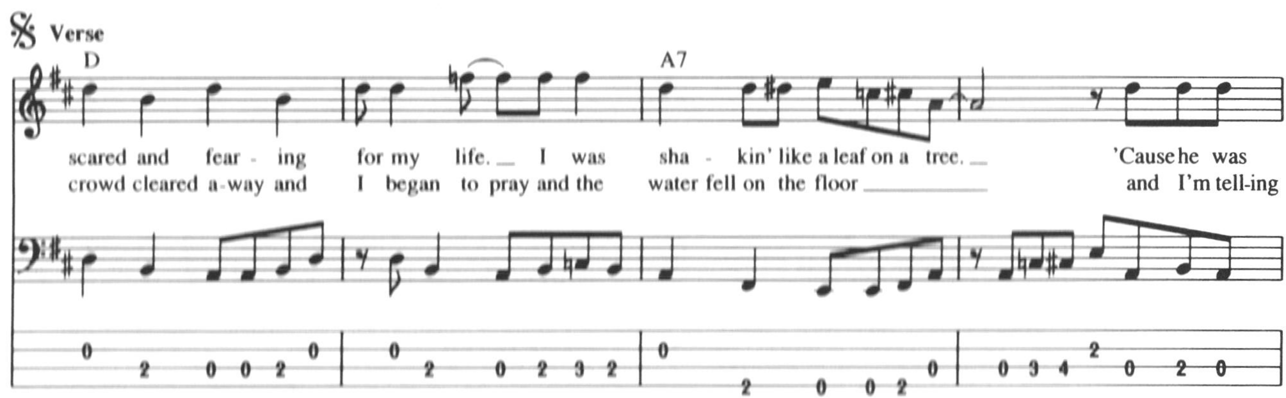
Verse
D
A7
scared and fear - ing for my life. I was sha - kin' like a leaf on a tree. 'Cause he was
crowd cleared a-way and I began to pray and the water fell on the floor and I'm tell-ing

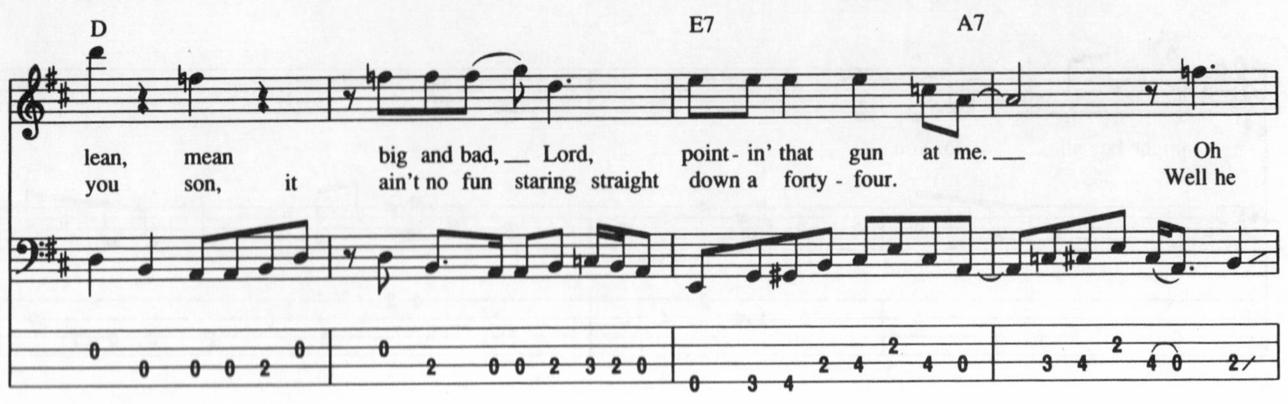
D
E7
A7
lean, mean big and bad, — Lord, point- in' that gun at me. — Oh
you son, it ain't no fun staring straight down a forty - four. Well he

D
G
E7
wait a min-ute, mis-ter. I did-n't e - ven kiss her. Don't want no trou-ble with you. — And I know
turned — and screamed at Lin-da Lu. — That's the break I was look- ing for — and you could

D
A7
D
— you don't owe me but I wish you 'o let — me ask one fa - vor from you. —
— hear me scream-ing a mile a - way as I was head-ed out to - ward the door. —

Chorus
Oh won't you gim-me three steps, gim - me
last verse

A7
D
three steps mis - ter. Gim-me three steps to-ward the door. _
Gim-me three steps, gim-me

To Coda
A7
D
three steps mis - ter and you'll nev- er see me no more. _

Solo
D
A

D
E7
A7

D

G
E7
D
A
D
D.S. al Coda
Coda
D
A
D
E7
A7
D
G
E7
D
A
D
Fade
A

Give It Away

By Anthony Kiedis, Flea, John Frusciante and Chad Smith

Chorus
N.C.(A5)
Give it a-way, give it a-way, give it a-way now.
Give it a-way, give it a-way, give it a-way now.
Give it a-way, give it a-way, give it a-way now.
1.
I can't tell if I'm a king-pin or a pau-per!
2.
Bass tacet
Oh. Oh, yeah!
Give it a-way, give it a-way, give it a-way now.
Give it a-way, give it a-way, give it a-way now.
Give it a-way, give it a-way, give it a-way now.
Guitar Solo
N.C.(E5)
I can't tell if I'm a king-pin or a pau-per!
Bass Fig. 2
End Bass Fig. 2

D.S. al Coda 1
Bass: w/ Bass Fig. 2, 6 times
6
3. Luck - y
Bass Fig. 3
End Bass Fig. 3
6
0 10 0 9 0 7 0 5 0 4 0 3 0 2 0
Coda 1
Chorus
N.C.(A5)
play 3 times
Give it a-way, give it a-way, give it a - way now.
I can't tell if I'm a king-pin or a pau - per!
* Played 1st time only.
Guitar Solo
Bass: w/ Bass Fig. 2, 3 times, simile
Bass: w/ Bass Fig. 3, simile
N.C.(E5)
D.S. al Coda
3
Coda 2
Out-Chorus
Bass: w/ Bass Fig. 1, 1 1/2 times, simile
Bass: w/ Bass Fig. 1, 1 1/2 times, simile
N.C.(A5)
play 4 times
play 3 times
Give it a-way, give it a-way, give it a way now.
Give it a-way now.
Give it a-way now.
Bass: w/ Bass Fig. 1, 1 1/2 times, simile
Bass: w/ Bass Fig. 1, 1 1/2 times, simile
play 3 times
play 3 times
Give it a-way now.
Give it a-way now.
Give it a-way now.

Additional Lyrics

3. Lucky me swimmin' in my ability,
   Dancin' down on life with agility.
   Come and drink it up from my fertility,
   Blessed with a bucket of lucky mobility.
   My mom, I love her 'cause she loves me,
   Long gone are the times when she scrub me.
   Feelin' good, my brother gonna hug me,
   Drink up my juice, young love, chug-a-lug me.
   There's a river born to be a giver,
   Keep you warm, won't let you shiver.
   His heart is never gonna wither,
   Come on everybody, time to deliver.

Got to Get You Into My Life

Words and Music by John Lennon and Paul McCartney

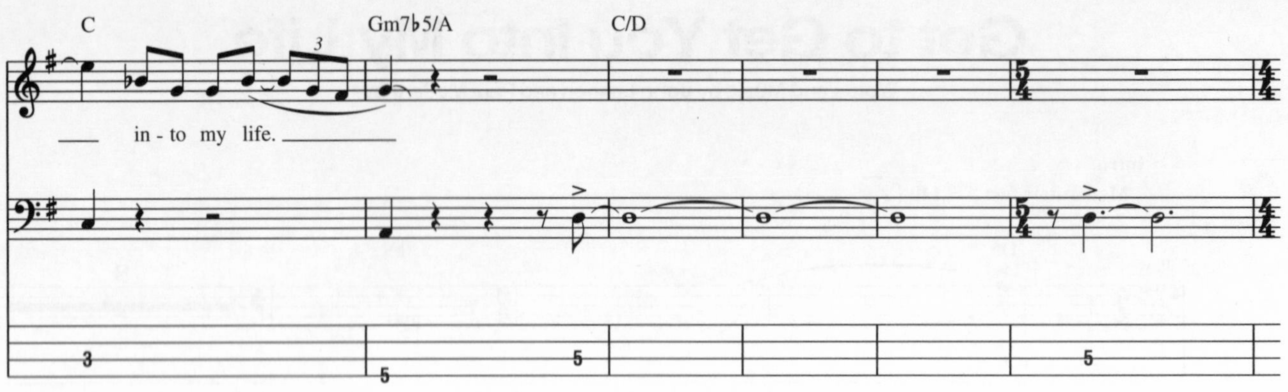
C
Gm7♭5/A
C/D
in - to my life.

Gmaj7
Fmaj9/G
Do, do, do, do, do, do, do, do. Do, do, do, do, do, do, do.

Gmaj7
Do, do, do, do, do, do, do, do. Do, do, do, do, do, do,

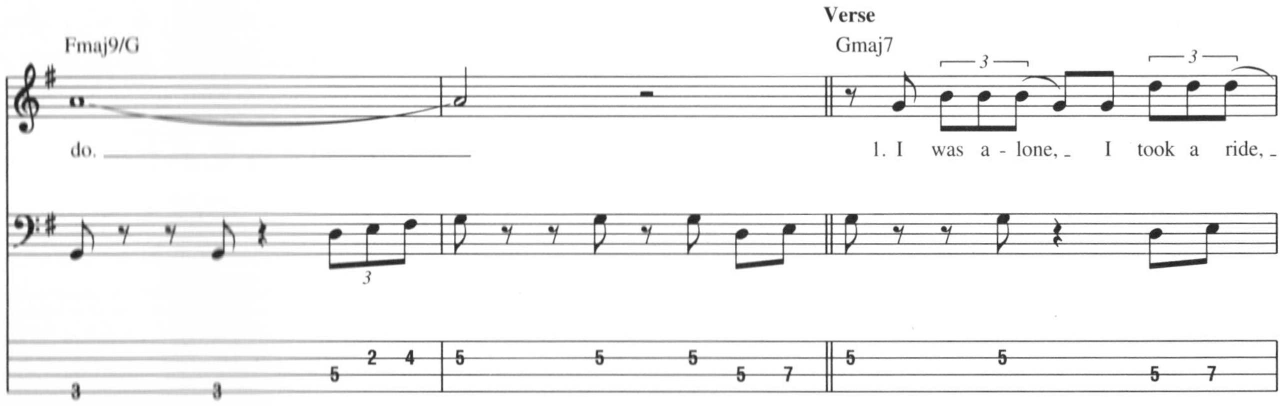
Fmaj9/G
Verse
Gmaj7
do.
1. I was a - lone, I took a ride,

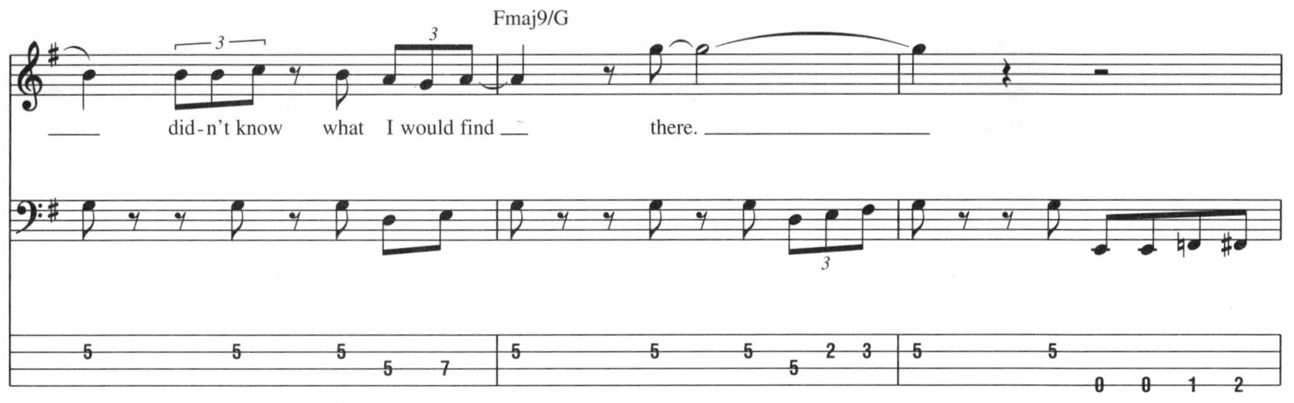
Fmaj9/G
did-n't know what I would find there.

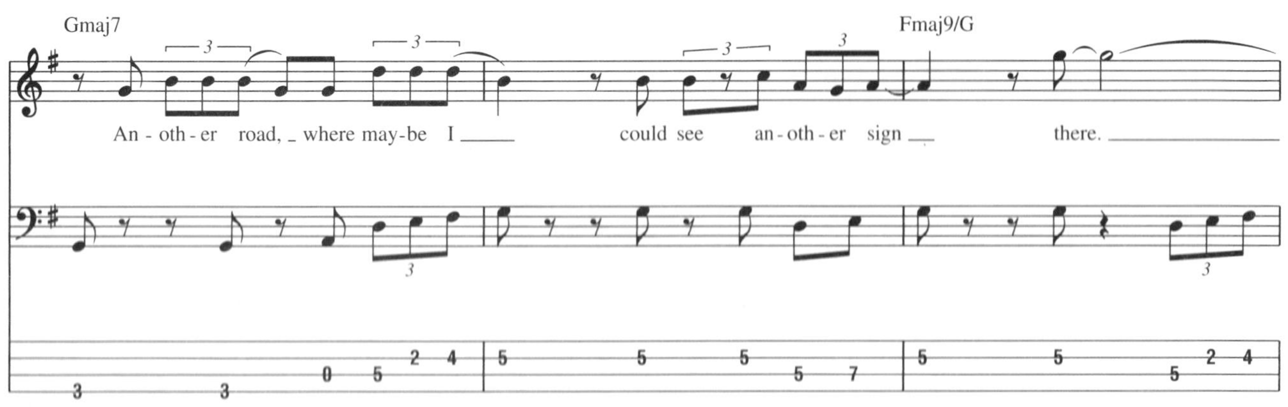
Gmaj7
Fmaj9/G
An-oth-er road, where may-be I could see an-oth-er sign there.

Bm7
Ooh, and then I sud-den-ly see you. Ooh,
Bass Fig. 1

C G/B Am7 D
and did I tell you that I need you ev-'ry sin-gle day of my life?
End Bass Fig. 1

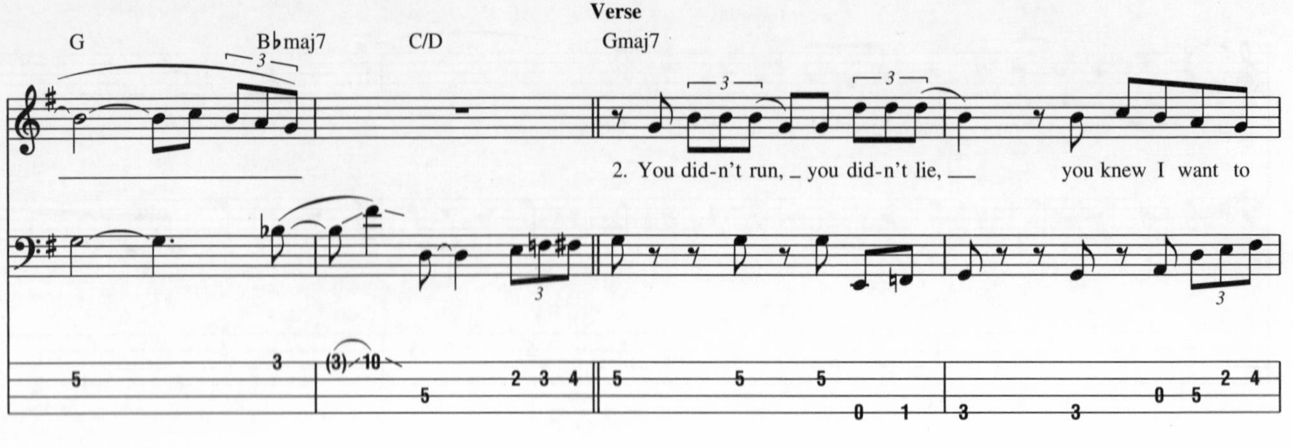
Verse
G
B♭maj7
C/D
Gmaj7
2. You did-n't run, you did-n't lie, you knew I want to

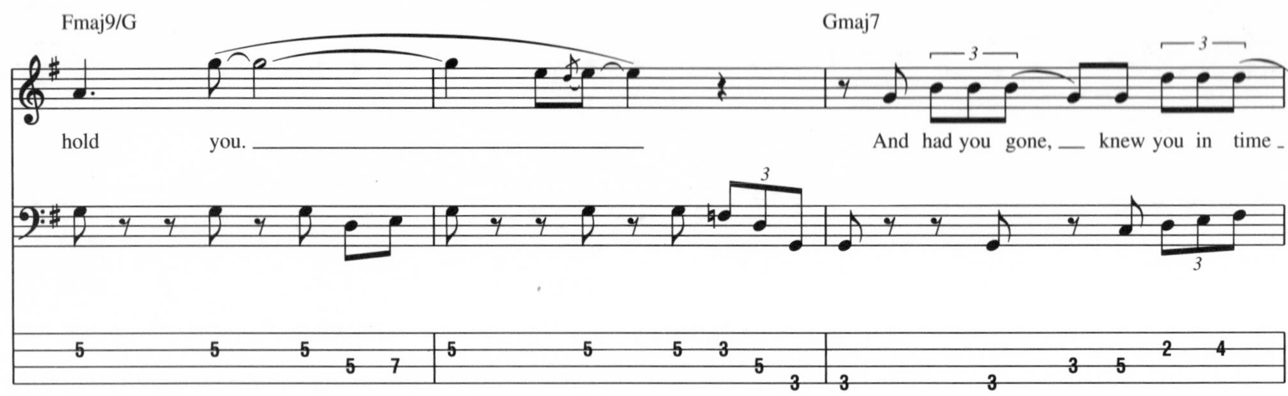
Fmaj9/G
Gmaj7
hold you. And had you gone, knew you in time

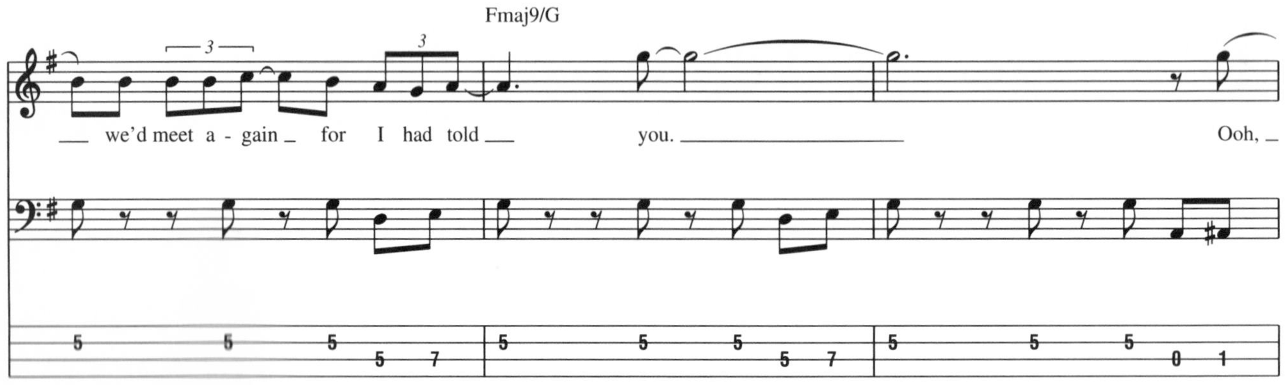
Fmaj9/G
we'd meet a - gain for I had told you. Ooh,

Bass: w/ Bass Fig. 1
Bm7
you were meant to be near me. Ooh, I real - ly

C
G/B
Am7
D
want for you to hear me say we'll be to - geth - er ev - 'ry day.

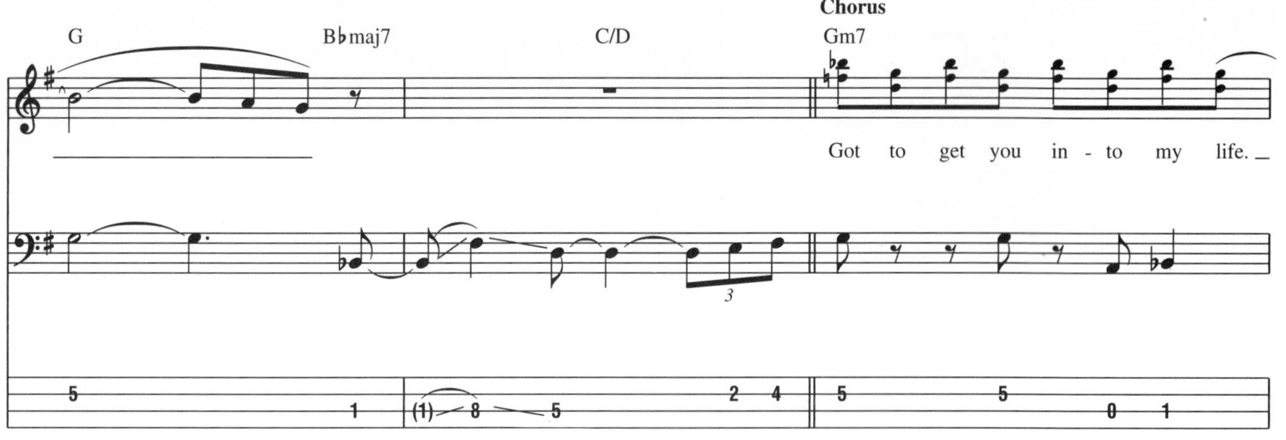
Chorus
G
B♭maj7
C/D
Gm7
Got to get you in - to my life.
5 1 (1) 8 5 2 4 5 5 0 1

C7
Am7
Dm7
D♭
Got to get you in - to my life.
3 3 3 2 0 0 0 3 5 5 4

C7
Am7
Dm7
Gm7
Got to get you in - to my, got to get you in - to my life,
Got to get you in, got to get you in - to my life.
3 3 0 3 2 0 5 5 7 5 5 5 0 1 2

C7
Am7
Dm7
D♭
yeah.
Ah, huh.
Got to get you in - to my life.

C7
Am7
Dm7
Gm7
Got to get you in - to my, got to get you in - to my life.
Got to get you in - to my life.

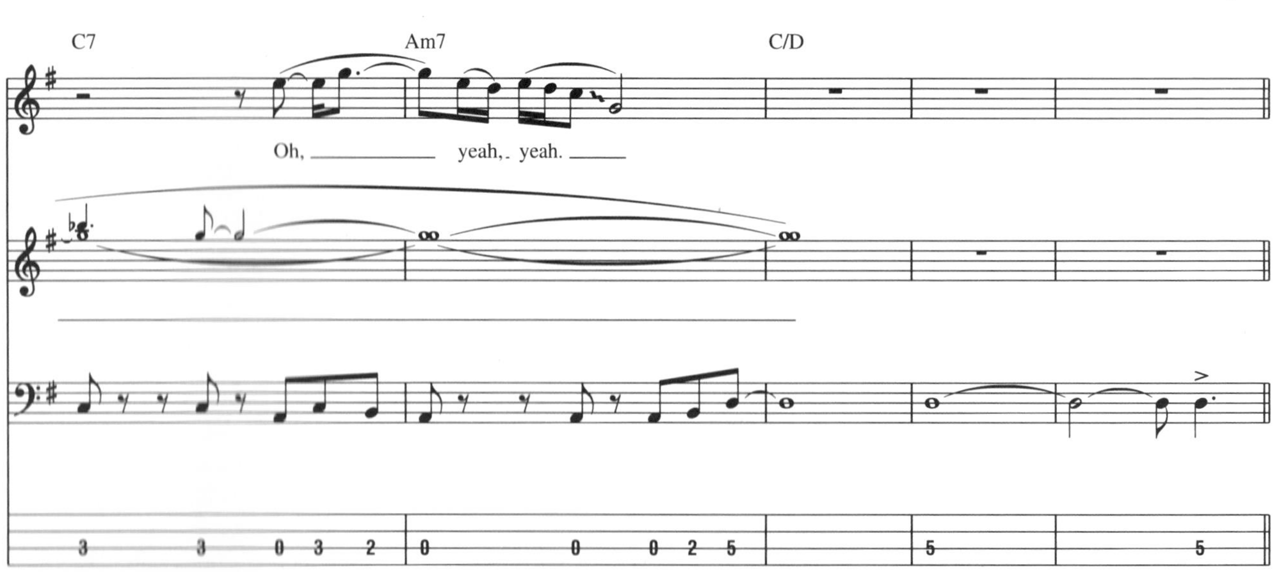
C7
Am7
C/D
Oh, yeah, yeah.

Guitar Solo
Gmaj7
Fmaj9/G
Gmaj7
Famj9/G
Bm7
Ooh, then I
sud - den - ly see you. Ooh, did I tell you that I need you
C G/B Am7 D G B♭maj7 C/D
ev - 'ry sin - gle day of my life?

Chorus
Gm7
C7
Am7
Dm7
D♭
Got to get you in - to my life.
Got to get you in - to my life.
C7
Am7
Dm7
Gm7
C7
My life.
Got to get you in, got to get you in - to my life.
Am7
Dm7
D♭
C7
Am7
Dm7
Got to get you in - to my life. yeah.
Got to get you in - to my life.

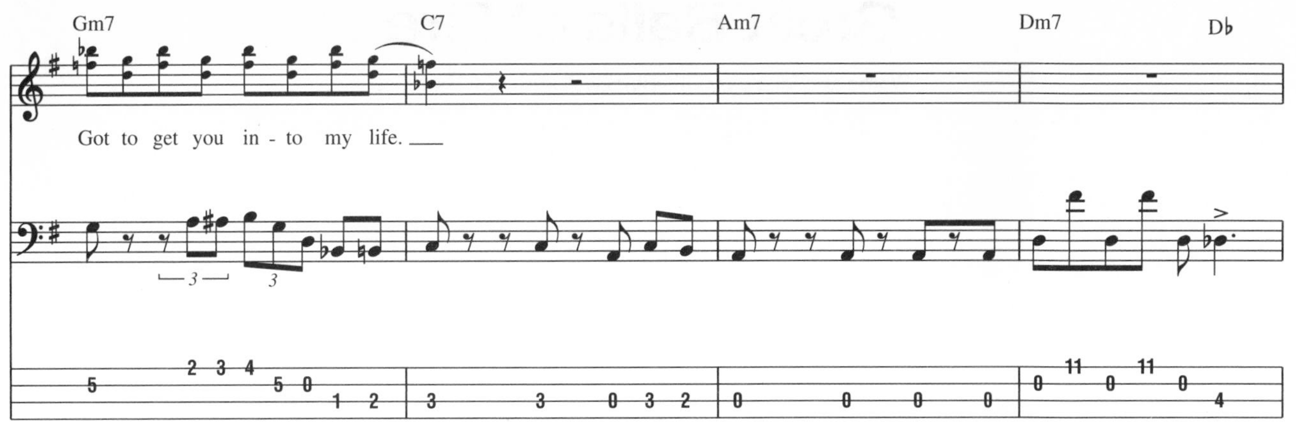
Gm7
C7
Am7
Dm7
D♭
Got to get you in - to my life.
3
3
5
2 3 4
5 0
1 2
3 3 0 3 2
0 0 0 0
0 11 0 11 0
4

C7
Am7
Dm7
Gm7
C7
Got to get you in, got to get you in, got to get you in, got to get you in, in - to my life.
3
3
3 3 0 3 2
0 5 5 7 5
5
2 3 4
5 0
1 2
3 3 0 3 2

Am7
Dm7
D♭
Band tacet
N.C.
Got to get you in - to my life.
0 0 0 2 0
0 11 0 11 0
4

Repeat and fade
C7
Am7
Dm7
Gm7
C7
Got to get you in, got to get you in, got to get you in, got to get you in, in - to my life.

Great Balls of Fire

Words and Music by Otis Blackwell and Jack Hammer

Bright Rock (♩ =166)

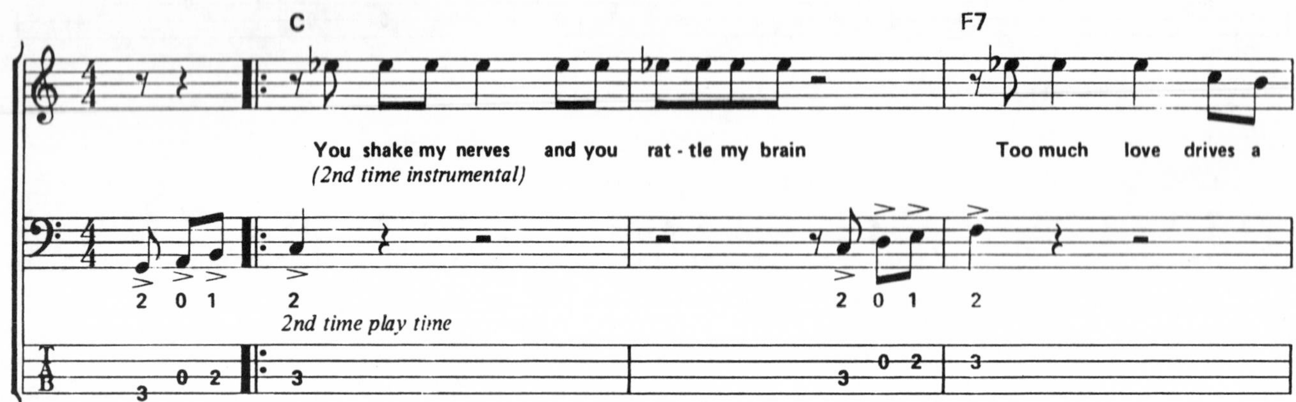
C
F7
You shake my nerves and you rat - tle my brain
Too much love drives a
(2nd time instrumental)
2nd time play time
2 0 1 2 2 0 1 2
3 0 2 3 3 0 2 3

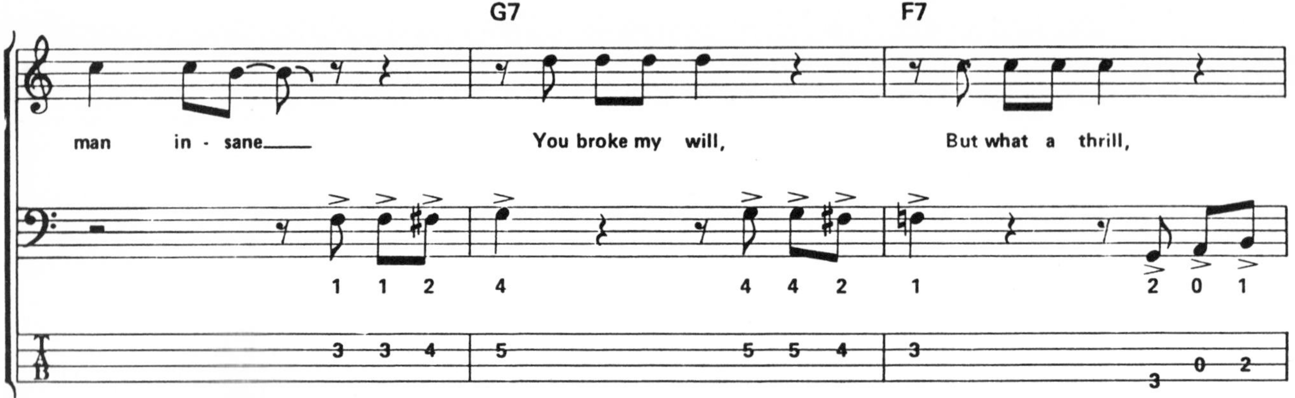
G7
F7
man in - sane
You broke my will,
But what a thrill,
1 1 2 4 4 4 2 1 2 0 1
3 3 4 5 5 5 4 3 3 0 2

C
N.C.
C
Good - ness gra - cious, great balls of fire!
I laughed at love 'cause I
2 2 1 0 2 0
3 3 3 2 2 0 0 2 0

F7
thought it was fun - ny
You came a - long and moved ___ me, hon - ey.
G7
F7
C N.C.
I changed my mind,
This love is fine.
Good - ness gra - cious, great ___
F7
C
___ balls of fire! ___
Kiss me ba - by,
Hmmm
feels
F7
G7
good
Hold me, ba - by!
Well, ___ I wan - na love ya like a

lov - er should___ You're fine___ so kind___ I got to tell this world that you're
G7
mine, mine, mine, mine.
C
I chew my nails and I twid - dle my thumbs
F7
I'm real ner - vous but it sure is fun.___
G7
Come on ba - by, you drive me cra - zy,
C N.C.
Good - ness gra - cious, great___ balls of fire!
1
2
___ balls of fire!___
C

Green-Eyed Lady

Words and Music by Jerry Corbetta, J.C. Phillips and David Riordan

Am7/E
Em7
slow - ly towards the sun.
night, the waves, the sand.
Green-eyed
A7/E
Am7/E
la - dy, o - cean la - dy.
Sooth - ing ev - 'ry rag - ing
Child of na - ture,
Em7
wave that comes.
friend of man.
Green-eyed la - dy pas - sions
A7/E
Am7/E
la - dy. Dressed in love, she lives for life to be.
Em7
A7/E
Green-eyed la - dy feels life, I nev - er see
To Coda
Am7/E
Em7
set - ting suns and lone - ly lov - ers free.
Organ Solo
Em7 F#m7 Gmaj7 F#m7 Em7 F#m7 Gmaj7
1., 2., 3.
4.
F#m7
F#m7 Em7 F#m7 Gmaj7 F#m7 Em7

Guitar Solo
F#m7
Gmaj7
F#m7
N.C.(Em7)
(B/E)
(B7/E)
Interlude
Em(maj7)
N.C.
D.S. al Coda
Am7/E
Em7
Coda
Outro
Begin fade
Fade out
Bass: w/ Bass Fig. 1 (till fade)
Em7

Hair of the Dog

Words and Music by Dan McCafferty, Darrell Sweet, Pete Agnew and Manuel Charlton

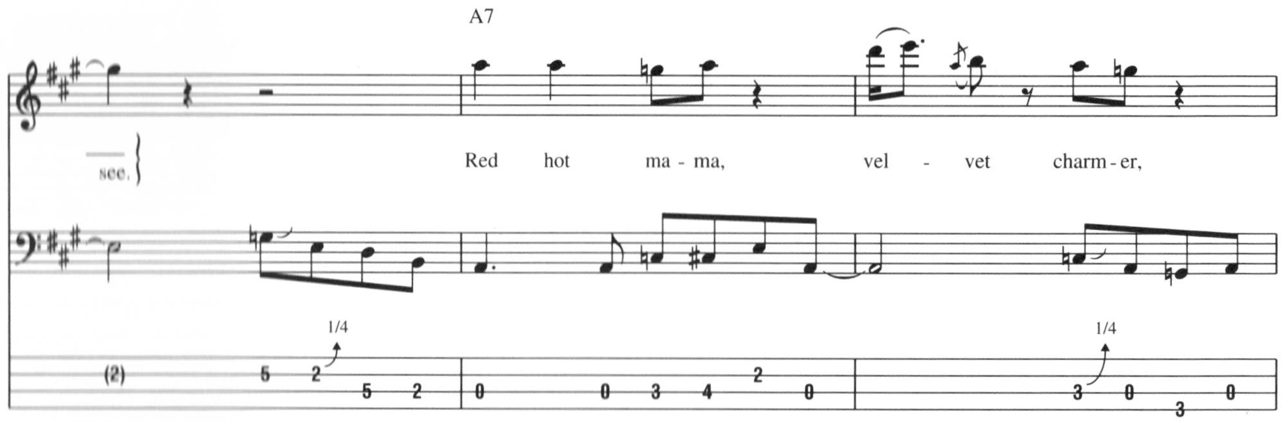

E7
time's come to pay your dues.
1/4

Chorus
E5
G5
Now you're mess-in' with a...
1/4
1/4

A5
E5
D5
E5
Now you're mess - in' with a son of a bitch.
Voc. Fig. 1
End Voc. Fig. 1
(A son of a bitch.)

Bkgd. Voc.: w/ Voc. Fig. 1
E5
G5
A5
E5
D5
E5
Now you're mess-in' with a…
Now you're mess-in' with a son of a bitch.
Interlude
E7
1/4
1/4
E5
3
E5
G5
A5
E5
G5
A5
E5
1.
2.
D5
C5
B5
D5
C5
B5
E7
1/4

Chorus
Bkgd. Voc.: w/ Voc. Fig. 1
E5
G5/E
A5/E
Now you're mess-in' with a. . .
1/4
E5
D5/E
E5
G5/E
Now you're mess-in' with a son of a bitch.
Now you're mess-in' with a...
Bass Fig. 2
Bkgd. Voc.: w/ Voc. Fig. 1
A5/E
E5
D5/E
E5
Now you're mess-in' with a son of a bitch.
End Bass Fig. 2
Outro
w/ Bass Fig. 2 (till end)
Bkgd. Voc.:w/ Voc. Fig. 1
E5
G5
A5
E5
D5
E5
Now you're mess-in' with a...
Now you're mess-in' with a son of a bitch.
(Spoken: Son of a bitch.)
Bkgd. Voc.: w/ Voc. Fig. 1
Play 4 times and fade
E5
G5
A5
E5
D5
E5
Now you're mess-in' with a...
Now you're mess-in' with a son of a bitch.

Hard to Handle

Words and Music by Allen Jones, Alvertis Bell and Otis Redding

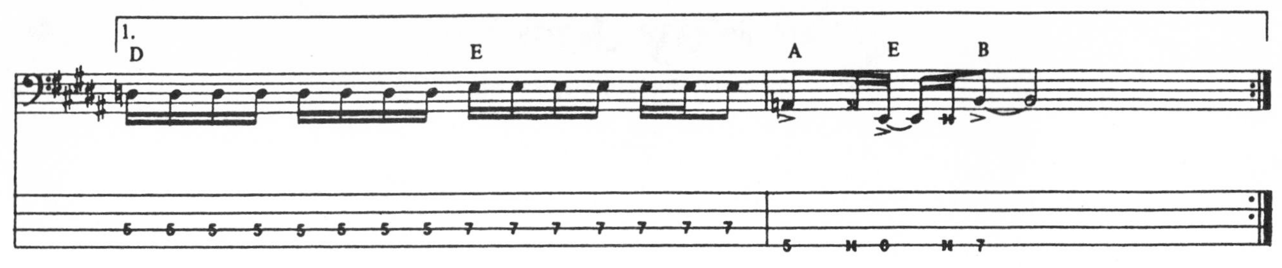
1.
D
E
A
E
B

2nd time to Coda I;
3rd time to Coda II
D.S. (take 2nd ending) al Coda I
2.
A
E
B
A E B
A E B
A
E
B

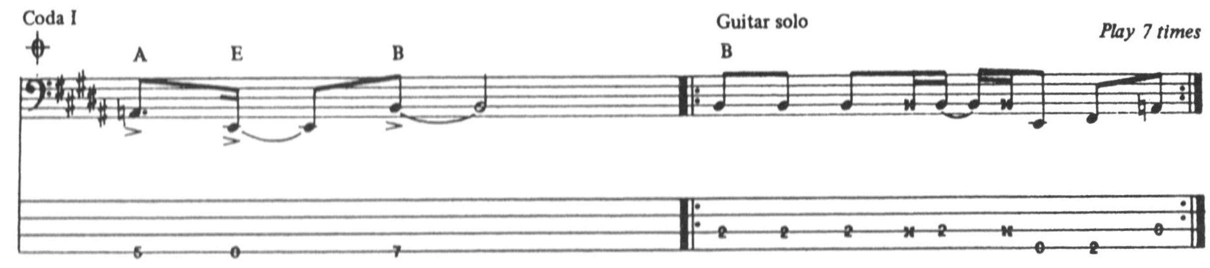
Coda I
A
E
B
Guitar solo
B
Play 7 times

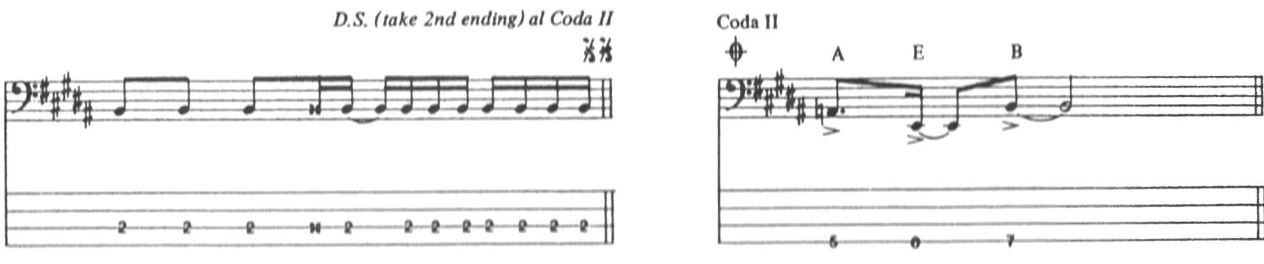
D.S. (take 2nd ending) al Coda II
Coda II
A
E
B

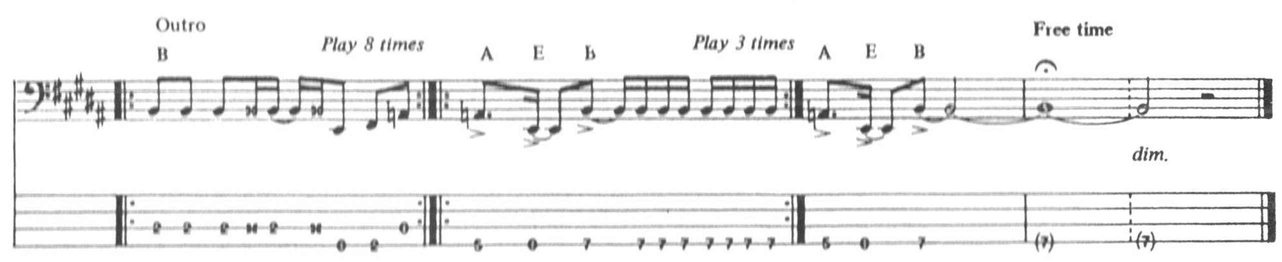
Outro
B
Play 8 times
A
E
B
Play 3 times
A
E
B
Free time
dim.

Hey Joe

Words and Music by Billy Roberts

D
Aadd9
E
you know I caught her mess-in' 'round with an-oth-er man.
5 5 5 5 5 5 5 6
7 7 7 5 7 5 6
C
Gadd9
Yeah!
I'm go-in' down to shoot my old la-dy,
Ooh.
7 7 7 7 7 7 7 7 7 7 7
3 3 3 2 2 3
D
A
E
you know I caught her mess-in' 'round with an-oth-er man.
Huh!
And that ain't
5 5 5 5 5 5 4 4 5
7 7 7 7 5 7 5 6
Verse
C
G
D
A
too cool.
)
2. Uh, hey, Joe,
I heard you shot your
(Ah.
7 7 7 7 7 7 7 7 7 7 7
3 3 3 3 2 2 3
5 5 5 5 5 3 3 5

E
C
G
wom-an down, you shot her down, now.
Uh, hey, Joe,
Ah.
D5
Aadd9
E
I heard you shot your old la - dy down, you shot her down in the ground.
C
Gadd9
Yeah!
Yes I did, I shot her,
Ah.
D5
A
E
you know I caught her mess-in' 'round, mess-in' 'round town.

C
Gadd9
D
A
Uh, yes I did, I shot her,
you know I caught my old la - dy mess-in' 'round
Ah.
E
E7
town.
And I gave her the gun,
I shot her!
Guitar Solo
C
Gadd9
D
A
E
N.C.
Al - right!
Woo!
Ah!
Hey,
Joe!
E
E7
C
Gadd9
Dsus4
A
N.C.
Shoot her one more time a - gain, ba-by!
Ooh.
Hey,

Interlude
E7
N.C.(C)
(G)
Yeah!
Ah, dig it!
Ah!
Joe! ______)
(Hey, ______
(D)
(A)
E
Ah!
Joe, where you gon - na go? ______)
Ooh, al - right! _
Verse
C
G
D
A
E7
3. Hey, __ Joe, said now, uh, where you gon-na run to now, __ where you gon-na run to? ___
(Hey, ______ Joe, where you gon - na go? ______
C
Gadd9
D
A
Yeah.
Hey, ___ Joe, __ I said, where you gon-na run _
Hey, ______

E
N.C.
C
Gadd9
_ to now, _ where you, where you gon-na go?
Well, dig it!
I'm go-in' way down south, _
Joe!
Hey,
D
A
E
N.C.
way down to Mex - i - co way!
Joe!
E
N.C.(C)
(G)
(D)
(A)
Al - right! _
I'm go-in' way down south, _
way down where I _
Hey,
Joe, where you gon - na
E
C
Gadd9
can be free! Ain't no one _ gon-na find me babe!
Ain't no hang-man gon-na,
go?
Hey,

Dsus4
A
E
he ain't gon-na put a rope a-round me! You bet-ter be-lieve it right
Joe, where you gon - na go?
Begin Fade
N.C.(C)
(G)
now! I got-ta go now!
Hey, hey, hey, Joe,
Hey,
(D)
(A)
E
E7
E
you bet-ter run on down! Good - bye ev-'ry-bod-y. Ow!
Joe, where you gon-na go?
Fade Out
N.C.(C)
(G)
(D)
(A)
(E)
Hey, hey, Joe, what'd I say, run on down!
(Hey, Joe, where you gon - na go?)

Hide Away

Words and Music by Freddie King and Sonny Thompson

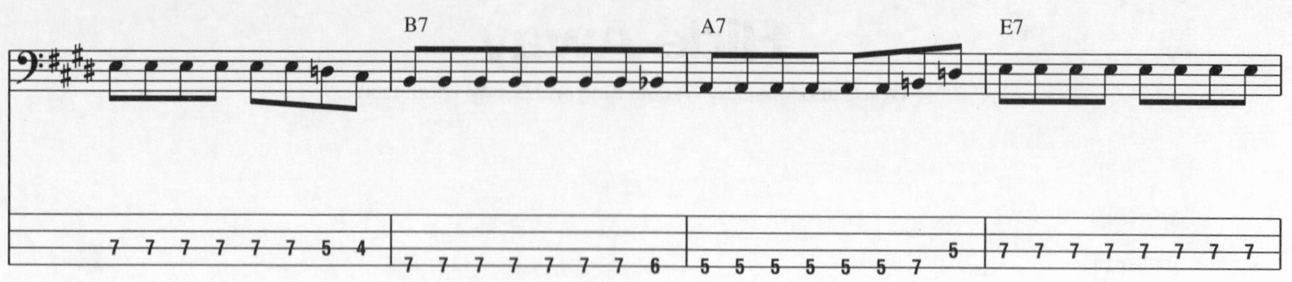
B7
A7
E7

C
B7
E7

A7
E7

B7
E7

D
E7

A7
E7
B7
A7
E7
B7
E
E7
A7
E7
B7
A7
E7
B7
F
E7

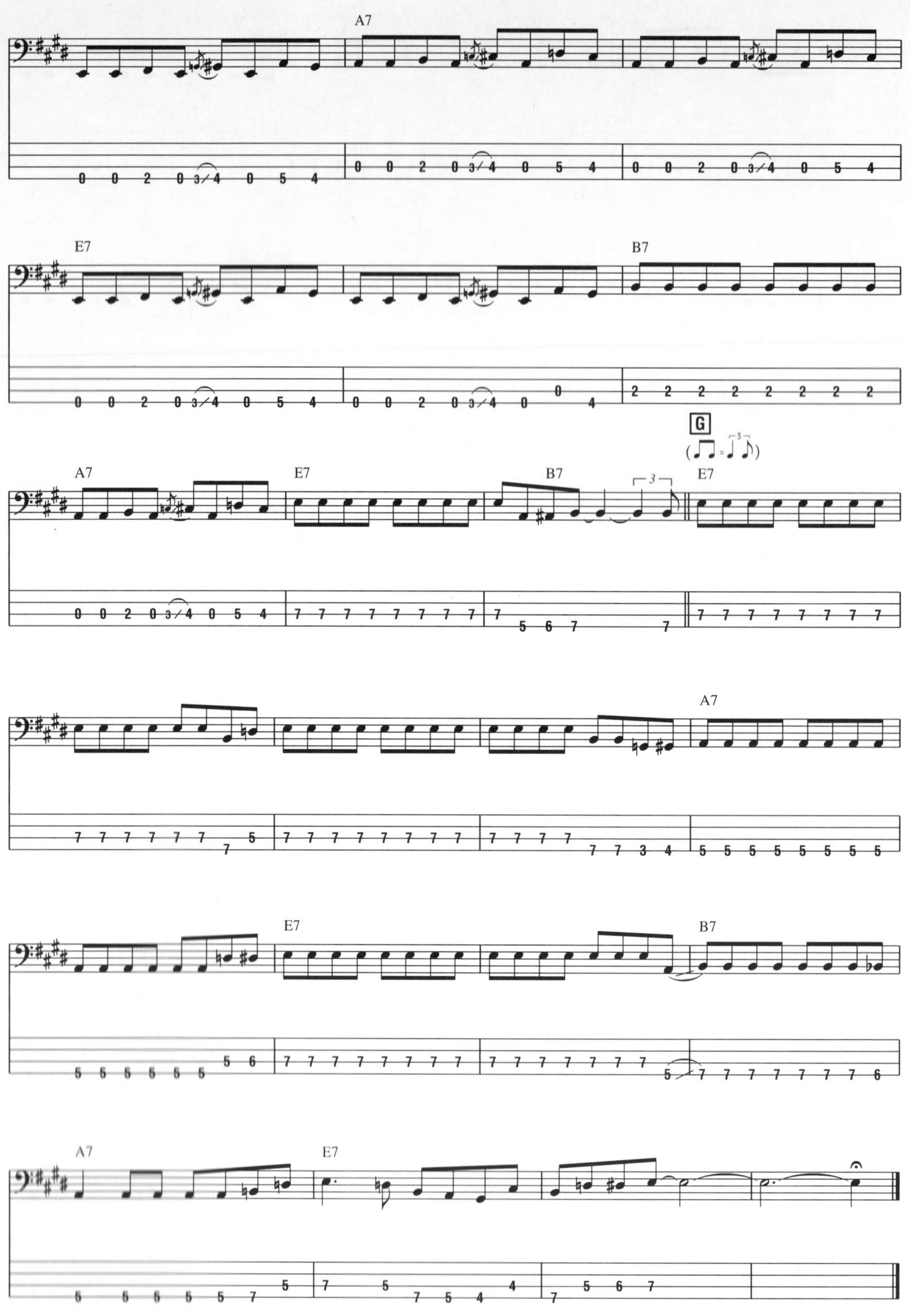

A7
E7
B7
A7
E7
B7
G
E7
A7
E7
B7
A7
E7

The House Is Rockin'

Written by Stevie Ray Vaughan and Doyle Bramhall

F7
noth - in' to lose. Seen it all for years, a – start spread-in' the news.
C7
G7
We got room on the floor, come
on ba – by shake sump- in' loose!
C7
Well, the
D Chorus
house is a – rock - in', don't both – er knock - in'. Well, the house is a – rock – in', don't

G7
both – er knock-in'. Well, the house is a – rock- in', don't both- er, come on in.
C7
E Piano Solo
F7
C7
G7
C7
F Guitar Solo
F7

C7 G7

G7#9 C7

Well,_ the

G Chorus

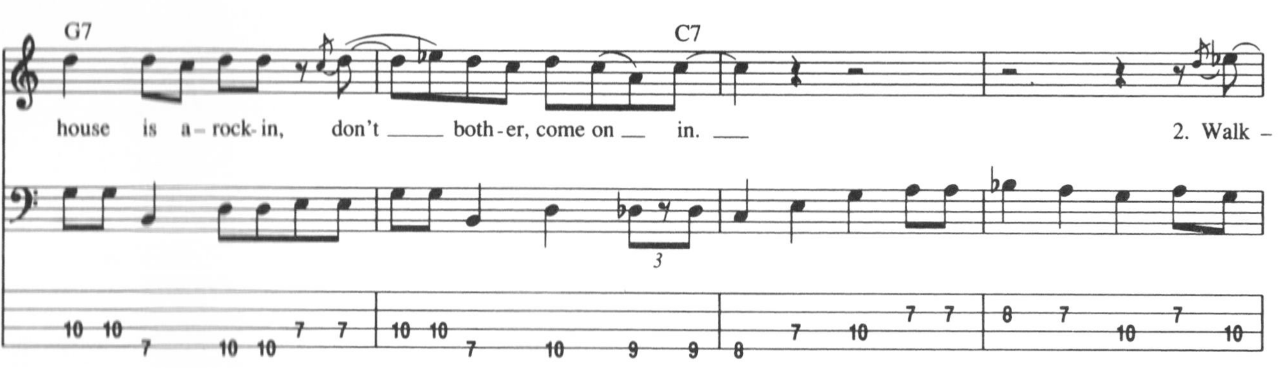

H Verse
– in' up the street you can hear the sound _ of some bad honk-y tonk-ers real-ly
F7
lay-in' it down. They've seen it all for years, ___ and got noth-in' to lose. _
C7
G7
So get out on the floor, _ shim –
C7
– my 'til you shake sump-in' loose! _ Well, the

I Chorus
house_ is a-rock-in', don't __ both - er knock-in'. Well, the house_ is a-rock-in', don't __
10 10 7 10 10 7 7
8 8 7 10 10 7 10
8 8 7 10 7

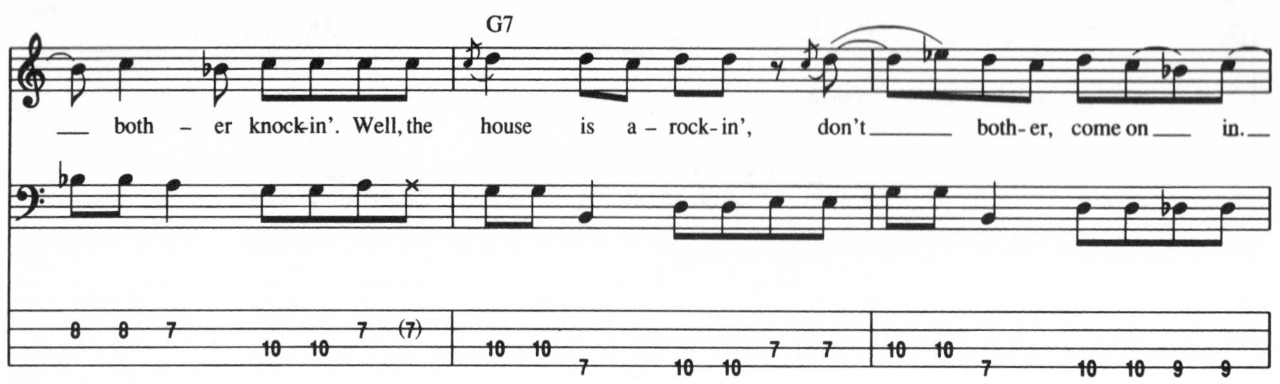
G7
__ both - er knock-in'. Well, the house is a - rock-in', don't ___ both-er, come on ___ in. __
8 8 7 10 10 7 (7)
10 10 7 10 10 7 7
10 10 7 10 10 9 9

C7
G7
__
I said the house is a-rock-in', don't ___ both-er, come on __ in. __
8 8 7 10 10 7 (7)
10 10 7 7 8 8 9 9
10 10 7 10 10 7 7
10 10 7 10 10 9 9

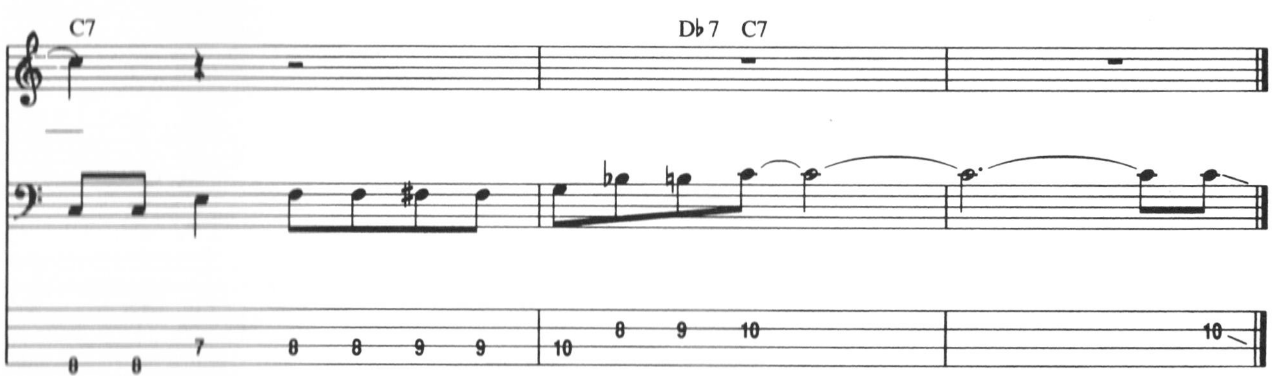
C7
Db7 C7
8 8 7 8 8 9 9
10 8 9 10
10

I Can See for Miles

Words and Music by Peter Townshend

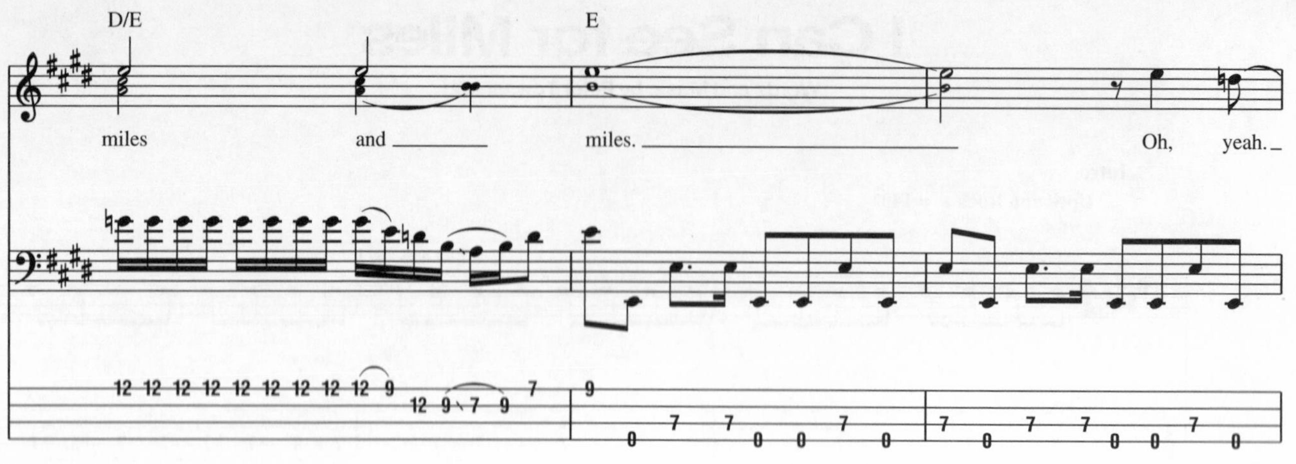

D/E
E
miles and miles. Oh, yeah.

To Coda
Verse
E5
2. If you think that I
3. You took ad - van - tage of my

G5
A5
2nd time, w/ Bass Fill 1
E5
G5
A5
don't know a - bout the lit - tle tricks you play
trust in you when I was so far a - way.

Bass Fill 1

E5
G5
A5
E
and nev - er see you when de - lib - 'rate - ly you put things in my way.
I saw you hold - in' lots of oth - er guys, and how you've got the nerve to say
Pre-Chorus
A5
B
A5
Well, here's a poke at you. You're gon - na choke on it, too. You're gon - na lose that smile, be -
that you still want me. Well, that's as may be, but you got - ta stand trial be -
B
Chorus
A
E
cause all the while,
cause all the while,
I can see for miles and miles. I can see for
A
E
G6
A
miles and miles. I can see for miles and miles and

C
D/E
E
miles
and
miles
and
miles.
Oh,
yeah.
1.
2.
Guitar Solo
E5
G5
A5
E5
G5
A5
1.
2.
E5
D.S. al Coda
4. I

Coda
Verse
A5
C5
D5
A5
5. The Eif - fel Tow - er and the Taj Ma - hal are mine to see on clear _ days. _
C5
D5
A5
C5
D5
You thought that I _ would need a crys - tal ball to see right
A5
Pre-Chorus
D
E5
through the haze. _ Well here's a poke at you. _ You're gon - na choke on it, too. _ You're gon - na
Dsus2
E5
Chorus
D5
E5
lose that smile, _ be - cause all _ the while, I can see for miles and

A5
D5
E5
A5
C/A
miles. I can see for miles and miles. I can see for miles and
D/A
F/A
G/A
miles and miles and miles and miles and
miles and miles and miles.
A5
Repeat and fade
D5
E5
A5
I can see for miles and miles. I can see for

I Can't Quit You Baby

Written by Willie Dixon

sl.
(E7)
(D7)
N.C.
A
B♭
Guitar solo
N.C.(A7)
(D7)
(A7)
(D7)
(A7)
sl.
(E7)
sl.
(D7)
sl.
sl.
sl.
N.C.
A
B♭
A
B♭
N.C.(A7)
(D7)
H

(A7)
(E7)
(D7)
A
B♭
N.C.(A)
(B♭)
sl.
3rd Verse
N.C.(A7)
C♯9
D9
N.C.(A7)
H
(D7)
(A7)
C♯9
E9
D9
N.C.

I Fought the Law

Words and Music by Sonny Curtis

Moderately (♩ = 154)

G
D7
G
I need - ed mon- ey 'cause I
3
3 3 3 3 3 3 3 3
5 5 5 3 3 3 3
3 3 3 3 3 3 3 3
C7
G
C7
G
had none,
I fought the law and the
law won,
3 3 3 3 3 3 3 3
3 3 3 3 3 3 3 3
3 3 3 3 3 3 3 3
D7
G
C7
D7
I fought the law and the
law
won.
3 3 3 3 3 3 3 3
5 5 5 5
3 3 3 3 3 3 3 3
3 3 3 5 5 5 5
G
D7
G
C
I left my ba - by and I feel so bad, I
3
3 3 3 3 3 3 3 3
5 5 5 3 3 3 3
3 3 2 3 5 3 3 2

G
C
guess my race is run.
She's the best girl I've ev - er had,
G
C7
G
D7
I fought the law and the law won,
I fought the law and the law
G
C7
D7
G
To Coda
D7
G
won.
C
G

C
G
C7
G
D7
G
A - rob - bin' peo - ple with a
3
N.C.
G
C7
G
six gun, I fought the law and the law won,
D7
G
C7
D7
I fought the law and the law won.

G
D7
G
I miss my ba - by and the
3
C7
G
C7
G
good fun,
I fought the law and the law won,
D7
G
C7
D7
I fought the law and the law won.
G
D7
G
D.S. al Coda
I
3
CODA
3
rit. . . . .

I Know a Little

Words and Music by Steve Gaines

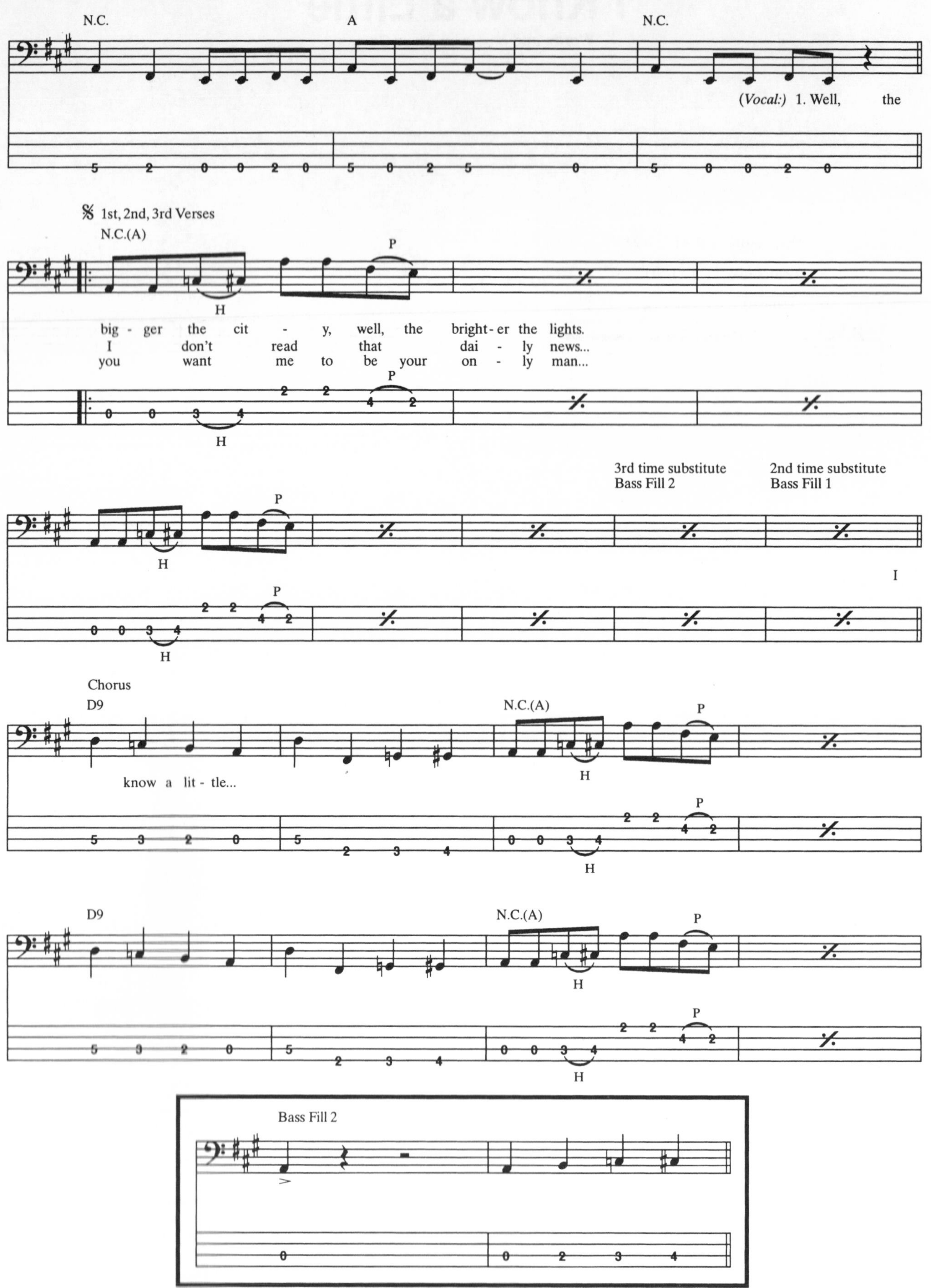
N.C.
A
N.C.
(Vocal:) 1. Well, the
1st, 2nd, 3rd Verses
N.C.(A)
big - ger the cit - y, well, the bright- er the lights.
I don't read that dai - ly news...
you want me to be your on - ly man...
3rd time substitute Bass Fill 2
2nd time substitute Bass Fill 1
I
Chorus
D9
know a lit - tle...
N.C.(A)
D9
N.C.(A)
Bass Fill 2

2nd time substitute Bass Fill 3
To Coda
E7
D7
G
G♯
A
P
N.C.
1.
2.
2. Well, now
Guitar solo
N.C.(A)
Play 8 times
D9
H
Bass Fill 3

A5
Piano solo
D9
N.C.(A)
E7
D7
G
G♯
A
N.C.
D.S. al Coda
3. Well, now
Coda
A5

I Wish It Would Rain

Words and Music by Phil Collins

2nd Verse
Ab
Ebadd9/G
Fm7
Ebadd9/G
sl.
P sl.
You said you did-n't need_me in your life,_ (etc.)
Ab
Ebadd9/G
Fm7
Chorus
Db
Ebsus4
Eb
Db
Eb
Ebsus4
Eb
Ebsus4
Eb
Db
Ebsus4
Eb
Db
Eb
Fm7
Eb/G
Bridge
Ab
Bb/Ab
Though your hurt is gone,_(etc.)
Db/Ab
Ab
Bb/Ab
Db/Ab
Ab
3rd Verse
Ab
Ebadd9/G
Fm7
Ebadd9/G

Ab
Ebadd9/G
Fm7
Chorus
Db
Ebsus4
Eb
Db
Eb
Ebsus4
Eb
Ebsus4
Eb
Db
Ebsus4
Eb
Db
Eb
Fm7
Eb/G
Outro
Ab
Ebadd9/G
Fm7
let ring
Ebadd9/G
Ab
Ebadd9/G
Fm7
Ebadd9/G Ab
Ebadd9/G
Fm7
Ebadd9/G
Ab
Ebadd9/G
Fm7
Free time
Ab

I'm Your Hoochie Coochie Man

Written by Willie Dixon

jump and shout,
then the world wan-na know,
what this all a - bout." But you know I'm here.

Chorus
D7
A7
Ev - 'ry - bod - y knows I'm here.

E7
Well, you know I'm the Hooch - ie Cooch - ie Man,

D7
A7
E7
ev - 'ry - bod - y knows I'm here.

Verse

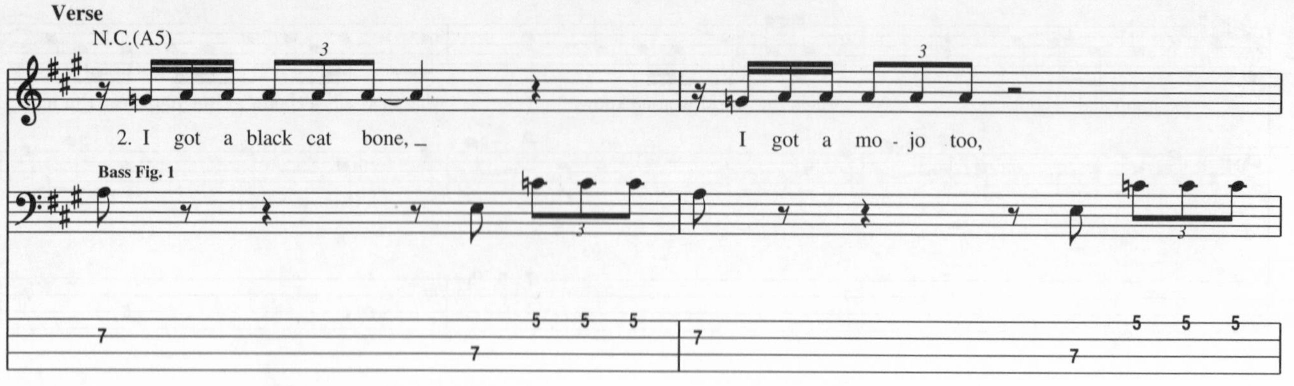
N.C.(A5)
2. I got a black cat bone,
I got a mo - jo too,
Bass Fig. 1

I got a John the Con - quer-root,
I got to mess with you.

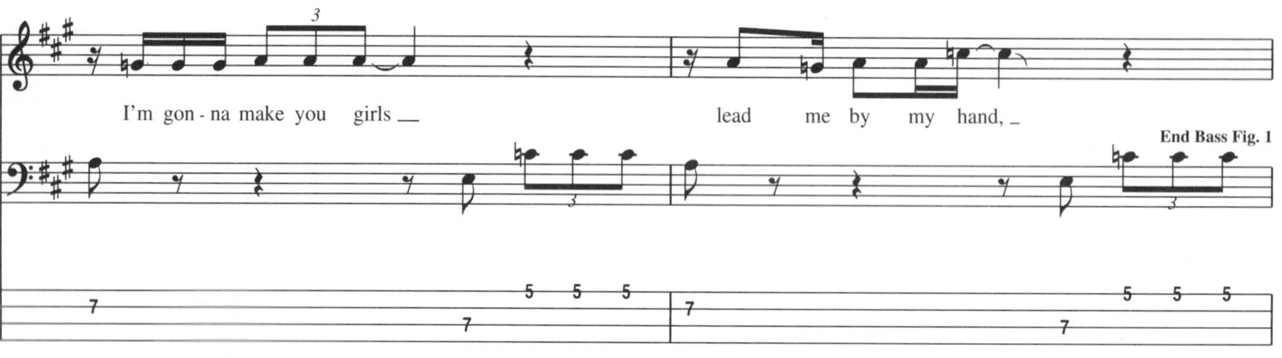
I'm gon - na make you girls
lead me by my hand,
End Bass Fig. 1

then the world - 'll know
I'm the Hooch - ie Cooch-ie Man.
But you know I'm here.

Chorus

D7
A7
Ev - 'ry - bod - y knows _ I'm here.
7 7 7 9
4
4 7 4 7
5
7
7 7 7 7 7
5

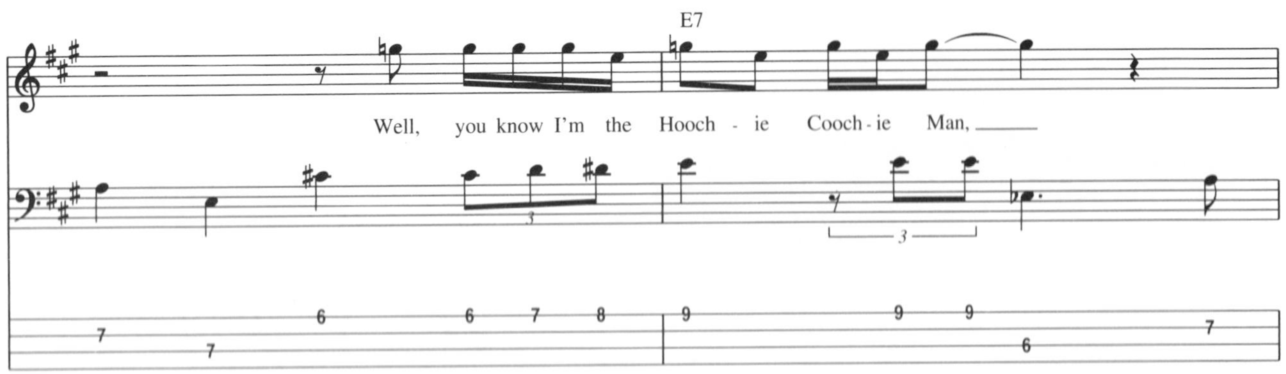
E7
Well, you know I'm the Hooch - ie Cooch - ie Man, ___
6 6 7 8
7
7
9 9 9
6
7

D7
A7
E7
ev - 'ry - bod - y knows I'm here... _
7 8 9
6
14 13 12 12 11
12 12 10 12 10
12 7
5 9
7

Verse

Bass: w/ Bass Fig. 1
N.C.(A5)
3. On the sev-enth hour, _ on the sev-enth day, _ on the sev-enth month,

the sev-enth doc - tor say, "You were born _ for good luck, and that you'll see." __

I've got sev - en hun-dred dol-lars, don't you mess with me. But you know I'm here.
Bass

Chorus

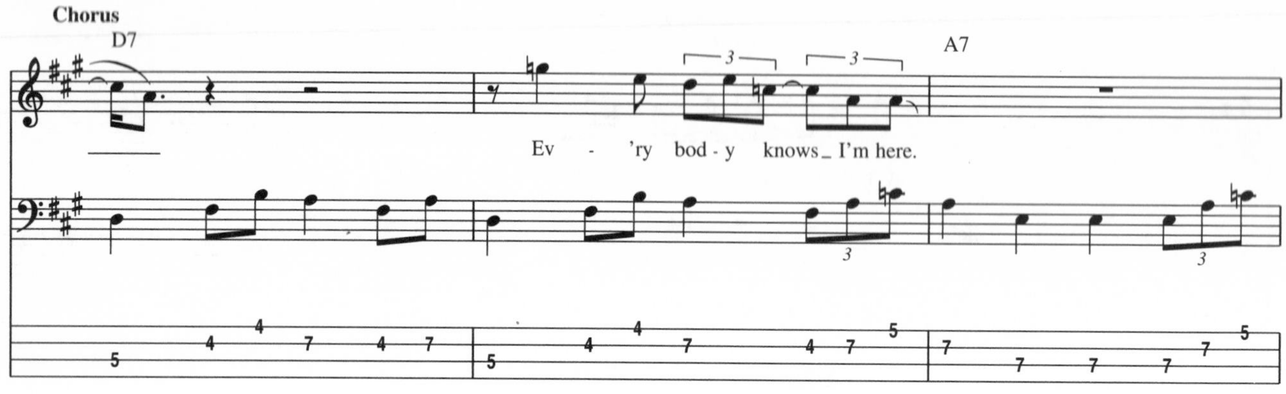
D7
A7
Ev - 'ry bod - y knows I'm here.

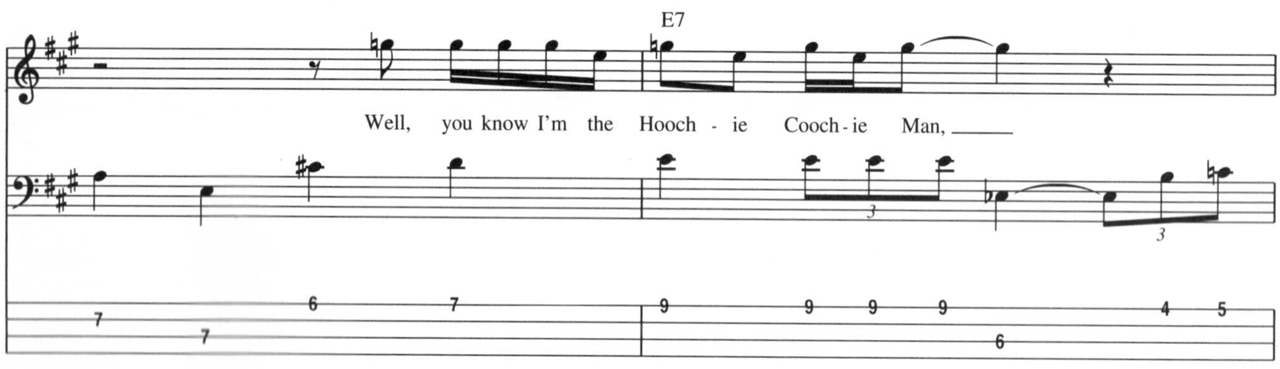
E7
Well, you know I'm the Hooch - ie Cooch - ie Man,

D7
A7
yeah, all a-round the world, I'm here.

In 2 Deep

Words and Music by Mark Selby, Kenny Wayne Shepherd and Danny Tate

Intro
Moderately ♩ = 100
N.C.
(drums)
Bass
Am
Bass Fig. 1
End Bass Fig. 1
Verse
Bass: w/ Bass Fig. 1, 2 times
Am
1. Ev - 'ry - bod - y's scared and there's a mad - man on the run,
2. Caught up in the hur - ri - cane that nev - er seems to end.
stum - blin' through the wreck - age like a blind man with a gun.
Ought to know the dev - il when he looks like your best friend.
No - where to hide,
Chorus
C5
Bb5
I'm in too deep.
Bass
Bass Fig. 2
End Bass Fig. 2

Bass: w/ Bass Fig. 1
Am
Bass: w/ Bass Fig. 2
C5
B♭5
Can't see the light
'cause I'm in too deep,

Am
o - ver my head.
Bass
Bass Fig. 3
End Bass Fig. 3

Bridge
E5
Oh, I should have known, but I can't let

Bass: w/ Bass Fig. 1, 2 times

Am

o - ver my head.

Oh!

Guitar Solo

Bass

Bm

Gm

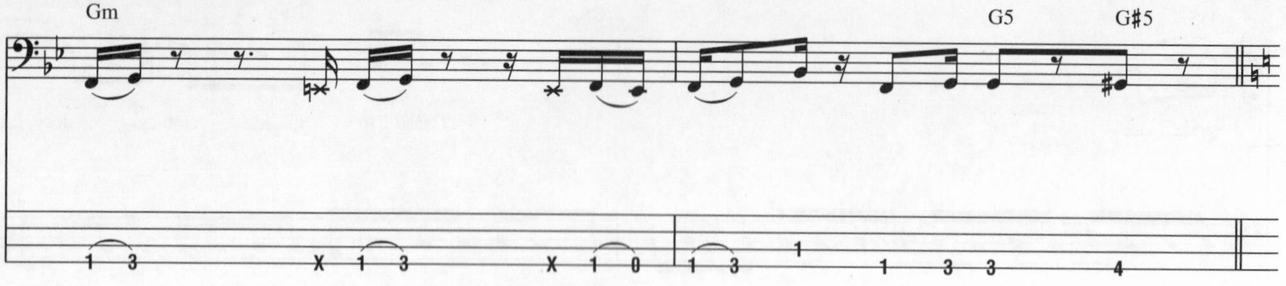
Gm
G5
G♯5

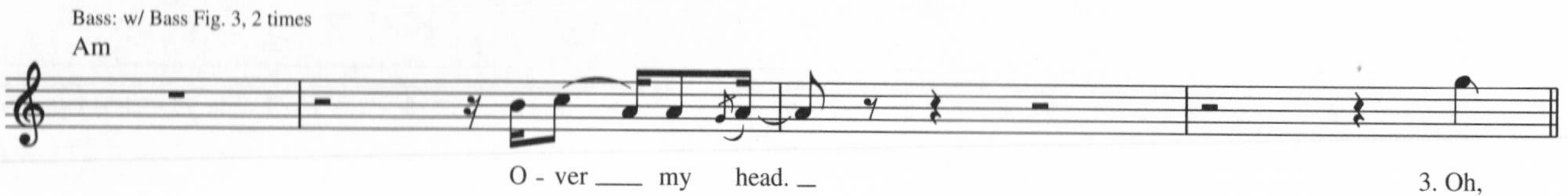
Bass: w/ Bass Fig. 3, 2 times
Am
O - ver my head.
3. Oh,

Verse
Bass: w/ Bass Fig. 1, 2 times
Am
some-one call some - bod - y, the a - sy - lum's un - der siege. The

in - mates took a hos - tage, I'll be damned if it's not me. No - where to hide,

Chorus
Bass: w/ Bass Fig. 2
C5
B♭5
Bass: w/ Bass Fig. 1
Am
'cause I'm in too deep.

Bass: w/ Bass Fig. 2
C5
B♭5
They'll real - ize, 'cause I'm in too deep.

Bass: w/ Bass Fig. 1
Am
Bass: w/ Bass Fig. 2
C5
Can't see the light,

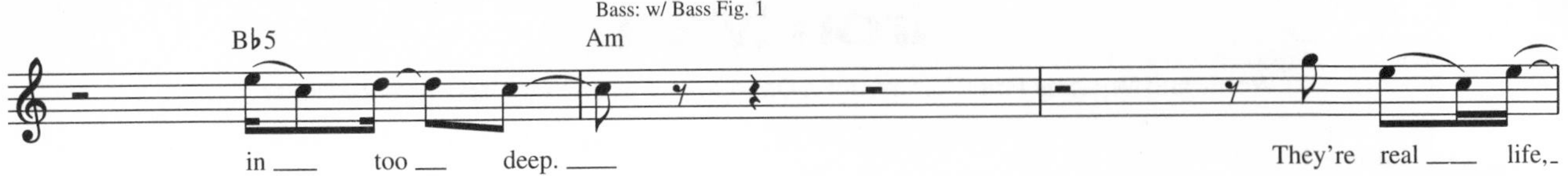
Bass: w/ Bass Fig. 1
B♭5
Am
in too deep.
They're real life,

Bass: w/ Bass Fig. 2
C5
B♭5
oh no,
I'm in too deep.

Outro

Bass: w/ Bass Fig. 3, 3 times
Am
I'm o - ver my head,

o - ver my head,
o - ver my head.

Bass

Iron Man

Words and Music by Frank Iommi, John Osbourne, William Ward, and Terence Butler

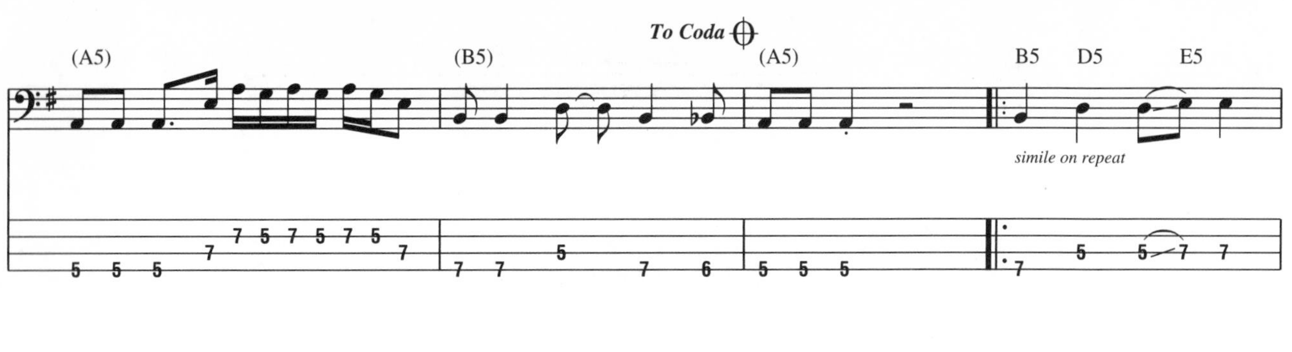
To Coda
(A5)
(B5)
(A5)
B5 D5 E5
simile on repeat

G5 F♯5 G5 F♯5 G5 D5 E5
B5 D5 E5
G5 F♯5 G5 F♯5 G5 D5 E5

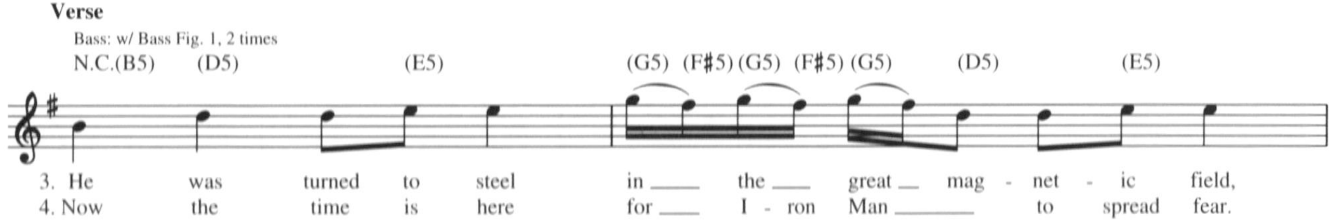
Verse
Bass: w/ Bass Fig. 1, 2 times
N.C.(B5) (D5) (E5)
(G5) (F♯5) (G5) (F♯5) (G5) (D5) (E5)
3. He was turned to steel in the great mag - net - ic field,
4. Now the time is here for I - ron Man to spread fear.

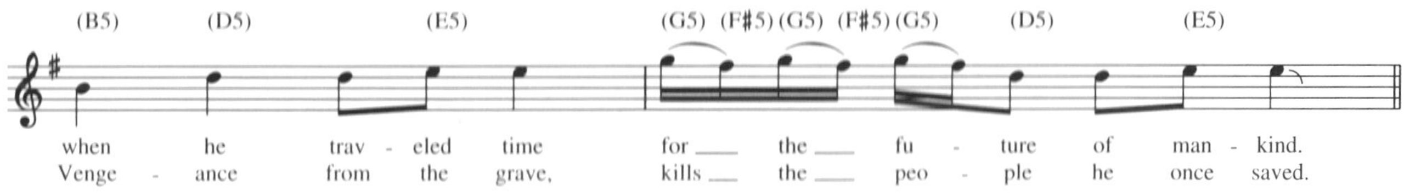
(B5) (D5) (E5)
(G5) (F♯5) (G5) (F♯5) (G5) (D5) (E5)
when he trav - eled time for the fu - ture of man - kind.
Venge - ance from the grave, kills the peo - ple he once saved.

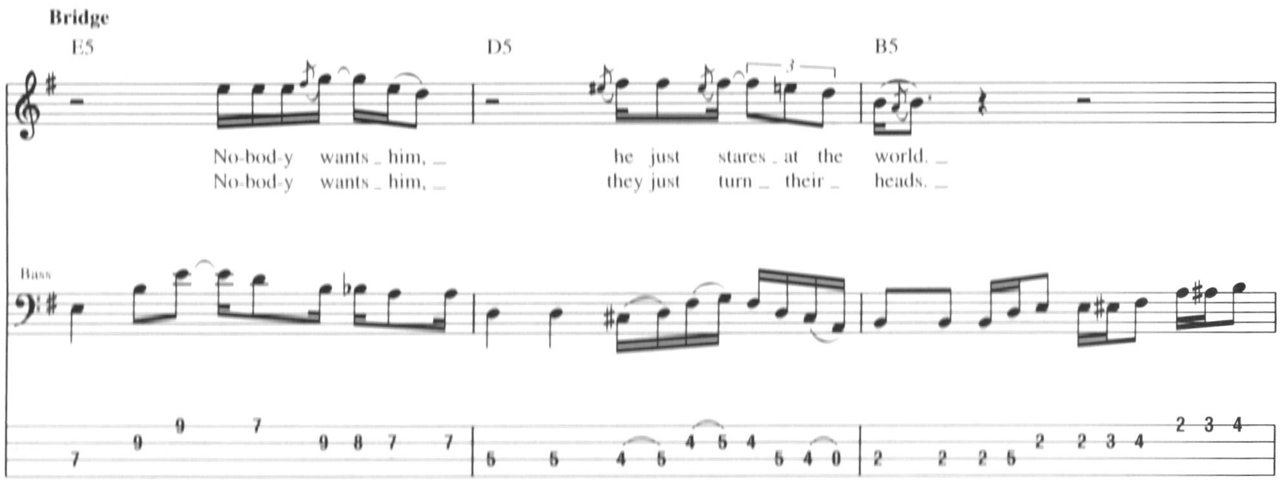
Bridge
E5
D5
B5
No-bod-y wants him, he just stares at the world.
No-bod-y wants him, they just turn their heads.
Bass

E5
D5
Plan - ning his venge - ance _ that he will _ soon un -
No - bod - y helps _ him, _ now he has _ his re -
B5
furl. _
venge. _
Interlude
Double-Time ♩ = 164
N.C.(C♯m)
Guitar Solo
N.C.(C♯m)

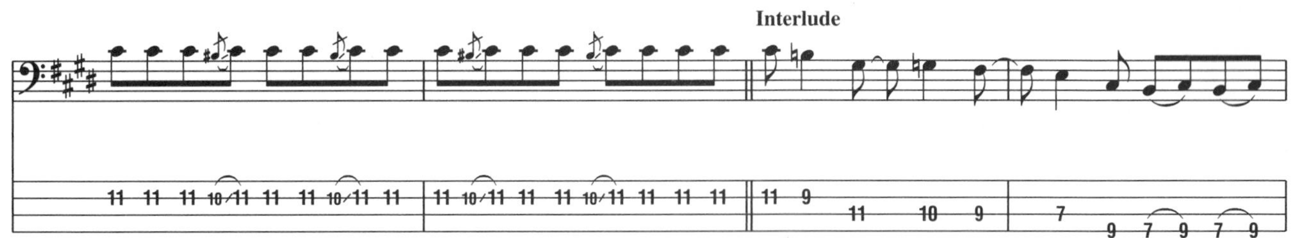
Interlude

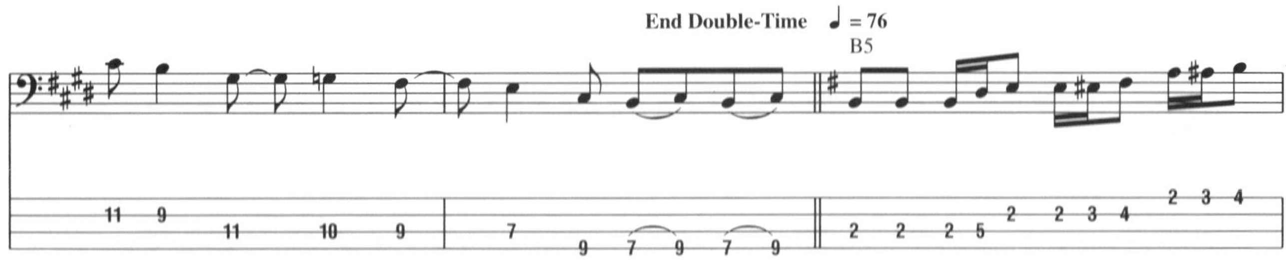
End Double-Time ♩ = 76
B5

D.S. al Coda
(take 2nd ending)
B5 D5 E5 G5 F#5 G5 F#5 G5 D5 E5 B5 D5 E5 G5 F#5 G5 F#5 G5 D5 E5

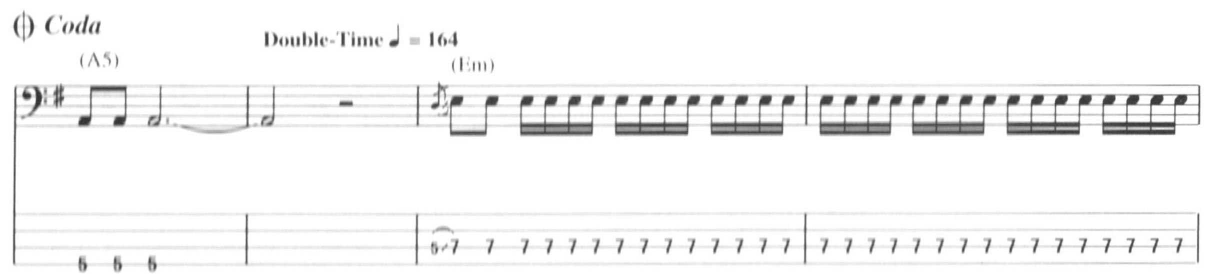
Coda
Double-Time ♩ = 164
(A5)
(Em)

N.C.(E)
*N.C.(E5)
(D5)
* Chords implied by bass.
Guitar Solo
(C#5)
(C5)
N.C.(E5)
(D5)
(C#5)
(C5)
(E5)
(D5)
(C#5)

(C5)
(E5)
(D5)
(C#5)
(C5)
Outro
(E5)
(D5)
(C#5)
(C5)
(E5)
(D5)
(C#5)
(C5)
(E5)
(D5)
(C#5)
(C5)
(E5)

Jeremy

Music by Jeff Ament
Lyric by Eddie Vedder

Intro
Moderate Rock ♩=96
N.C.
Bass 1
mf
* 12-stg. bass
Harm.
Bass 2
* 12-stg. bass (overdub)
mf let ring
Harm.
* Each string (E A D G) is tripled, with a second string 8va, and a third string 15ma.

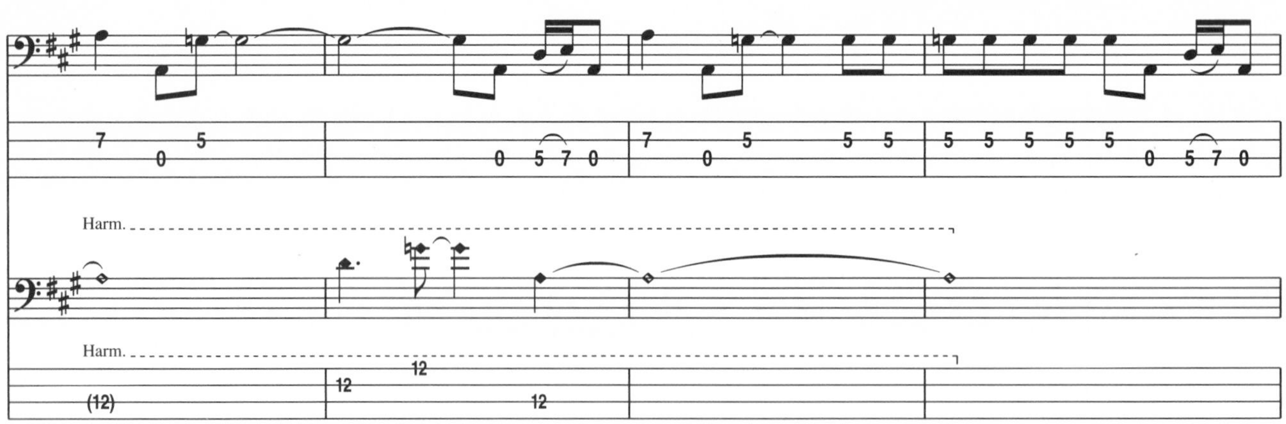
Harm.
Harm.

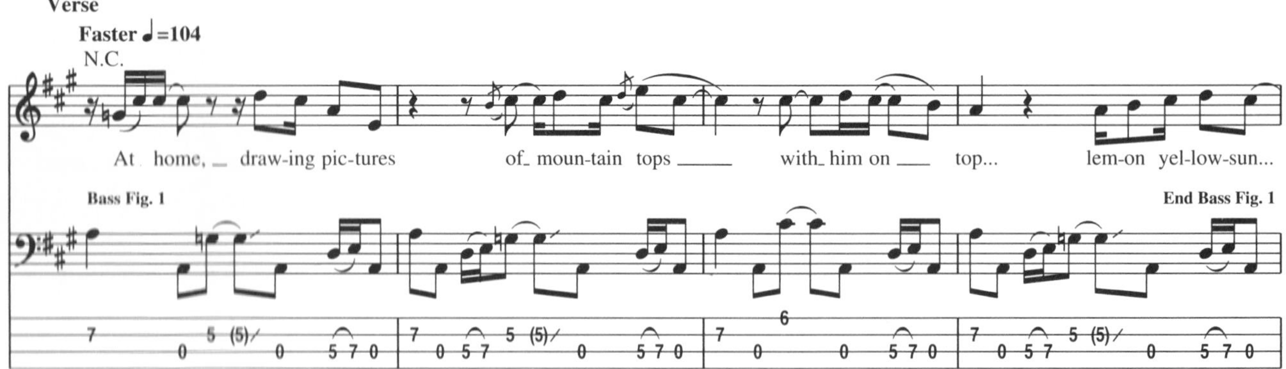
Verse
Faster ♩=104
N.C.
At home, drawing pictures of mountain tops with him on top... lemon yellow sun...
Bass Fig. 1
End Bass Fig. 1

w/Bass Fig. 1
arms raised in a V... an' the dead lay in pools of maroon below..

*A5 G5 D/F# A7sus4 A5
Dad-dy didn't give at-ten-tion... oh, to the fact that Mom-my didn't
Bass Fig. 2
f
* Chords refer to guitar.
G5 D/F# A7sus4 A5
care... King Jer-e-my the wick-ed... oh, ruled his world.
End Bass Fig. 2
Chorus
A7sus2 Fsus2 D5 E5 F5 A5
Jer-e-my spoke in class to-day.
A7sus2 Fsus2 D5 E5 F5/C A5
Jer-e-my spoke in class to-day.
w/Bass Fig. 1, 4 times
Verse
N.C.
Clear-ly I re-mem-ber... pick-ing on the boy... seemed a harm-less
lit-tle fuck... oo, but we un-leashed a li-on... gnashed
his teeth an' bit the re-cess lad-y's breast... how could I for-
get... an' he hit me with a sur-prise left... my jaw left hurt-in'...

oo, dropped wide o-pen... just like the day... oh,
w/Bass Fig. 2
A5 G5
like the day I heard... Dad-dy did-n't
D/F# A7sus4 A5
give af-fec-tion, no... and the boy was some-thing that Mom-my would-n't
G5 D/F# A7sus4 A5
wear... King Jer-e-my the wick-ed... oh, ruled his world.
Chorus
A7sus2 F(sus2) D5 E5 F5 A5
Jer-e-my spoke in class to-day.
(...day.)
A5 G5 Dm E5 F5/C A5
Jer-e-my spoke in class to-day.
(...day.)
A7sus2 Fsus2 D5 E5 F5 A5
Jer-e-my spoke in class to-day!
(steady gliss.)
Interlude
N.C.
Oo, oo, oo, oo, oo, oo, oo, oo, oo, oo, oo, oo, oo, oo. Try to for-get

this...
(Try to forget this...)
Try to e-rase this...
(Try to e-rase
7 0 5 (5) 0 5 7 0
7 0 3 5 7 5 0 5 7 0
7 0 5 (5) 0 5 7 0
Chorus
Asus2 N.C.(F) D5 E5 F5 A5 N.C.
from the black - board.
this...)
7 0 0 0 7 7 5 7 0
7 8 8 5 7 8 0 2
Am/C Asus2 Gsus4 D5 E5 N.C. A5
Jer - e-my spoke in class to - day.
3 5 0 5 7 0 7 10 10 5 7 (7) 3 0 0 7 0 0 0 7 0 5 7 0
A7sus2 Fsus2 D5 E5 F5 A5
Jer - e-my spoke in class to - day.
(day...)
7 8 8 5 7 8 0 0 7 0 0 0 7 0 5 7 0
Asus2 Gsus4 D5 E5 N.C. A5
Jer - e-my spoke in, spoke in, Jer - e-my spoke in, spoke in,
7 10 10 10 (10) 5 7 (7) 3 0 0 7 0 7 7 0 0 0 7 0 7 0
3

*F5
G5
A5
Jer - e - my spoke in class to - day.
* Chords refer to bass.
Outro w/Vocal ad lib
F5
G5
A5
Play 4 times
(Band out)
N.C.
mf
let ring
rit.
Harm.
8va

Jerry Was a Race Car Driver

Lyrics by Les Claypool
Music by Les Claypool, Larry LaLonde and Tim Alexander

* 6 str. fretless bass

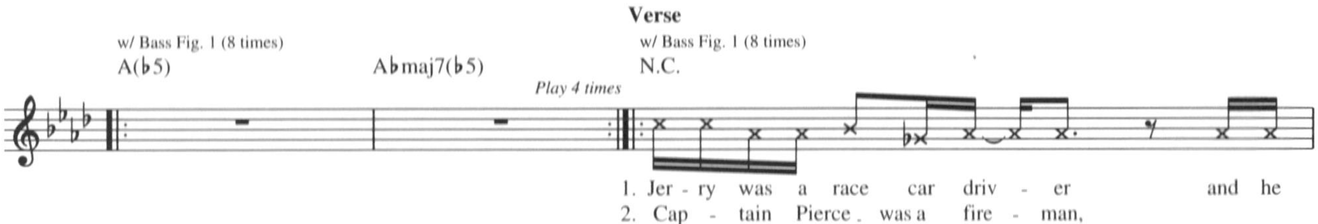

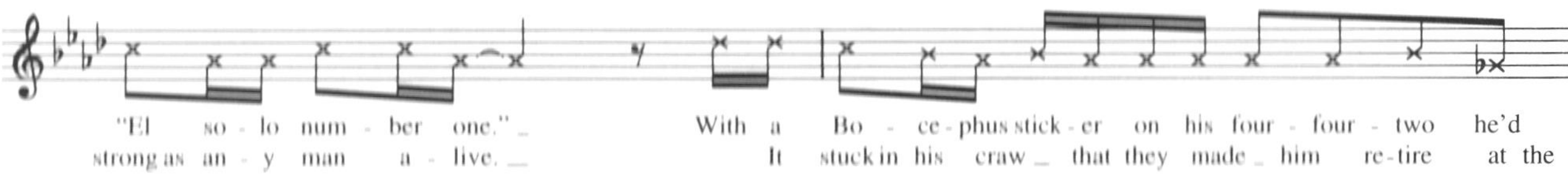

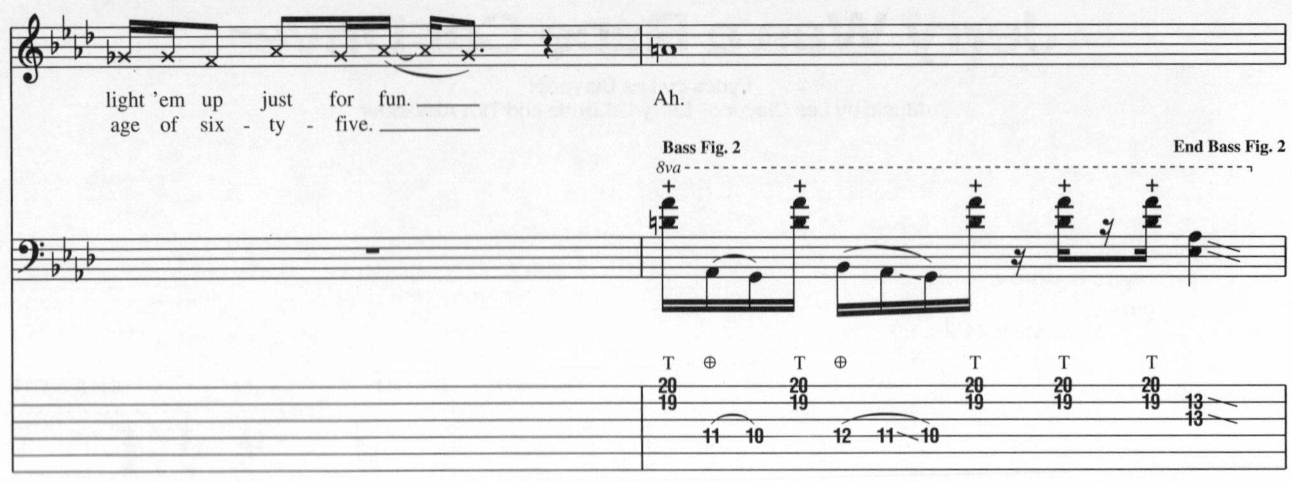
light 'em up just for fun.
age of six - ty - five.
Ah.
Bass Fig. 2
End Bass Fig. 2
8va
T ⊕ T ⊕ T T T
20 19 20 19 20 19 20 19 20 19 13 13
11 10 12 11 10

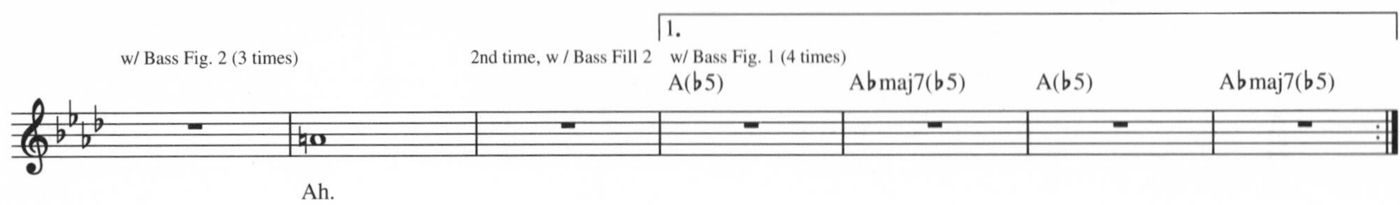
w/ Bass Fig. 2 (3 times)
2nd time, w / Bass Fill 2
1.
w/ Bass Fig. 1 (4 times)
A(♭5)
A♭maj7(♭5)
A(♭5)
A♭maj7(♭5)
Ah.

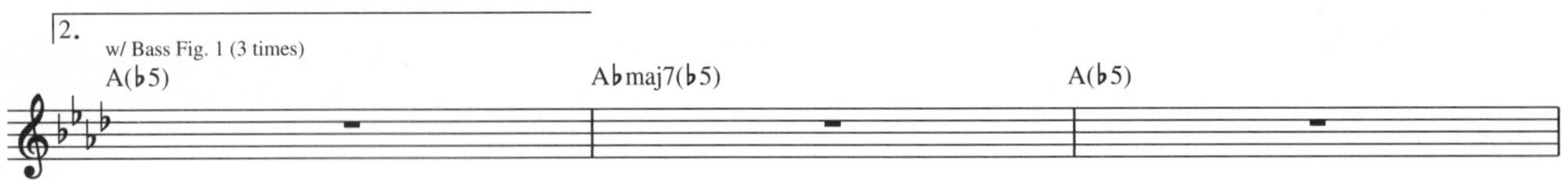
2.
w/ Bass Fig. 1 (3 times)
A(♭5)
A♭maj7(♭5)
A(♭5)

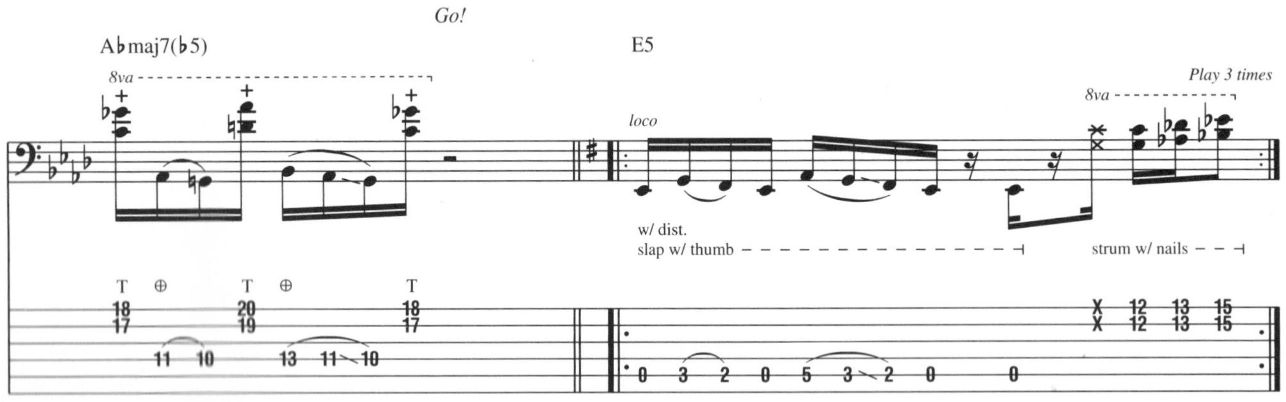
Go!
A♭maj7(♭5)
E5
8va
loco
Play 3 times
w/ dist.
slap w/ thumb
strum w/ nails
T ⊕ T ⊕ T
18 17 20 19 18 17
11 10 13 11 10
X X 12 12 13 13 15 15
0 3 2 0 5 3 2 0 0

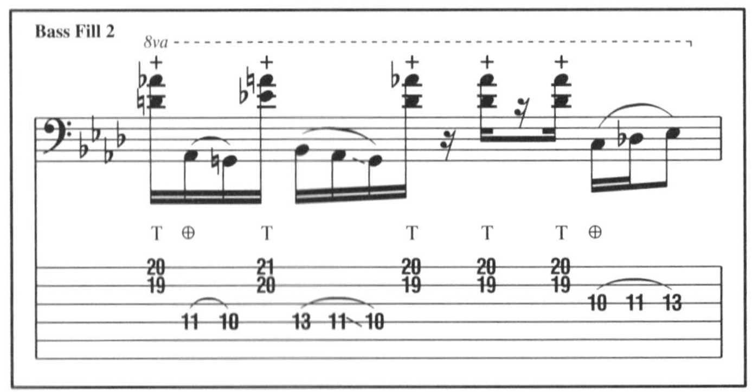
Bass Fill 2
8va
T ⊕ T T T T ⊕
20 19 21 20 20 19 20 19 20 19
11 10 13 11 10 10 11 13

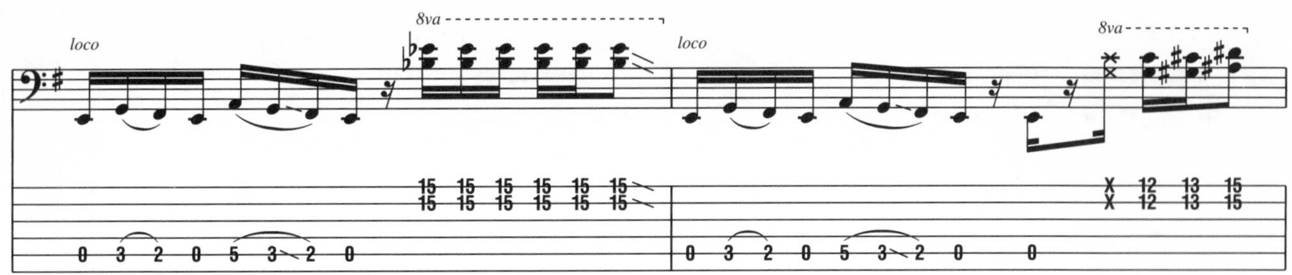
loco
8va
loco
8va

loco
8va
loco
dist. off

Dog will hunt.

Guitar Solo
w/ Bass Fig. 1 (3 times)
3
w/ Bass Fill 1
w/ Bass Fig. 1 (8 times)
8

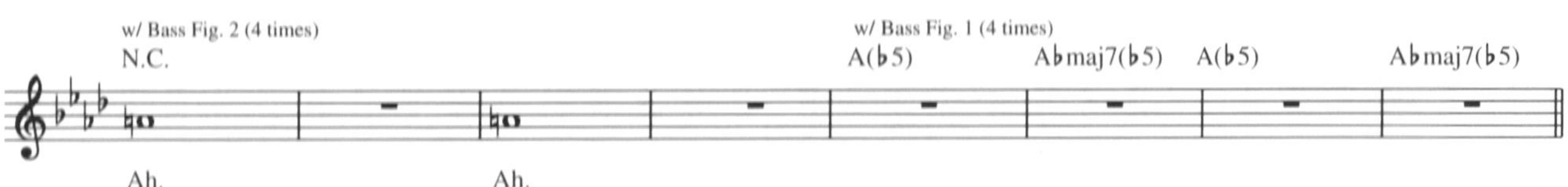
w/ Bass Fig. 2 (4 times)
N.C.
w/ Bass Fig. 1 (4 times)
A(♭5)
A♭maj7(♭5)
A(♭5)
A♭maj7(♭5)
Ah.
Ah.

Verse
w/ Bass Fig. 1 (4 times)
N.C.
3. Jer - ry was a race car driv - er,
twen - ty - two years old.
Had

one too man - y cold beers one night and wrapped him - self a - round a tel - e - phone pole. Go.

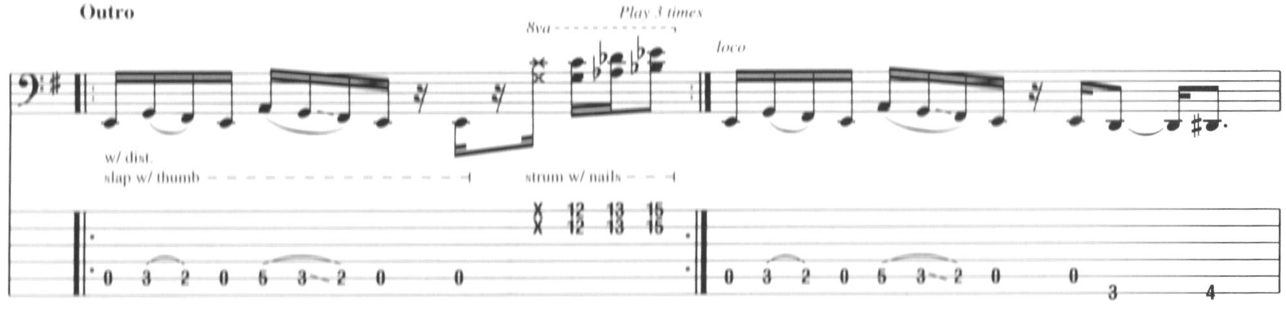
Outro
8va
Play 3 times
loco
w/ dist.
slap w/ thumb
strum w/ nails

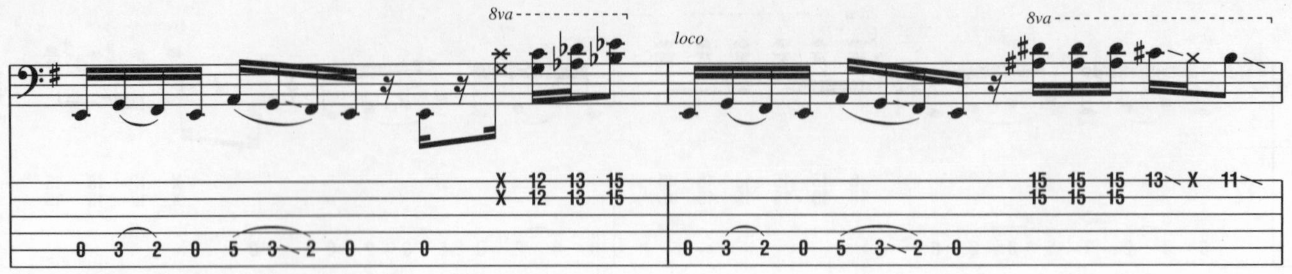
8va
loco
8va

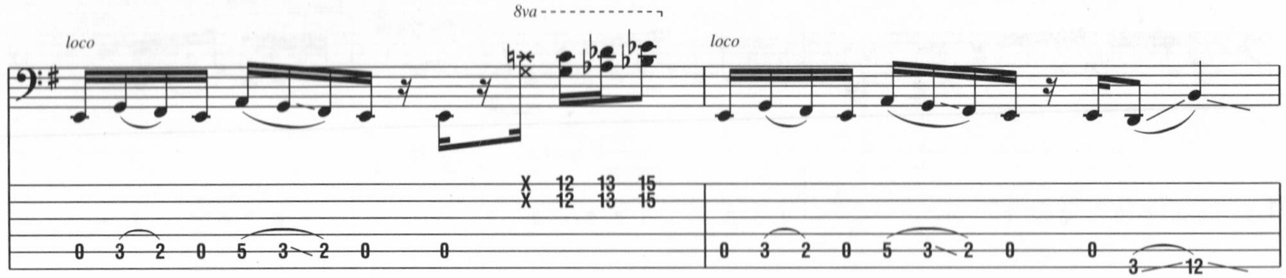
loco
8va
loco

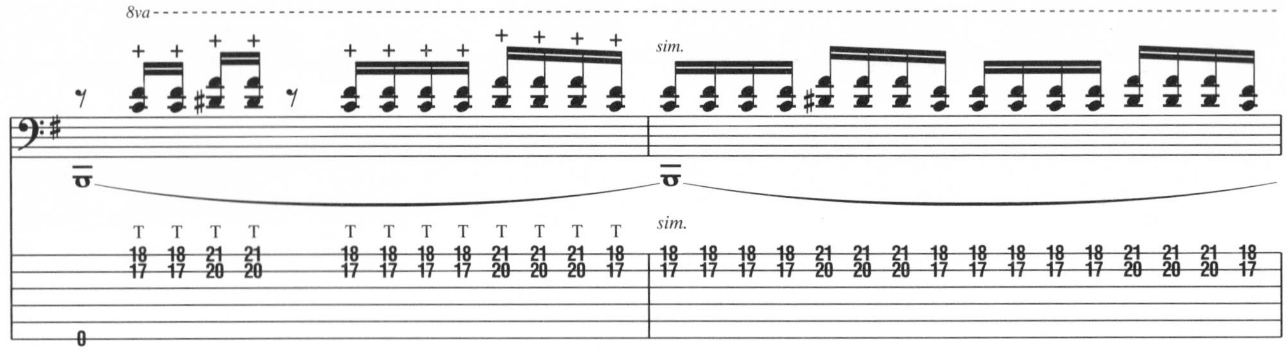
8va
sim.
sim.

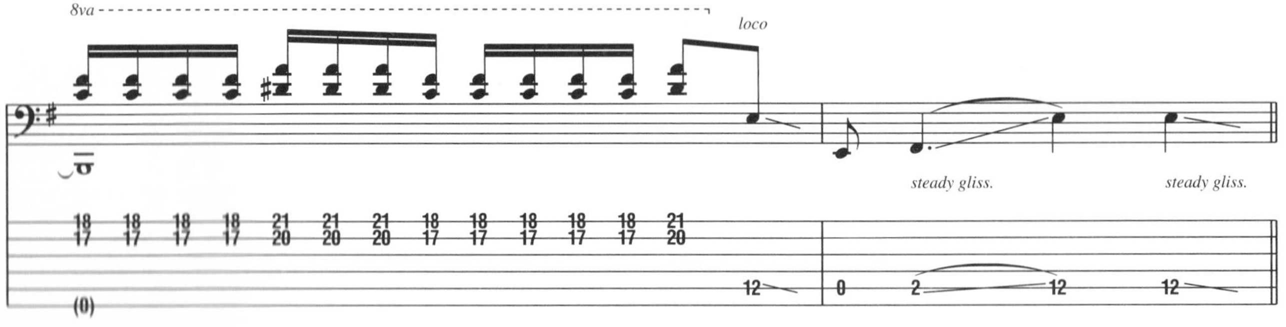
8va
loco
steady gliss.
steady gliss.

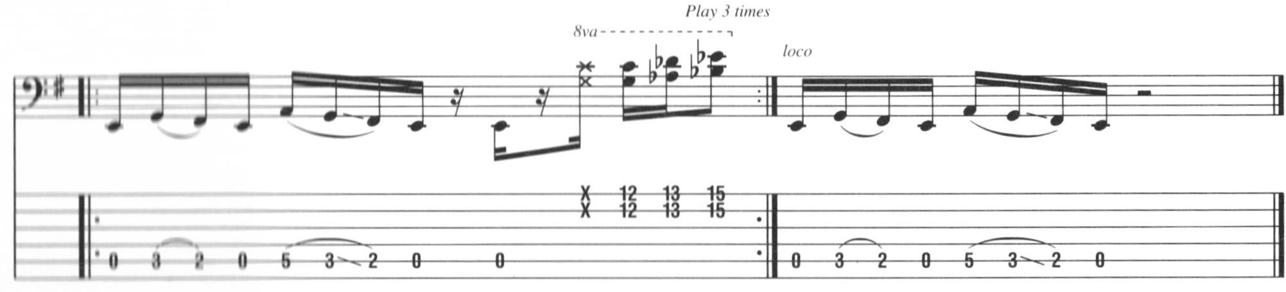
Play 3 times
8va
loco

Johnny B. Goode

Words and Music by Chuck Berry

Fast Rock 'n' Roll ♩= 176
Intro
B♭5
*E♭
mf
sl.
* Root names of chords shown only; see gtr. part for complete chord names.
B♭
F
E♭
1st Verse
Deep down in Lou'-si - an - a, close to
New Or - leans,_ (etc.)

Chorus
B♭
Go! Go!
Go,
Johnny! Go! Go! (etc.)
E♭
sl.
B♭
F
B♭
2nd Verse
B♭
He used to carry his guitar in a gunny sack (etc.)
E♭
B♭
F
B♭
Chorus
B♭

Eb
Bb
F
Guitar solo
Bb
Eb
Bb
Eb
Bb
F
sl.
Bb
Eb
Bb
Eb
Bb

F
Bb
His
3rd Verse
Bb
sl.
moth - er told him, "Some-day you will be a man, _ (etc.)
Eb
sl.
Bb
F
Bb
Chorus
Bb
Eb
Bb
F
Bb
Bb7

Juke Box Hero

Words and Music by Mick Jones and Lou Gramm

Verse
E5
D
N.C.(E)
eyes. 2. And the ver-y next day bought a beat up six - string in a sec-ond hand
7
0
5
0
7
X X 0 X X 0

Bass: w/ Bass Fig. 1 (2 times)
(D)
(E)
store. Did - n't know how to play it, but he knew for

Double-time feel
(D)
E5
D
sure, that one gui-tar felt good in his hands. Did - n't take
7
X X 0 X X 0
7
0 0 0 0 0 0 0 0 0 0 0
0 5

E5
D
E5
long to un - der-stand. Just one gui-tar slung way
0 7
0 5
0 7

D
E5
D
down_ low,
was a one - way
tick-et,
on-ly one _ way to go. __
So he start-ed
Pre-Chorus
B5
B7sus4
B5
B7sus4
B5
B7sus4
rock-in',
ain't nev-er gon-na stop.
Got-ta keep on
rock - in',
some day gon-na
(Rock - in'.) ______
(Rock - in'.) ______
Chorus
End Double-time feel
B5
E5
G5
D5
E5
make it to the top. _
And be a
juke box he - ro.
(Got stars in his _ eyes.)
He's a
Bass Fig. 2
G5
N.C.(D)
(Em)
E5
G5
juke box he - ro.
He took one gui - tar. _ Juke box he - ro.
End Bass Fig. 2
Bass Fig. 3

D5
E5
G5
N.C.(D)
E5
Juke box he - ro, he'll come a - live to - night.
(Stars in his eyes. Stars in his eyes.)
End Bass Fig. 3
Bass: w/ Bass Fig. 1 (4 times)
N.C.(E)
(D)
(E)
(D)
3. In a town with-out a
Verse
Bass: w/ Bass Fig. 1 (3 times)
N.C.(E)
(D)
(E)
name, in a heav-y down - pour, thought he cast his own shad-ow by the back-stage
Double-time feel
(D)
E5
D
door. Like a trip through the past to that day in the rain. And that one gui-tar
Pre-Chorus
E5
D
B5
B7sus4
made his whole life change. Now he needs to keep a - rock-in', he just can't
(Rock - in'.)
Bass Fig. 4

End Double-time feel
B5 B7sus4 B5 B7sus4 B5
stop. Got-ta keep on rock-in', that boy has got to stay on top, and be a
(Rock-in'.)
End Bass Fig. 4
Chorus
Bass: w/ Bass Fig. 2
E5 G5 D5 E5 G5
juke box he - ro. He's a juke box he - ro.
(Got stars in his eyes.) (Got
Bass: w/ Bass Fig. 3
N.C.(D) (Em) E5 G5 D5 E5
Yeah, juke box he - ro. With that one gui - tar
stars in his eyes.) (Stars in his eyes.
G5 N.C.(D) E5
he'll come a - live, come a - live to - night.
Stars in his eyes.)
Guitar Solo
Double-time feel
N.C.(E5) D5 N.C.(E5) D5 N.C.(E5) D5
1., - 4.
D
5.
N.C.(E5) D
Yeah. He's got - ta keep a -

Pre-Chorus
Bass: w/ Bass Fig. 4
B5 B7sus4 B5 B7sus4 B5 B7sus4
rock-in', he just can't stop. Got-ta keep on rock - in' that boy has
(Rock - in'.) (Rock - in'.)
Chorus
End Double-time feel
Bass: w/ Bass Fig. 2 (2 times)
B5 E5 G5 D5 E5
got to stay on top, and be a juke box he - ro. He's a
(Got stars in his eyes.)
G5 N.C.(D) (Em) E5 G5
juke box he - ro It took one gui-tar to put
(Got stars in his eyes.) (Juke box he - ro.)
D5 E5 G5 N.C.(D) (Em)
stars in his eyes. Now he's just a juke box he - ro.
(Stars in his eyes.) (Ah.)
Outro
Bkgd. Voc.: w/ Voc. Fig. 1
Bass: w/ Bass Fig. 2
E5 G5 D5 E5 G5 N.C.(D) (Em)
Juke box he - ro. Juke box he - ro, he's got stars in his eyes.
(Ah.)
E5 G5 D N.C.
Stars in his eyes.
(Stars in his eyes.)
5 5 5 5 5 5 5 5 5 5 5 5 5 5 5 5
0 3
5 5 5 5 5 5 5 5 5 2 4 5 4 2 0 2 0
Voc. Fig. 1
Star. Star. Star. Star. Star.

Killing Floor

Words and Music by Chester Burnett

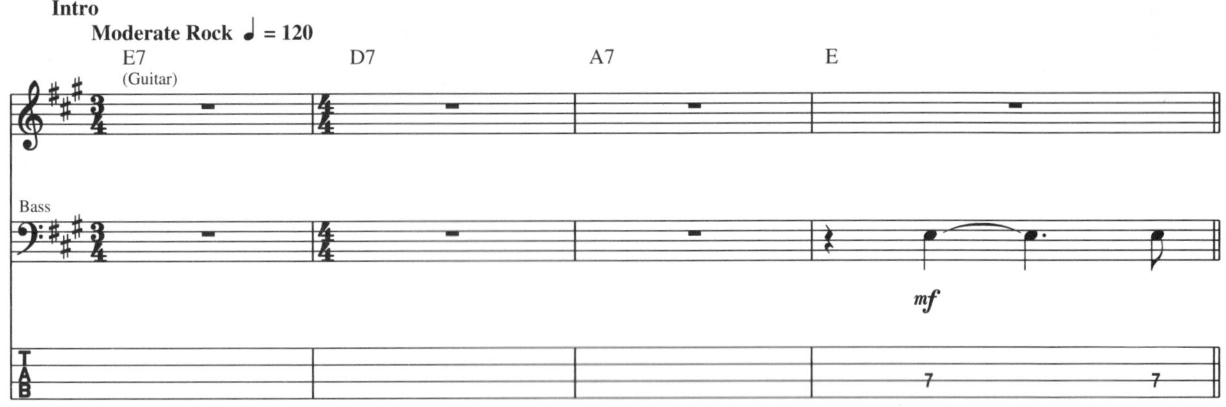

A7
E7
go.
I should have quit you
D7
1., 2., 4.
A
E7
and went off to Mex - i - co.
2. I should have
3. If I had a-
5. Oh, no
3., 5.
To Coda
A7
time.
floor.
Guitar Solo
A
D

Additional Lyrics

3. If I had a followed my first mind,
   If I had a followed my first mind,
   I'd a been gone since my second time.

4. I should have went on when my friend come from Mexico with me.
   I should have went on when my friend come from Mexico with me.
   But no foolin' with you, baby, I let you put me on the killing floor.

5. Oh no, I should have been gone.
   Oh no, I should have been gone.
   Then I wouldn't have been here, down on the killing floor.

Killing in the Name

Written and Arranged by Rage Against The Machine

Verse
N.C.
1., 2., 3.
Bass: w/ Bass Fill 1, 5th time
Some of those _ that work forc - es
are the same _ that burn cross - es.
mf

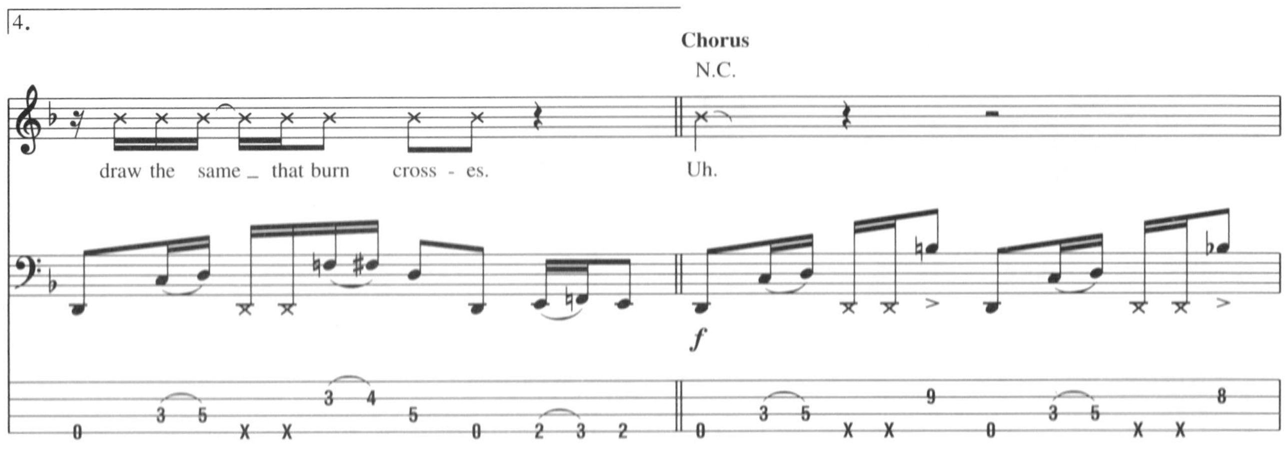
4.
Chorus
N.C.
draw the same _ that burn cross - es.
Uh.
f

Kill - ing in the name of...

Bass Fill 1

Interlude
Swing Feel
C5
N.C.(D5)
play 4 times
Kill-ing in the name of...
(Whispered:) Now you do what they told ya.
1., 2., 3.
w/ Voc. Fig. 1, on D.S. only
N.C.(D5)
Now you do what they told ya.
Now you do what they told ya.
4.
N.C.(D5)
Now you do what they told ya!
Those who died are jus-ti-fied by
4th time to Coda
wear-ing your badge and your cho-sen white. You'll jus-ti-fy those that died by
Voc. Fig. 1
play 6 times
Now you're un-der con-trol.
Now you're un-der con-trol!

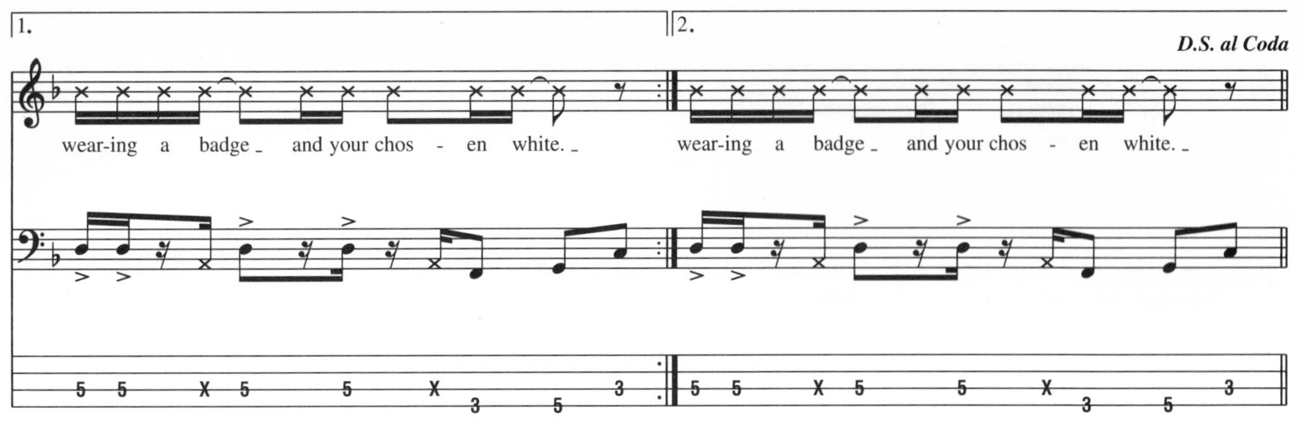
1.
2.
D.S. al Coda
wear-ing a badge _ and your chos - en white. _
wear-ing a badge _ and your chos - en white. _

Coda
Guitar Solo
N.C.(D5)
wear-ing a badge _ and your chos - en white. _ Come on!

1.
Bass Fill 2
End Bass Fill 2

2.
Bridge
Freely
N.C.
Fuck you, I won't do what ya tell __ me.

A Tempo
play 3 times
Fuck you, I won't do what ya tell _ me.
Fuck you, I won't do what ya tell _ me.
Fuck you, I won't do what ya tell _ me.
Bass: w/ Bass Fill 2, 4th time
N.C.(D5)
play 8 times
Fuck you, I won't do what ya tell _ me!
Dm7
Moth-er - fuck - er!
Uh!

La Grange

Words and Music by Billy F Gibbons, Dusty Hill and Frank Beard

Lady Madonna

Words and Music by John Lennon and Paul McCartney

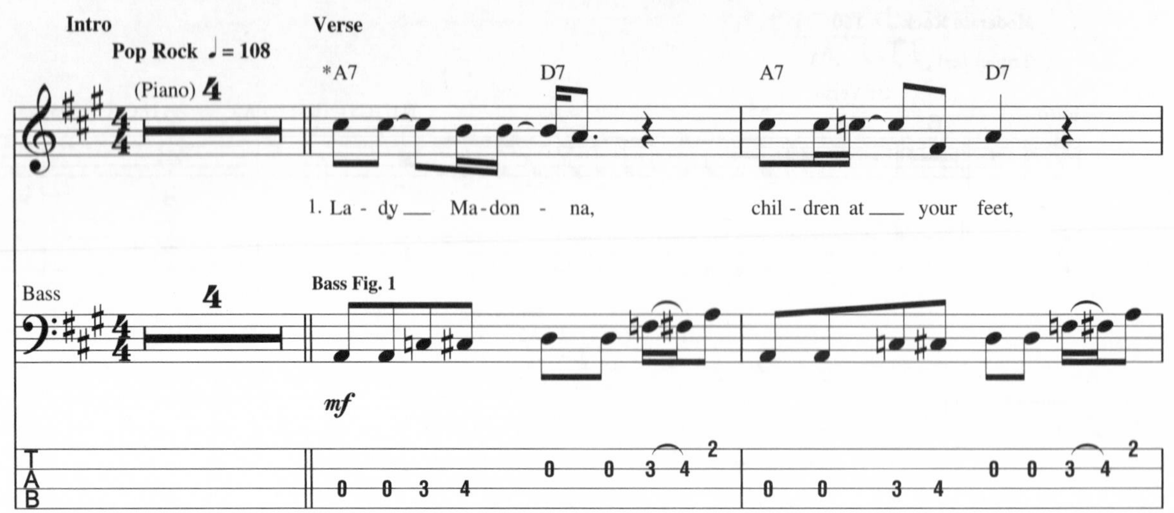

* Chord symbols implied by piano.

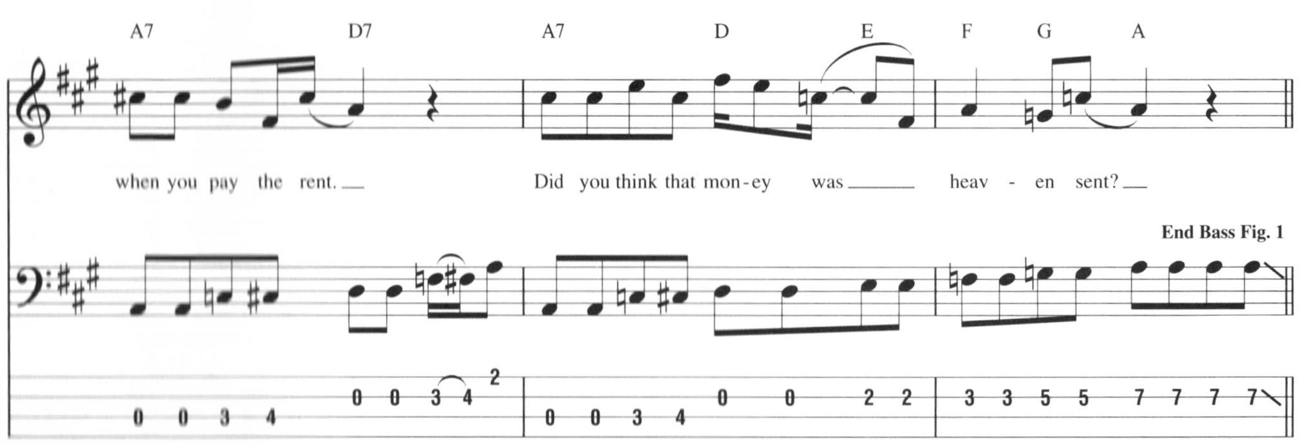

Bridge
Dm7
G7
Fri - day night ar - rives with - out a suit - case.
Bass Fig. 2
5 5 3 3 2 2 5 5
5 5 3 3 2 2 5 5
C
Am
Dm7
Sun - day morn - ing creep - ing like a nun.
Mon-day's child has learned to tie his
End Bass Fig. 2
3 3 2 2 5 5 3 3
5 5 2 2 3 3 7 7
5 5 3 3 2 2 5 5
Verse
Bass: w/ Bass Fig. 1
G7
C
Bm7
Esus4
E
A7
D7
boot lace.
See how they run.
2. La - dy Ma-don - na,
3. La - dy Ma-don - na,
5 5 3 3 2 2 5 5
3 2
7 0
A7
D7
A7
D
E
ba - by at your breast,
ly - ing on the bed,
won - ders how you man - age to feed
lis - ten to the mu - sic play - ing
To Coda
F G A
A7 D7 A7 D7 A7
D E F G A
the rest.
in your head.

Bridge
Dm7
Voc. Fig. 1
G7
C
Ba, ba, ba, ba, ba, ba, ba, ba, ba.
Ba, ba, ba, ba, ba, ba,
Am
D7
ba, ba, ba, ba, ba.
Ba, ba, ba, ba, ba, ba,
D.S. al Coda
G7
End Voc. Fig. 1
C
Bm7
Esus4
E
ba, ba, ba.
See how they run.
Coda
Bridge
Bkgd. Voc.: w/ Voc. Fig. 1
Bass: w/ Bass Fig. 2
Dm7
G7
Tues - day af - ter - noon is nev - er end - ing.
C
Am
Dm7
Wednes - day morn - ing pa - pers did - n't come.
Thurs - day night your stock - ings need - ed

G7
C
Bm7
Esus4
E
mend - ing.
See how they run.
Outro
A7
D7
Lady Ma - don - na,
chil - dren at your feet,
D
E
F
G
A
G/B
Cm
G/B A
won - der how you man - age to make ends meet?

Lay Down Sally

Words and Music by Eric Clapton, Marcy Levy and George Terry

Country Shuffle (𝅗𝅥 = 95)

Introduction

A7
8
Bass is tacet
muted bass

Verse

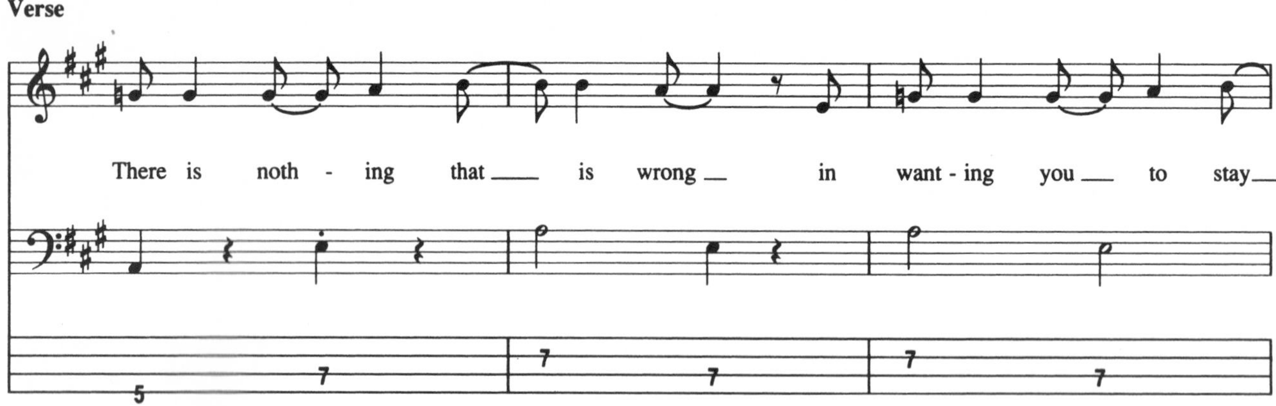
There is noth - ing that is wrong in want - ing you to stay

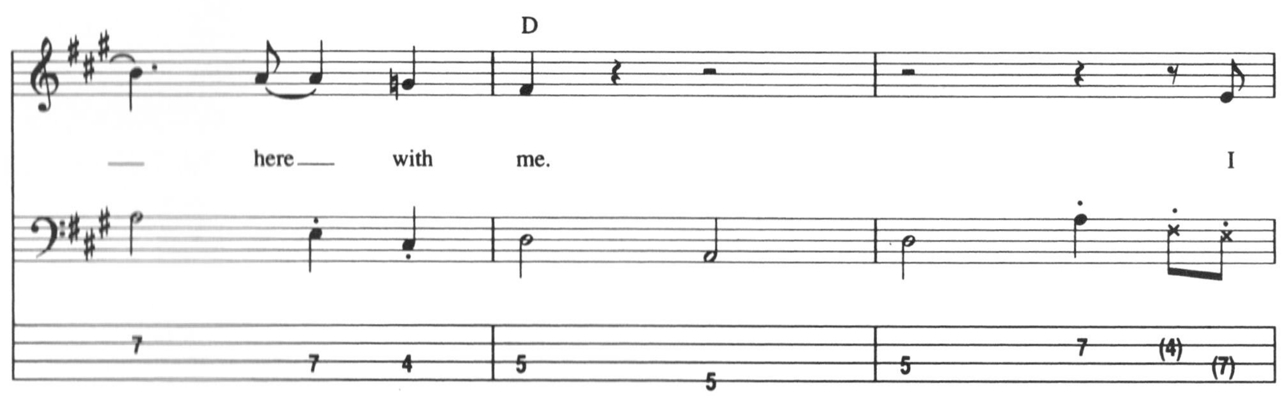
D
here with me.
I

A7
know you've got some - where to go, but won't you make your - self
D7
at home and stay with me? And don't you
Chorus
E7
A
ev - er leave. Lay down Sal -
D
- ly, and rest here in my arms.

E
A
Don't you think you want some - one to talk to?
Lay down Sal - ly, no
D
E
need to leave so soon.
I've been try - ing all
A
night long just to talk to you.

A7
The sun ain't near - ly on the rise, and
D
we still got the moon and stars a - bove.
A7
Un - der - neath the vel - vet skies,

D
love is all that mat - ters. Won't you stay with me?
E
And don't you ev - er leave.
A
D
Lay down Sal - ly, and rest here in my arms.
E
Don't you think you want some - one to talk

A
— to?
Lay down Sal -
- ly,
D
no need to leave — so soon. —
E
A
I've been try - ing all — night long — just to talk to you. —
Guitar Solo
A7

I
A7
long to see the morn - ing light col - or - ing your face
C
D
so dream - i - ly.
So
A7
don't you go and say good - bye, you can lay your wor -

D
-ries down and stay with me. And don't you
E
A
ev - er leave. Lay down Sal-
D
-ly, and rest here in my arms.
E
A
Don't you think you want some - one to talk to?

Lay down Sal - ly, no
7 7 4 7 4 7 5 7 7 4
D
need to leave so soon.
5 5 4 5 5 4 5 6
E
I've been try - ing all
7 7 4
night long just to talk to you.
7 4 7 7
A
4 7 7 7 7 4 7 4
Lay down Sal - ly, and rest here in my arms.
7 7 7 4 7
D
5 5

E
Don't you think you want some - one to talk
A
to?
Lay down Sal -
D
ly, no need to leave so soon.
E
A
I've been try - ing all night long just to talk to you.

A7
5
7
4
7
4
7
4
7
7
7
7
5
4

5
4
7
7
7
5
4
5
4
7
7
5
4

Begin fade
5
4
7
7
7
7
7
7
7
7

7
7
7
5
4
5
4
7
7
7
5
4

Fade-out
5
4
7
7
7
5
4
5
4
7
7
7
5
4

Leave It

Words and Music by Trevor Horn, Trevor Rabin and Chris Squire

Chorus
Gm F C B♭add9/D C F Gm F C B♭add9/D C F Gm
Voc. Fig. 3
End Voc. Fig. 3
(Ah, leave it.)
Bass
f
Bkgd. Voc.: w/ Voc. Fig. 3
F C B♭add9/D C F Gm F C B♭add9/D C F Gm
Bass Fig. 1
End Bass Fig. 1
Breakdown
Bass tacet
Gm F C B♭add9/D C F Gm
(Do, do, do, do, do, do, do.)
(Do, do, do, do, do, do, do, do.)
Verse
Bkgd. Voc.: w/ Voc. Fig. 4 (4 times)
Gm
2. Two down, there you go. Mc - Ar - thur Park in the driv - ing snow.
Up - town, they're dig - ging it out, bet - ter
Voc. Fig. 4
(Do, do, do, do, do, do, do.)
(Do, do, do, do, do, do, do, do.)
(Do, do, do, do, do, do, do, do, do, do, do.)

lay your claim.
Get home, you're not a - lone, you just broke out of the dan - ger zone.
Be there to show your face on an - oth - er dream - y day.
Chorus
Voc.: w/ Voc. Fig. 3 (2 times)
2nd time, Voc.: w/ Voc. Fill 1
2nd time, Bass: w/ Bass Fig. 1 (2 times)
Gm F C B♭add9/D C F Gm F C B♭add9/D
C F Gm F C B♭add9/D C F Gm
Voc. Fill 1
re - al.

To Coda
Breakdown
F C B♭add9/D C F Gm
Gm F C B♭add9/D
(Do, do, do, do,
C F Gm
do, do, do.
F C B♭add9/D C F Gm
Do, do, do, do, do, do, do.
(Do, do, do, do, do, do, do, do, do.)
F C B♭add9/D C F Gm
Do, do, do, do, do, do, do.
(Do, do, do, do, do, do, do, do, do.)
F C Gm F C Gm F C
Do, do, do, do, do, do, do, do, do, do, do,
Chorus
Bkgd. Voc.: w/ Voc. Fig. 2 (2 times)
B♭ Gm F C B♭add9/D C F Gm
Voc. Fig. 5
do, do, do, do.)
Good - bye, good - bye, good - bye bad.

F C B♭add9/D C F Gm F C B♭add9/D
Hel - lo, hel - lo, heav - en. Good - bye, good - bye,
C F Gm F C B♭add9/D B♭ Gm
Interlude
G F/G
good - bye bad. Hel - lo, hel - lo, heav - en. Oo,
Em/G E♭/G
Bridge
Bkgd. Voc.: w/ Voc. Fig. 1
D5
oo. I can feel... No il -
D.S. al Coda
E5 D5
- lu - sions... Ref - uge in... Break - ing down... We make

Coda

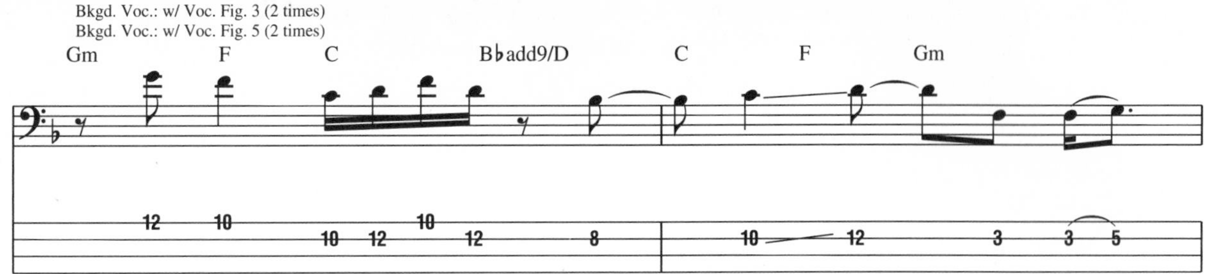
Bkgd. Voc.: w/ Voc. Fig. 3 (2 times)
Bkgd. Voc.: w/ Voc. Fig. 5 (2 times)
Gm F C B♭add9/D C F Gm

F C B♭add9/D C F Gm F C B♭add9/D

C F Gm F C B♭add9/D B♭ Gm

Outro

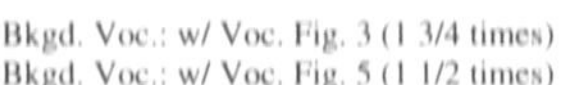
Bkgd. Voc.: w/ Voc. Fig. 3 (1 3/4 times)
Bkgd. Voc.: w/ Voc. Fig. 5 (1 1/2 times)

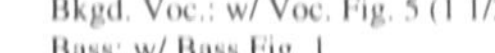
Bass: w/ Bass Fig. 1

Em F C B♭add9/D C F Gm F C B♭add9/D B♭ Gm
One down, one to go. An - oth - er town and one more show.

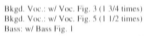

Gm F C B♭add9/D C F Gm G
One down and one to go. An - oth - er town and one more show!

Like a Rolling Stone

Words and Music by Bob Dylan

F
Em
Dm
C
Dm7
sl.
G
How does it feel...
Chorus
H
P
Play 4 times

Live Forever

Words and Music by Noel Gallagher

Em7
D
— May - be you're — the same — as me, — we see things they'll nev - er
Am7
F
F/E
F
F/E
F
F/E
F
F/E
see. You and I — are gon - na live for - ev - er. I said,
(end Bass Fig. 1)
2nd Verse
G5
D
Am7
may - be — I don't real - ly wan - na know how your gar - den grows 'cause I —
Bass Fig. 2
P
P
C
D
G5
D
— just wan - na fly. Late - ly, — did you ev - er feel the pain in the morn-
(end Bass Fig. 2)
P
P

Am7
C
D
ing rain as it soaks you to the bone?
Chorus
w/Bass Fig. 1 (1st 8 bars only)
Em7
D
May - be I will nev - er be all the things that I wan - na
Am7
C
D
be. Now is not the time to cry, now's the time to find out
Em7
D
why. I think you're the same as me, we see things they'll nev - er
w/Bass Fill 1
Am7
F
F/E F
F/E F
F/E F
see. You and I are gon - na live for - ev - er.
Guitar solo
w/Bass Fig. 2 (2 times)
G5
D
Am7
1.
C
D
2.
Substitute Bass Fill 2
w/Bass Fig. 1
C
D
Em7
D
Am7
C
D
Bass Fill 1
Bass Fill 2

Em7
D
Am7
F
F/E
F
F/E
F
F/E
F
F/E
3rd Verse
G5
D
May - be I don't real - ly wan - na know how your gar -
3
Am7
C
D
den grows 'cause I just wan - na fly.
H
H
sl.
H
12 14
12
12 14
12
(12)
H
sl.
w/Bass Fig. 2 (1st 3 bars only)
G5
D
Am7
Late - ly, did you ev - er feel the pain in the morn - ing rain as it soaks
w/Bass Fill 2
C
D
Chorus
w/Bass Fig. 1 (1st 7 bars only)
Em7
you to the bone? May - be I just wan - na
D
Am7
fly. Wan - na live, I don't wan - na die. May - be I just wan - na

C
D
Em7
breathe, may - be I just don't be - lieve. May - be you're the same as me,
D
Am7
we see things they'll nev - er see. You and I are gon - na live for - ev -
F
F/E
F
F/E
Am
er,
gon - na live for - ev -
Bass Fig. 3
(end Bass Fig. 3)
w/Bass Fig. 3
F
F/E
F
F/E
Am
er,
gon - na live for - ev - er,
w/Bass Fig. 3
F
F/E
F
F/E
Am
Play 3 times
w/Bass Fig. 3
F
F/E
F
F/E
Am
gon - na live for - ev - er.
Outro solo
w/Bass Fig. 3
F
F/E
F
F/E
Am
Play 7 times
Free time
F
F/E
F
F/E
Am7
Amsus2
sl.
sl.

Lonesome Whistle Blues

Words and Music by Alan Moore, Elson Teat and Rudy Toombs

F7
even
Why you packed up an' left me, did-n't e-ven tell me the rea-son
C7
G7
why. Well, if I did-n't please you, ba - by,
F7
C7
G7
ain't be-cause I did-n't try. 2. Well, then a -
Verse
C7
F7
C7
long a - bout mid-night when I heard that ol' lone - some can-non-ball,

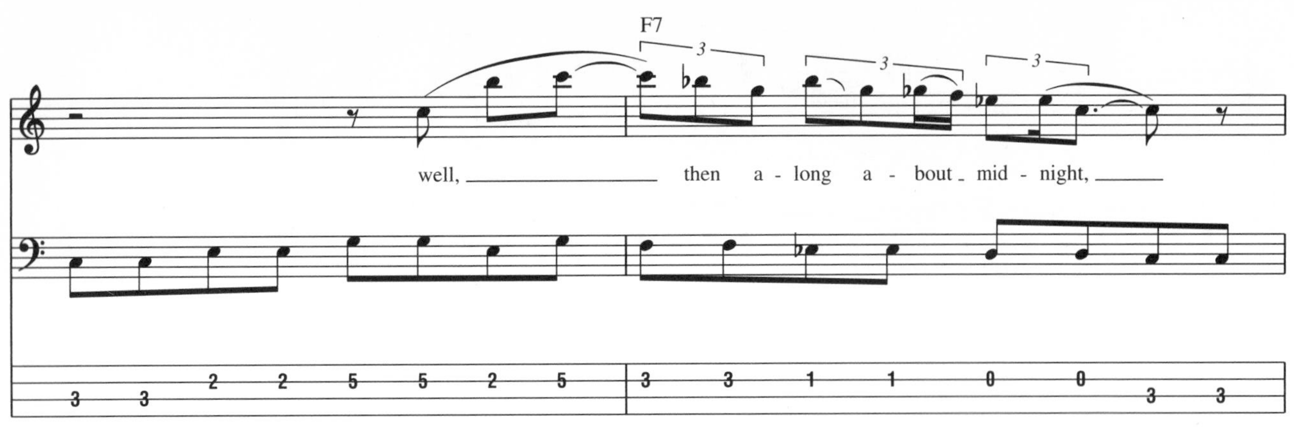
F7
well, then a - long a - bout - mid - night,
3 3 2 2 5 5 2 5
3 3 1 1 0 0 3 3

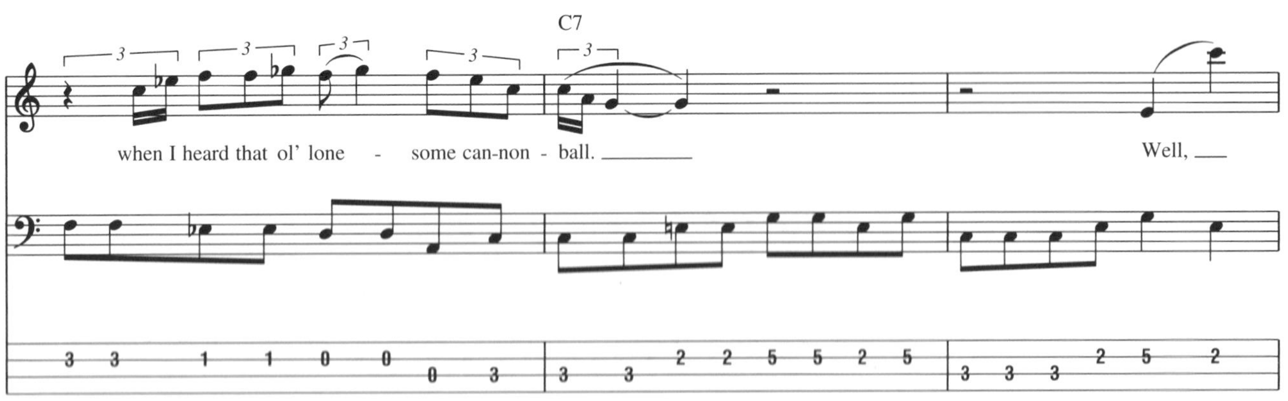
C7
when I heard that ol' lone - some can-non - ball.
Well,
3 3 1 1 0 0 0 3
3 3 2 2 5 5 2 5
3 3 3 2 5 2

G7
even
when I think a-bout you, ba - by,
tears be - gin to fall.
C7
3 3 2 2 5 5 2 5 2
1 1 0 0 3 3 0 3 0
3 3 2 2 5 5 2 5 2

G7
Chorus
C7
Woo.
3 3 1 3 5 2 5 2
3 3 2 2 5 5 2 5 2
3 3 2 2 5 5 2 5 2
3 3 2 2 5 5 2 5 2

F7
C7
Woo.
G7
F7
C7
Woo.
G7
Verse
C7
F7
3. I'm gon-na find you, ba - by, if it takes my whole life to track you
C7
down.
F7
I'm gon-na find you, ba - by,
* Sung behind the beat.

even
C7
if it takes my whole life to track you down.
Well,
G7
even
F7
C7
if I don't find you by plane, I gon-na use my ol' blood-hound.
Outro-Chorus
G7
C7
F7
C7
Woo.
Begin Fade
F7
C7
Woo.
G7
F7
C7
Fade Out
Woo.

Look at Little Sister

Words and Music by Hank Ballard

Tune down 1/2 step

Moderate Rock Shuffle ♫ = ♩♪ (3) ♩ = 114

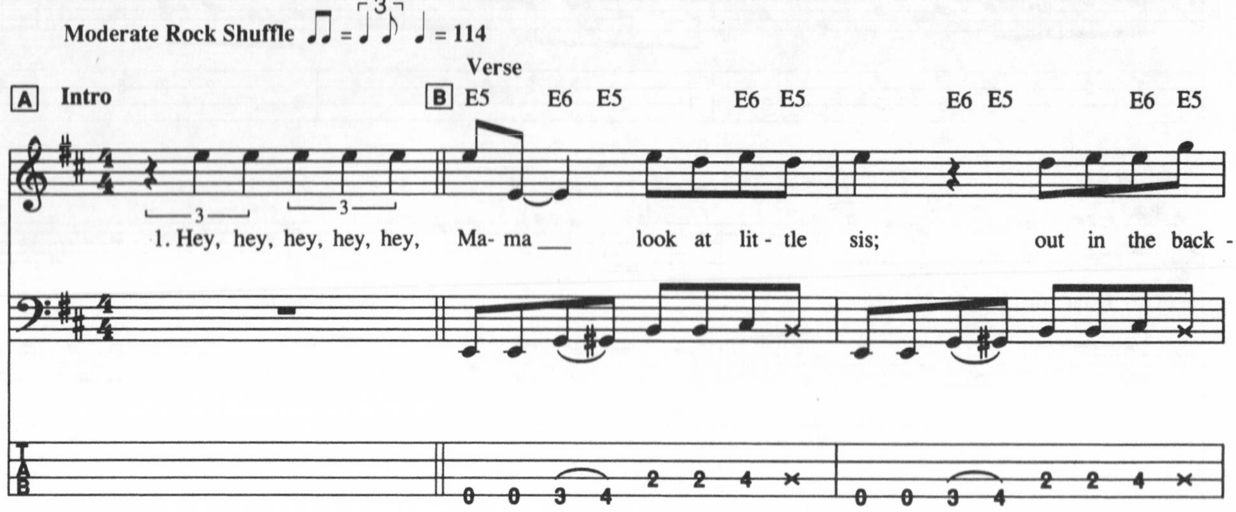

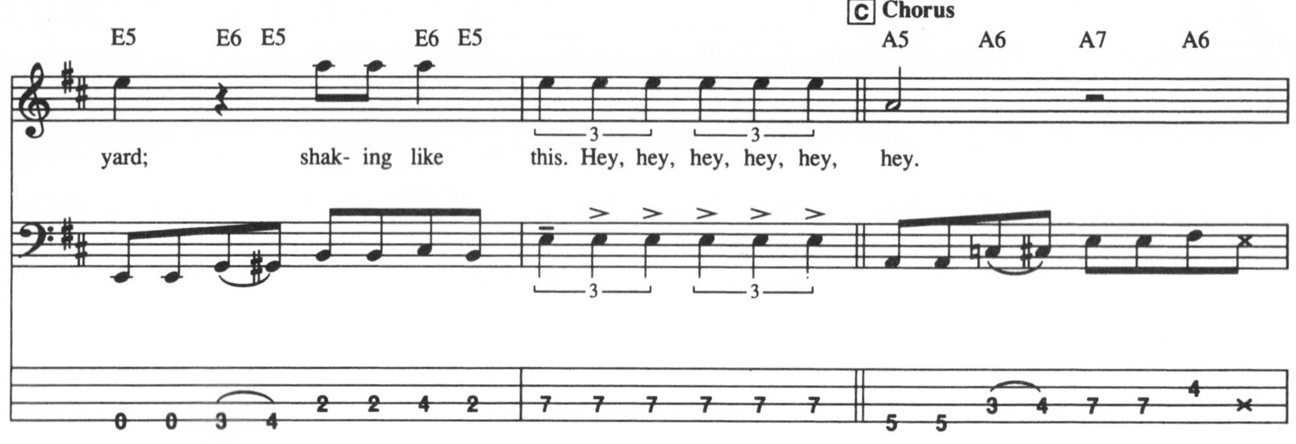

B5 B6 B5 B6 B5 A5 A6 A5 A6 A5 E5 E6 E5 E6 E5
hey, hey; look at lit - tle sis - ter.
D Verse
B5 E5 E6 E5 E6 E5 E6 E5 E6 E5
2. What a - bout the neigh - bors? What they gon - na say?
E Chorus
E5 E6 E5 E6 E5 A5 A6 A7 A6
Stop lit - tle sis - ter get - ting car - ried a - way, hey, hey, hey;
A5 A6 A7 A6 E5 E6 E5 E6 E5 E6 E5 E6 E5
look at lit - tle sis - ter. Hey, hey,

B5
B6
B5
B6
B5
A5
A6
A5
A6
A5
E5
E6
E5
E6
E5
hey,
hey;
look at lit - tle
sis - ter.
F Verse
B5
E5
3.Shak - in' like a tree,
roll - in' like a log,
G Chorus
A5
A6
A7
A6
shak- in' and a roll - in' now,
that ain't
all.
Hey, hey,
hey;
A5
A6
A7
A6
E5
E6
E5
E6
E5
E6
E5
E6
E5
look at lit - tle
sis - ter.
Hey, hey,

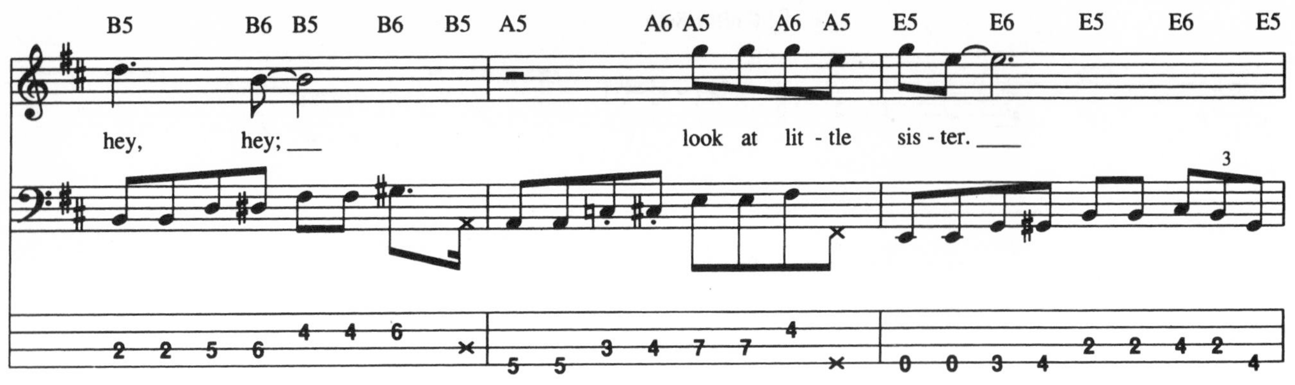
B5 B6 B5 B6 B5 A5 A6 A5 A6 A5 E5 E6 E5 E6 E5
hey, hey; ___ look at lit - tle sis - ter. ____

B5
H Sax Solo
E5

A5

E5

B5
A5
E5

I Guitar Solo
B5
E5

A5

E5

B5
A5
E5

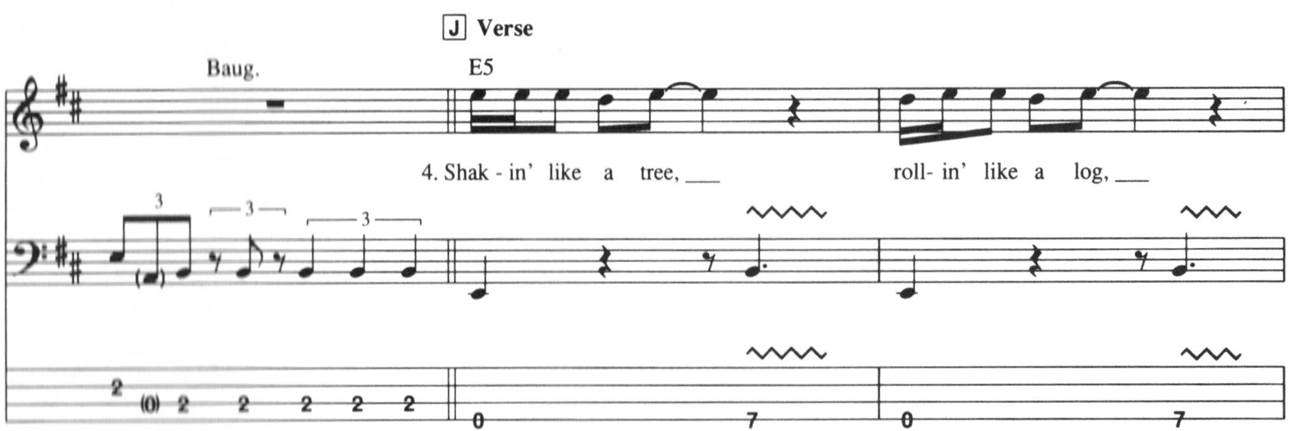
J Verse
Baug.
E5
4. Shak - in' like a tree, ___
roll- in' like a log, ___

K Chorus
A5 A6 A7 A6
shak- in' and a roll - in' now, that ain't all. ___ Hey, hey, hey;
A5 A6 A7 A6 E5 E6 E5 E6 E5 E6 E5 E6 E5
look at lit - tle sis - ter. ____ Hey, hey,
B5 B6 B5 B6 B5 A5 A6 A5 A6 A5 E5 E6 E5 E6 E5
hey, hey; ___ look at lit - tle sis - ter. ____
L Verse
B5 E5 E6 E5 E6 E5 E6 E5 E6 E5
5.What a - bout the neigh - bors? What they gon - na say?

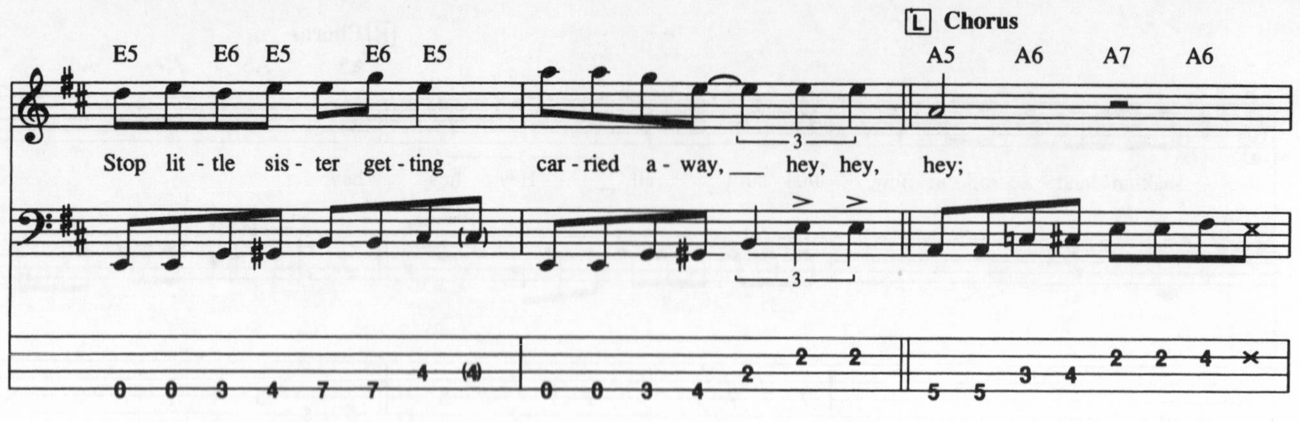
L Chorus
E5 E6 E5 E6 E5 A5 A6 A7 A6
Stop lit - tle sis - ter get - ting car - ried a - way, hey, hey, hey;

A5 A6 A7 A6 E5 E6 E5 E6 E5 E6 E5 E6 E5
look at lit - tle sis - ter. Hey, hey,

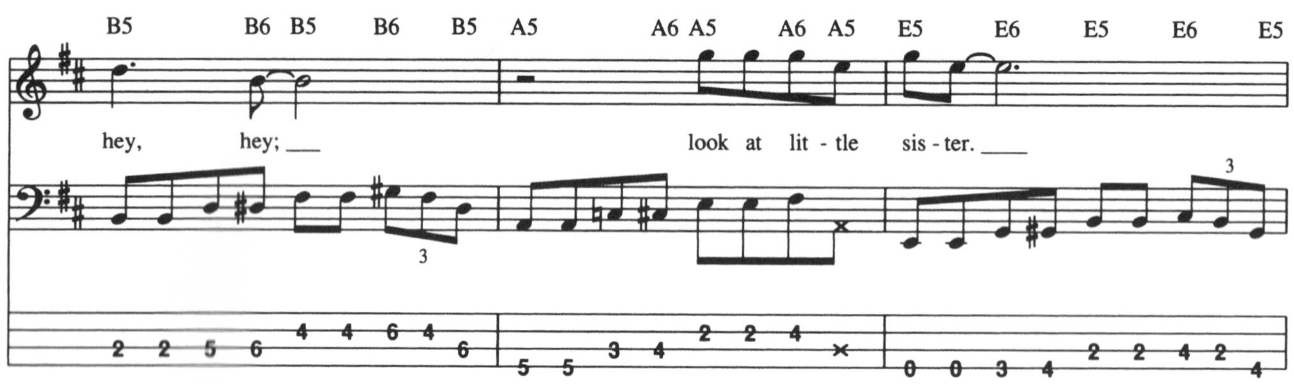
B5 B6 B5 B6 B5 A5 A6 A5 A6 A5 E5 E6 E5 E6 E5
hey, hey; look at lit - tle sis - ter.

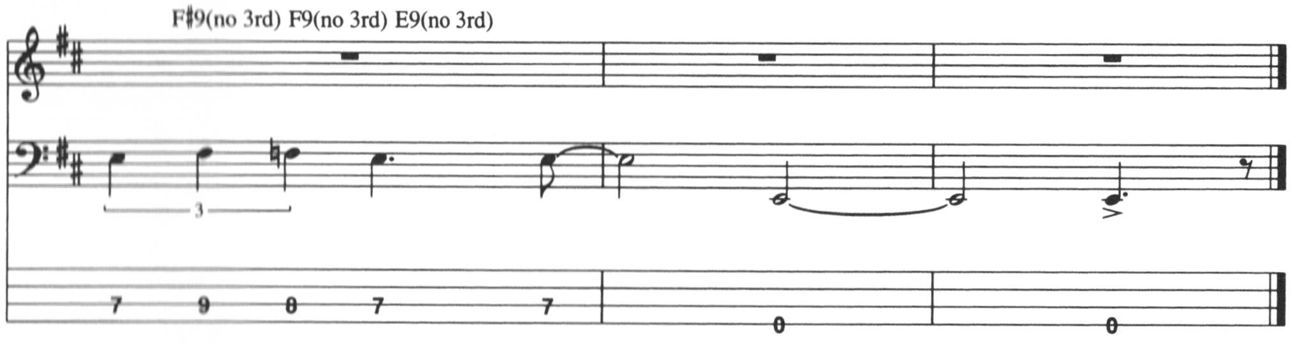
F♯9(no 3rd) F9(no 3rd) E9(no 3rd)

Loser

Words by Beck Hansen
Music by Beck Hansen and Karl Stephenson

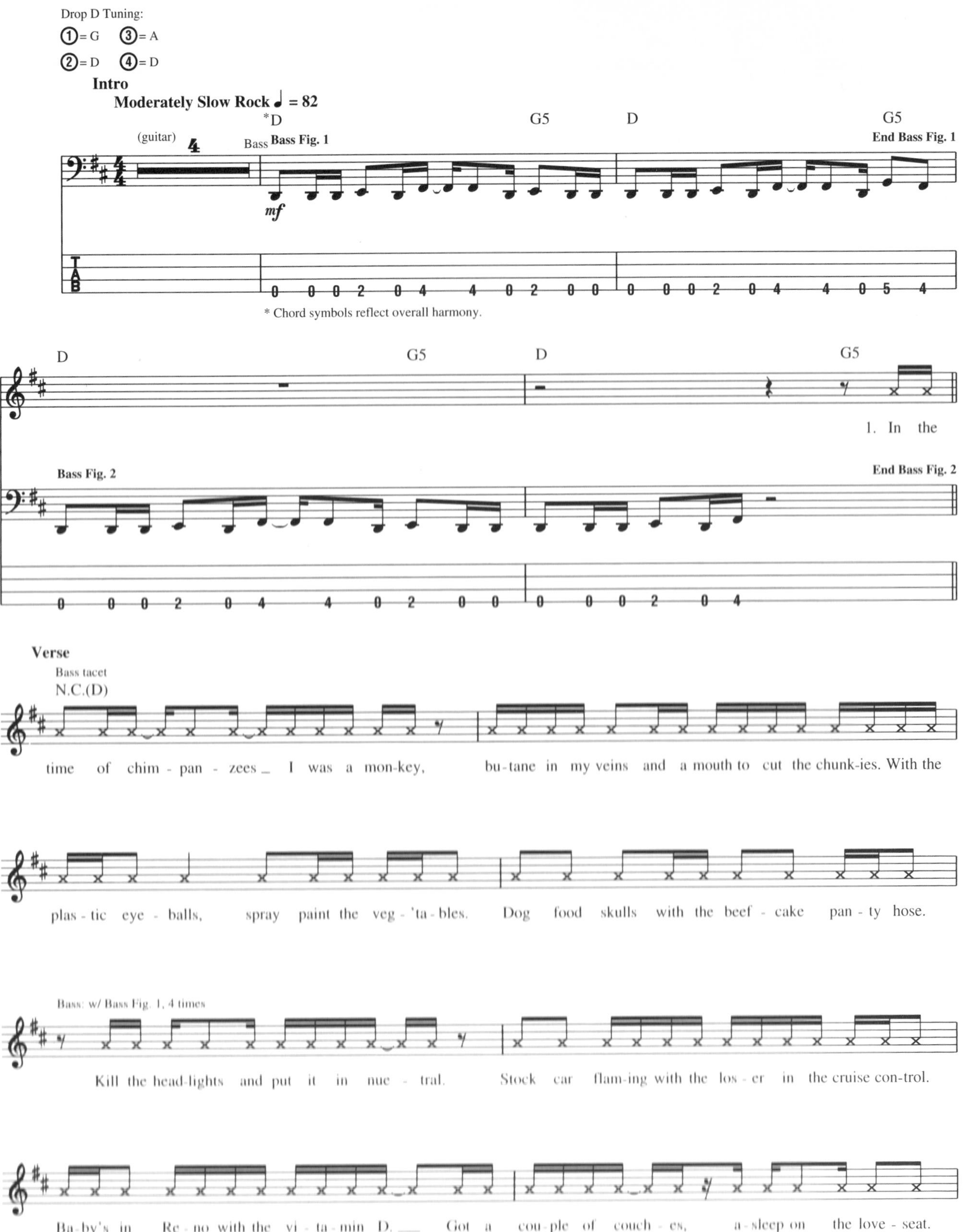

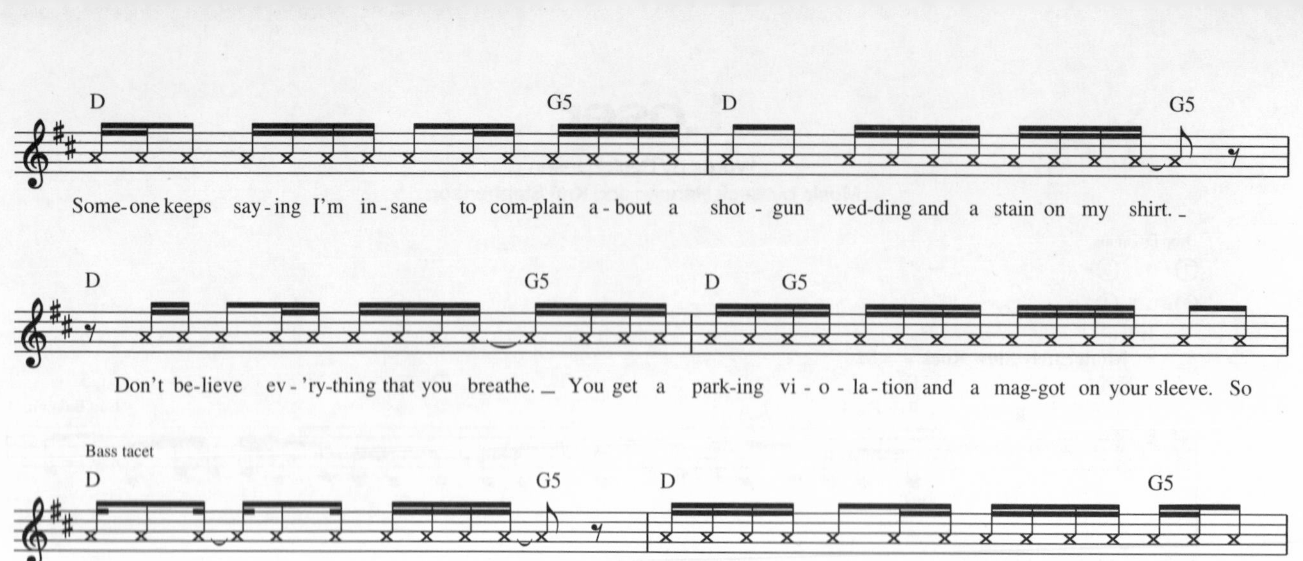
D G5 D G5
Some-one keeps say-ing I'm in-sane to com-plain a-bout a shot - gun wed-ding and a stain on my shirt.
D G5 D G5
Don't be-lieve ev-'ry-thing that you breathe. You get a park-ing vi-o-la-tion and a mag-got on your sleeve. So
Bass tacet
D G5 D G5
shave your face with some mace in the dark. Sav-ing all your food stamps and burn-ing down the trail-er park.

Chorus
Bass: w/ Bass Fig. 1, 4 times
D G5 D D G5 D G5
Yo. Cut it. Soy un per-di-dor. I'm a
* w/ multi-tracked vocals on Chorus and Bridge sections

D G5 D G5 D G5
los-er, ba - by, so why don't you kill me? Soy un
Spoken: Double barrell buck shy.

D G5 D G5 D G5
per-di-dor. I'm a los-er, ba - by, so why don't you kill me?

Verse
Bass: w/ Bass Fig. 1, 4 times
N.C.
2. Forc-es of e-vil and a bo - zo night-mare. Bent all the mu-sic with the pho-ny gas cham-ber, 'cause

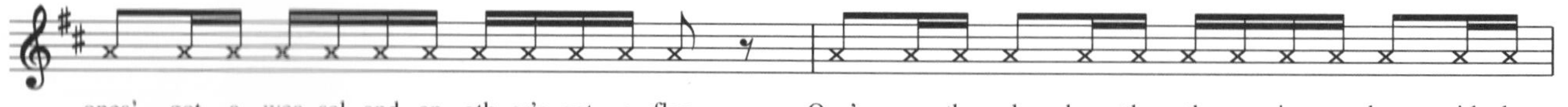
ones' got a wea-sel and an-oth-er's got a flag. One's on the pole; shove the oth-er in a bag with the

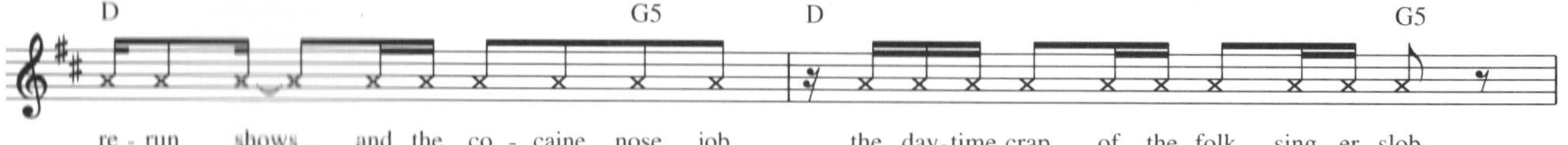
D G5 D G5
re-run shows and the co-caine nose job, the day-time crap of the folk sing-er slob.

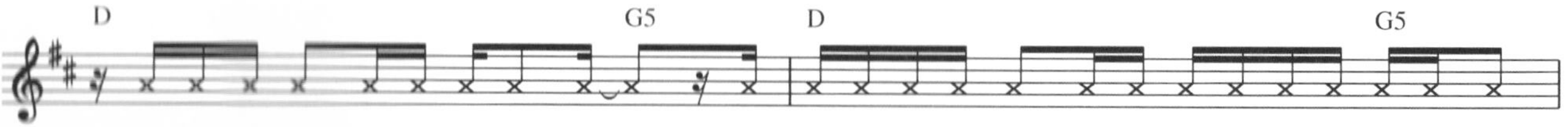
D G5 D G5
He hung him-self with a gui-tar string. A slab of tur-key neck, and it's hang-ing from a pi-geon wing.

Bass tacet
N.C.(D7)
a - get right if you can't re - late. Trade the cash for the beef, for the bod - y, for the hate. And my
time is a piece of wax fall - in' on a ter - mite who's chok - in' on the splin-ters.
Chorus
Bass: w/ Bass Fig. 1, 3 times
D G5 D G5 D G5 D G5
Soy un per - di - dor. I'm a los-er, ba - by, so why don't you kill me?
Spoken: Get crazy with the Cheez Whiz.
Bass: w/ Bass Fig. 2
D G5 D G5 D G5 D
Soy un per - di - dor. I'm a los-er, ba - by, so why don't you kill me?
Spoken: Drive-by body pierce.
Bridge
Bass tacet
N.C.
w/ Bkgd. voc. ad lib. next 4 meas.
D G5 D G5
Yo, bring it on down. Soy Soy.
Bass: w/ Bass Fig. 1, 1 1/2 times
Bass: w/ Bass Fill 1
D G5 D G5 D G5 D G5 G5 D G5
Spoken: I'm a driver, I'm a winner. Things are gonna change. I can feel it.
Chorus
4th time, Begin Fade
Bass: w/ Bass Fig. 1, till fade
1.
D G5 D G5 D G5 D G5
Soy un per - di - dor. I'm a los-er, ba - by, so why don't you kill me?
Spoken: I can't believe it.
2. 3. 4.
Outro
Repeat & Fade
D G5 D G5 D G5 N.C.(D)
don't you kill me? don't you kill me? don't you kill me?
Spoken: Uuuuuuuuuh. Spoken: Sprechen Sie Deutsch, baby? Spoken: You know what I'm sayin'?
Bass Fill 1
0 0 0 4

Love Struck Baby

Written by Stevie Ray Vaughan

Tune down 1/2 step:
(low to high) E♭–A♭–D♭–G♭

Intro

Moderately fast ♩ = 140

*Chord symbols reflect overall harmony.

Verse

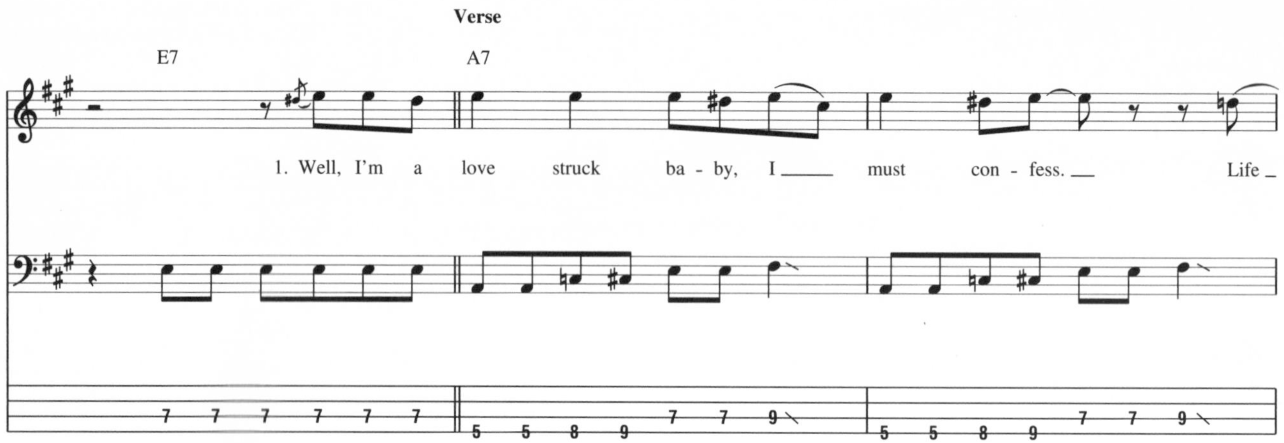

E7
A7
1. Well, I'm a love struck ba - by, I must con - fess. Life

D7
with - out ya dar - lin' is a sol - id mess. Think - in' 'bout you ba - by, give me

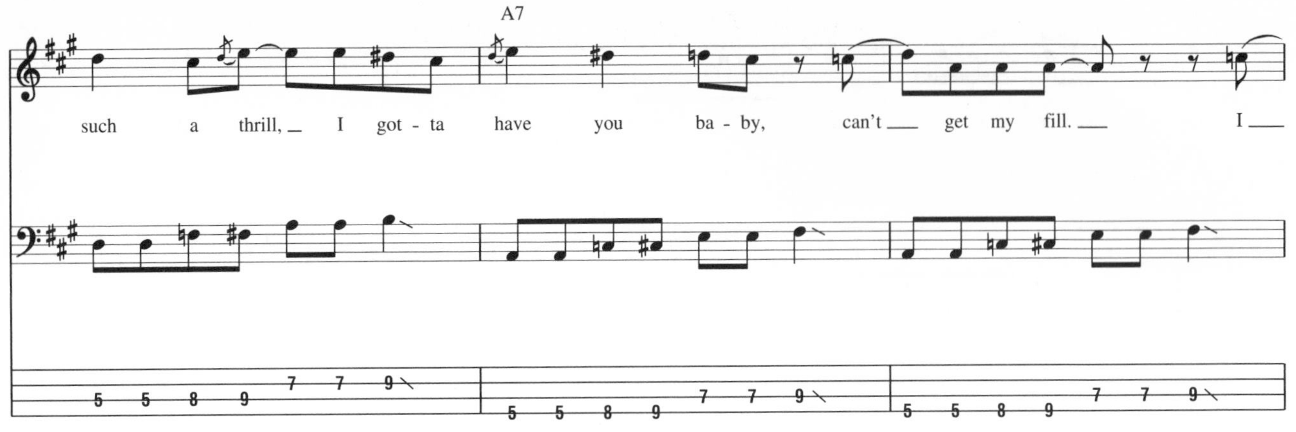
A7
such a thrill, I got - ta have you ba - by, can't get my fill. I

E7
A7
have you, ba - by, an' I know just what to do.

Pre-Chorus
D7
I still re - mem - ber, let it be said, the

A7
D7
way you make me feel _ it - 'll take a fool to for - get. ___ I swore a ton of bricks had hit me
5 5 8 9 7 7 9 7
5 5 8 9 7 7 9
5 5 8 9 7 7 9 7

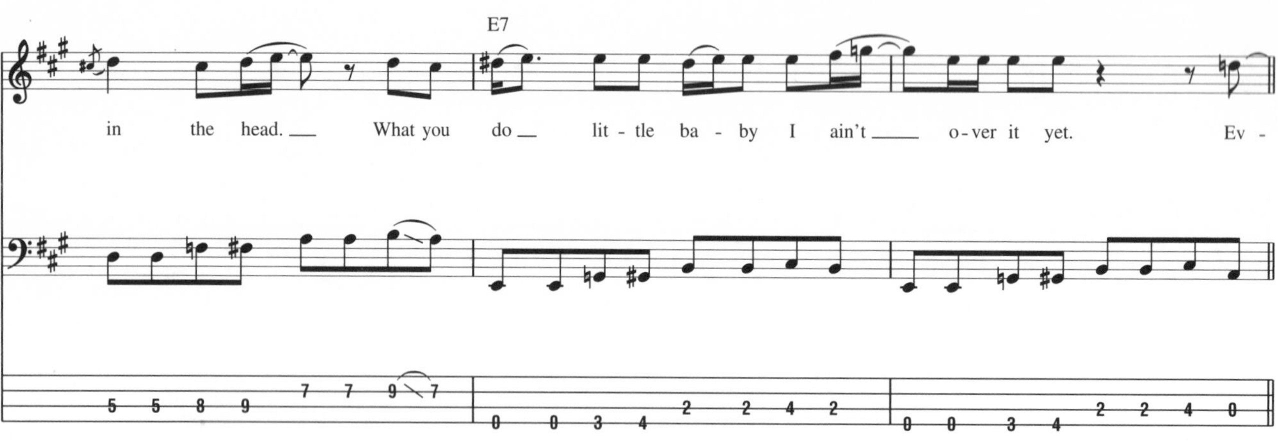
E7
in the head. ___ What you do ___ lit - tle ba - by I ain't ____ o - ver it yet. Ev -
5 5 8 9 7 7 9 7
0 0 3 4 2 2 4 2
0 0 3 4 2 2 4 0

Pre-Chorus
D7
A7
- 'ry time I see ya, make me feel so fine. ___ Heart beat - in' cra - zy, my blood _
5 5 8 9 7 7 9 7
5 5 8 9 7 7 9
5 5 8 9 7 7 9

D7
run - nin' wild.
Lov - in' make me feel like a might - y might - y man.
Love

Chorus
E7
A7
me ba - by, ain't I your man? I'm a love struck ba - by.

D7
Yeah, I'm a love struck ba - by.
You've got me

A7
E7
love struck ba - by and I know just what to do.

Guitar Solo

A7

D7

A7

E7
A7
7 7 5 5 7 7 5 6
7 0 4 0 7 7 6 4
5 5 4 4 7 7 4 4

7 7 6 6 4 4 5 4
5 5 4 4 7 7 4 4
5 5 4 4 7 7 4 4

D7
5 5 4 4 7 7 4 4
5 5 4 4 7 7 4 4
5 5 4 4 7 7 4 4

A7
5 5 4 4 7 7 4 4
5 5 4 4 7 7 4 4
5 5 4 4 7 7 4 4

E7
A7

D7

A7

E7
A7
7 4 4 7 7 4 4
7 7 4 4 7 7 4 4
5 5 4 4 7 7 4 4

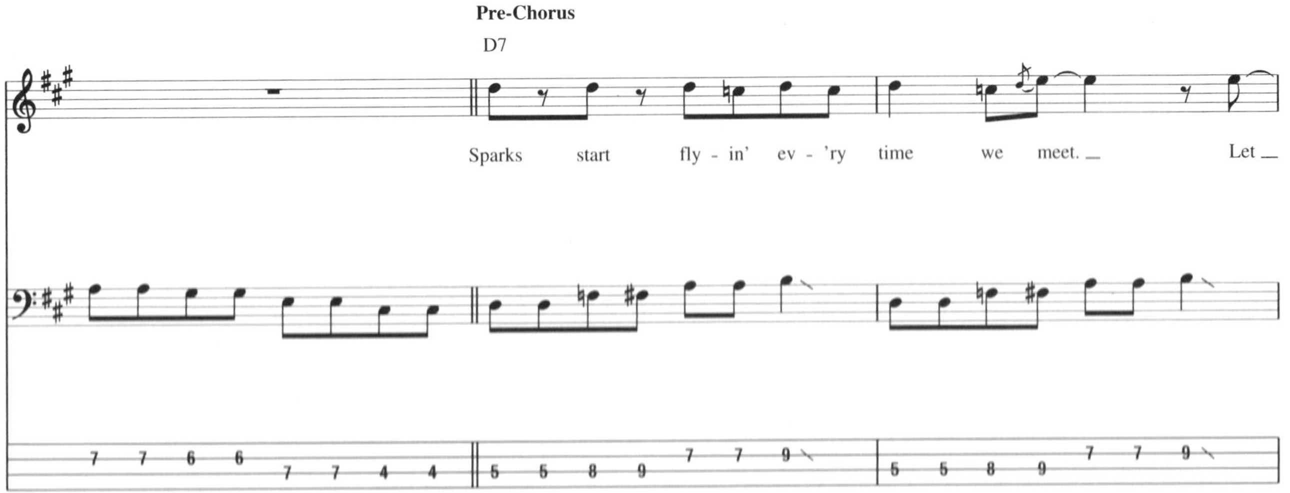
Pre-Chorus
D7
Sparks start fly - in' ev - 'ry time we meet. Let
7 7 6 6 7 7 4 4
5 5 8 9 7 7 9
5 5 8 9 7 7 9

A7
D7
me tell you ba - by, you knock me off my feet. Your kiss - es trip me up, they're so
5 5 8 9 7 7 9
5 5 8 9 7 7 9
5 5 8 9 7 7 9 7

E7
dog - gone sweet. Don't ya know ba - by you can't be beat? I'm a

Chorus

A7
D7
love struck ba - by. Yeah, I'm a love struck ba - by.

A7
You got me love struck ba - by and I

Outro
E7
E7
know just what to do.
0 0 3 4 2 2 4 2
0 0 3 4 2 2 5 5
7 7 7 7 7 7 5

D7
A7
A9
5 5 5 5 5 5 3
5 4 4 5 5 4 5 6
7 4 6 7

(7)

Low Rider

Words and Music by Sylvester Allen, Harold R. Brown, Morris Dickerson, Jerry Goldstein, Leroy Jordan, Lee Oskar, Charles W. Miller and Howard Scott

Intro

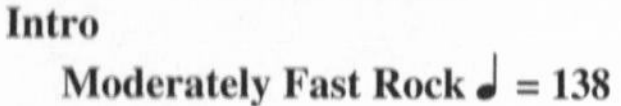

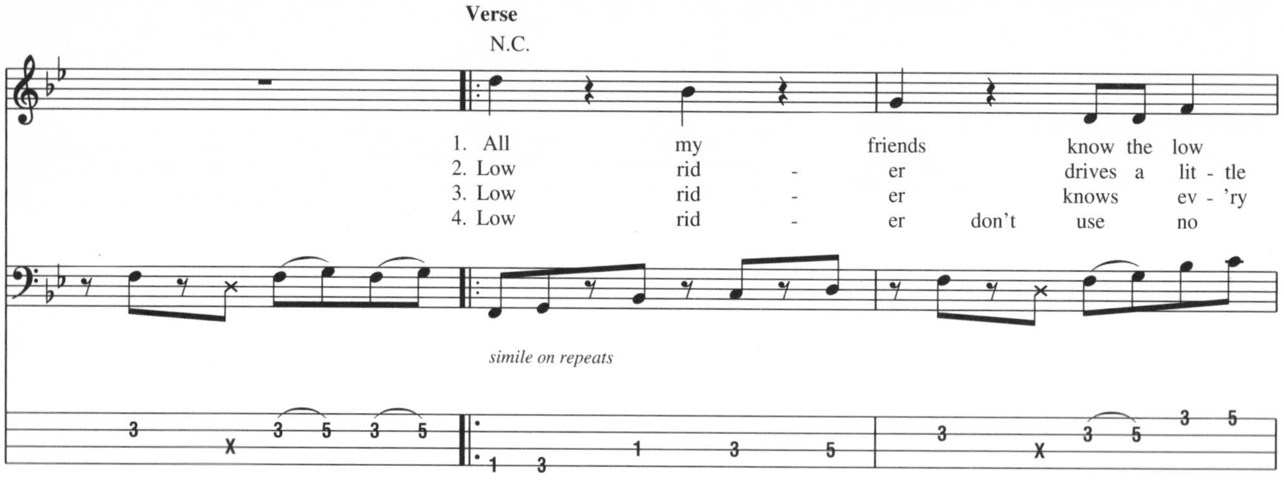

er is a lit - tle high - er.
er, he's a real go - er.
er, is the one to meet, yeah.
er don't drive too fast.
Chorus
N.C.
Horns
play 4 times

Outro

N.C.

Take a lit - tle trip, take a lit - tle trip, take a lit - tle trip and see.

Take a lit - tle trip, take a lit - tle trip, take a lit - tle trip with me.

Play 3 Times and Fade

Mama Kin

Words and Music by Steven Tyler

(Guitar)
4
(9) 9 9 9 9 9 9 9 9 9 7 7 8 9

E5
B5
A5
A5
7 7 (7) 5 5 3 4 7 5 6 7 (7) 7 7 7 7 5 7

1st Verse
(E5)
(B5)
It ain't eas-y, liv -
(7) 7 7 7 7 7 5 7 (7) 7 5 7 5 6 7 (7) 7 5 7 7 5 7 7

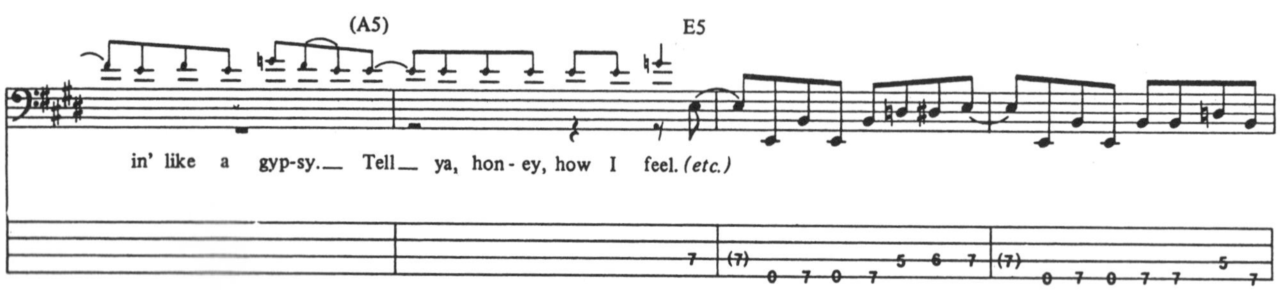
(A5)
E5
in' like a gyp-sy. Tell ya, hon-ey, how I feel. (etc.)
7 (7) 0 7 0 7 5 6 7 (7) 0 7 0 7 7 5 7

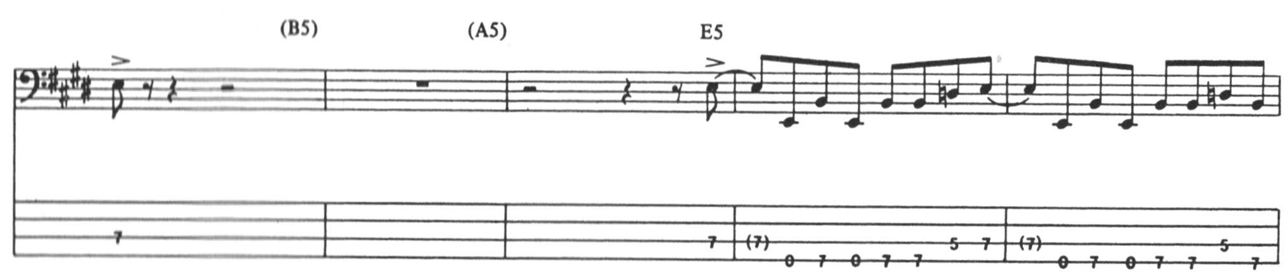
(B5)
(A5)
E5
7 7 (7) 0 7 0 7 7 5 7 (7) 0 7 0 7 7 5 7

(1st), 2nd, 3rd Verses
(E5)
(B5)
(A5)
3rd time substitute Bass Fill 1
E5
1. Whole - earth lov - er, keep - in' un - der cov - er, nev - er know-in' where you been. (etc.)
2.3. It ain't eas - y, liv - in' like you wan - na, it's so hard to find peace of mind. (etc.)
*2nd time bass rests on beat 1.
Pre-chorus
A5
1. Well, you've al - ways got your tail on the wag. (etc.)
2.3. Said, you're bald as an egg at eight-een. (etc.)
F♯5
B5
1.
2.
Bass Fill 1
sl.

Chorus
(E5)
(B5)
(E5)
5
B5
Keep - in' touch with ma - ma kin. (etc.)
E5 A5 G5 D5 B5 E5 A5 G5 D5 B5 E5 A5 G5 D5 B5
To Coda
Interlude
E5 A5 G5 D5 C5
B5
A5 G5 A5
D.S. (take 2nd ending) al Coda
Coda
C5 D5
Slower ♩ = 216
E9
E5

Manic Depression

Words and Music by Jimi Hendrix

(E)
(G)
(D)
(C)
Feel - ing, sweet feel - ing drops from my fin - gers,
(G)
(A)
(G)
fin - gers. Man - ic de - pres - sion's cap - tured my
(A7)
soul. Yeah
Verse
(A)
(G)
(A)
2. Wom - an so will - ing the sweet cause in vain.

(G)
even
You make love, you break love, it's a all the
(A)
same when it's, when it's o - ver.
(E)
Mu - sic, sweet
(G)
(D)
(C)
(G)
mu - sic, I wish I could ca - ress, ca - ress, ca - ress.
(A)
(G)
Ma - nic de - pres - sion's a frus - trat - ing mess.
Oo, ow!

Interlude
N.C.(A7)
(Cough)
Do, ___ do, do, ___
do, ___ do, do.
Guitar Solo
N.C.(A7)

Cry on gui - tar.
Verse
N.C.(A)
(G)
3. Well, I think I'll go turn my - self off and, uh, uh, huh, go on
(A)
down. Huh! All the way down. Real - ly ain't no
(G)
(A)
use in me hang - ing a - round in, uh, huh, your kind of scene.

(E)
(G)
(D)
(C)
Mu - sic, sweet mu - sic, I wish I could ca - ress and - a
(G)
(A)
(G)
kiss, kiss. Man - ic de - pres - sion's a frus - trat - in'
mess! Oo, ah! Dig. Ow!
Outro
N.C.
Mu - sic, sweet mu - sic, sweet mu - sic, sweet mu - sic, ah!
p
mp

Mu - sic, sweet mu - sic, sweet mu - sic. Yeah!
p
mp
mf
Do,
oo,
oo.
Free Time
A5
Fade Out
Hmm, hmm, hmm.
De - press...
(Tongue clicks)

Maria Maria

Words and Music by Wyclef Jean, Jerry Duplessis, Carlos Santana, Karl Perazzo, Paul Rekow, Marvin Hough and David McRae

*Chord symbols reflect overall harmony.

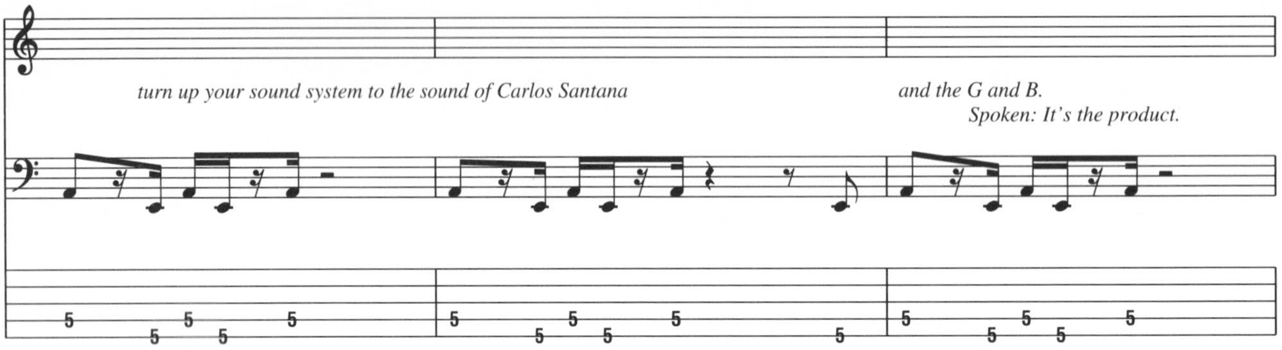

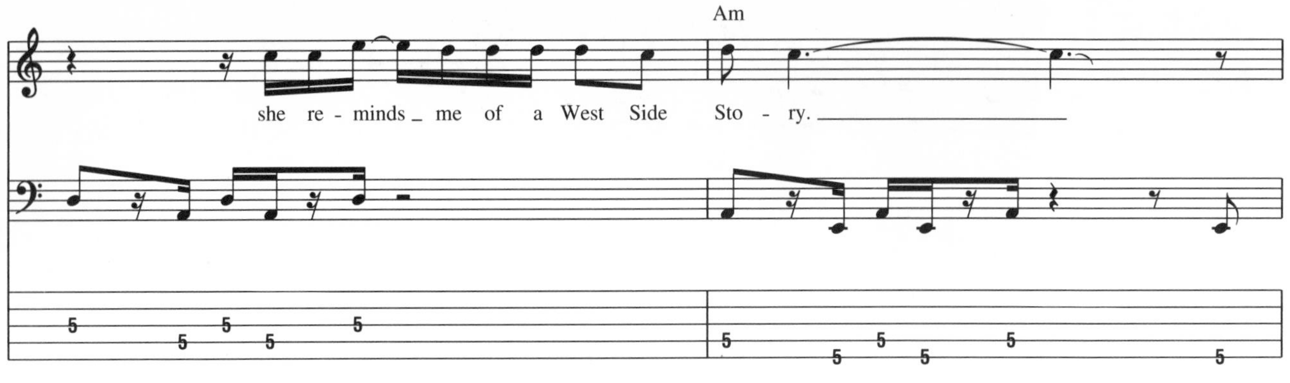
Am
she re - minds _ me of a West Side Sto - ry.

Em
Grow - ing up _ in Span - ish Har - lem,

E
Am
she's liv - ing the life _ just like a mov - ie star.
Oh, _

Dm
Ma - ri - a, Ma - ri - a,
Spoken: Hey you, Maria.

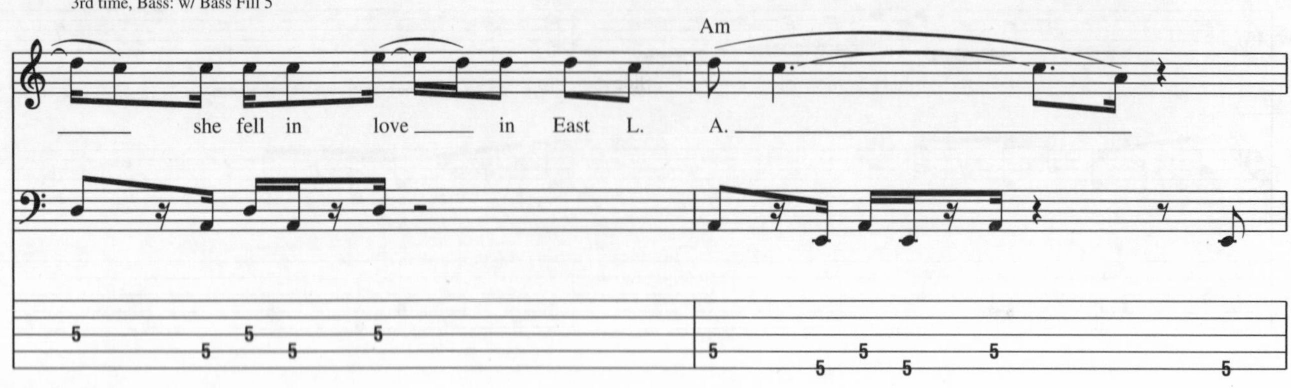
2nd time, Bass: w/ Bass Fill 1
3rd time, Bass: w/ Bass Fill 5
Am
she fell in love in East L. A.
5 5 5 5 5
5 5 5 5 5 5 5

Em
to the sounds of a gui - tar, yeah, yeah,
5 5 5 5 5
5 7 7 7 7 7

2nd & 3rd time, Bass: w/ Bass Fill 2
E
Am
played by Car - los San - tan - a.
7
5 5 5 5 5 5

Bass Fill 1
tr
5 5 5 5 5 5 (7)

Bass Fill 2
7 14

Bass Fill 5
5 5 5 5 5 5 7

To Coda 1
To Coda 2
1. Stop the loot -
Verse
Am
G
*Voc. Fig. 1
- ing, stop the shoot - ing, pick pock - ing on the cor - ner. See as the rich
Spoken: (Oh, yeah.
Bass Fig. 2
F
G
E
is get - ting rich - er the poor is get - ting poor - er. Se mí - ra Ma - ri -
Oh, yeah.
End Bass Fig. 2
Bass: w/ Bass Fig. 2
Am
G
- a on the cor - ner think - ing of ways to make it bet - ter. In my mail-
Oh, yeah.)

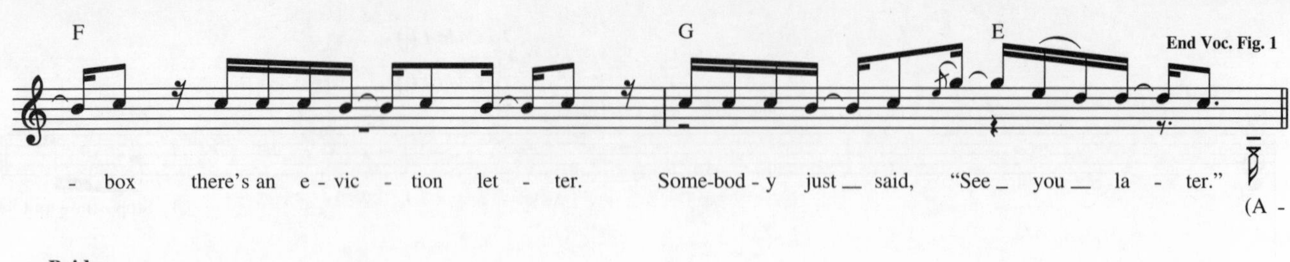
F
G
E
End Voc. Fig. 1
- box there's an e - vic - tion let - ter. Some-bod - y just said, "See you la - ter."
(A -

Bridge
Bass: w/ Bass Fig. 1 (2 times)
Am
*Voc. Fig. 2
3
End Voc. Fig. 2
Yeah.
hor - a ven - go ma - ma cho-la, ma-ma cho-la. A - hor - a ven - go ma-ma cho-la. A -
Spoken: (East coast.

*Downstemmed voc. only

D.S. al Coda 1
**Voc. Fig. 3
End Voc. Fig. 3
Ma - ri - a, Ma - ri -
hor - a ven - go ma-ma cho-la, ma-ma cho-la. A - hor - a ven - go ma-ma cho-la.)
West coast.)

**as before

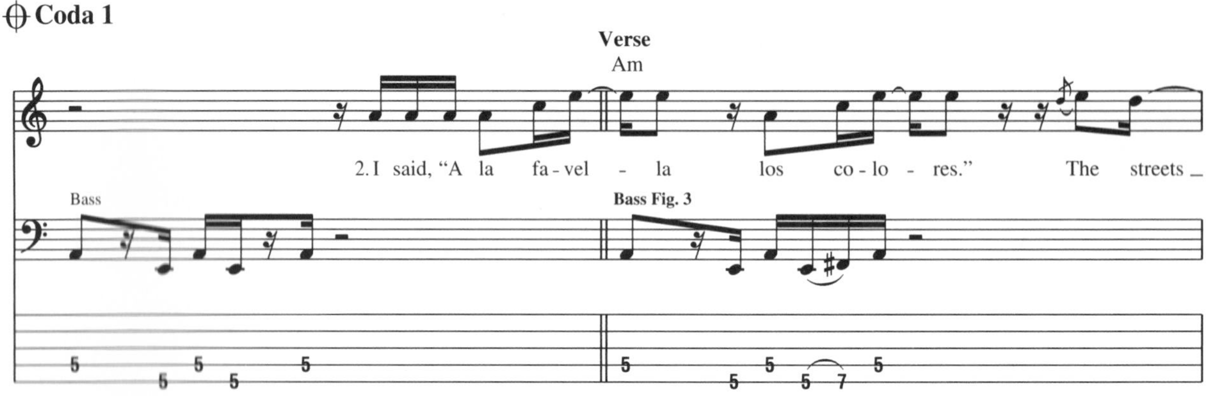
Coda 1
Verse
Am
2. I said, "A la fa-vel - la los co-lo - res." The streets
Bass
Bass Fig. 3

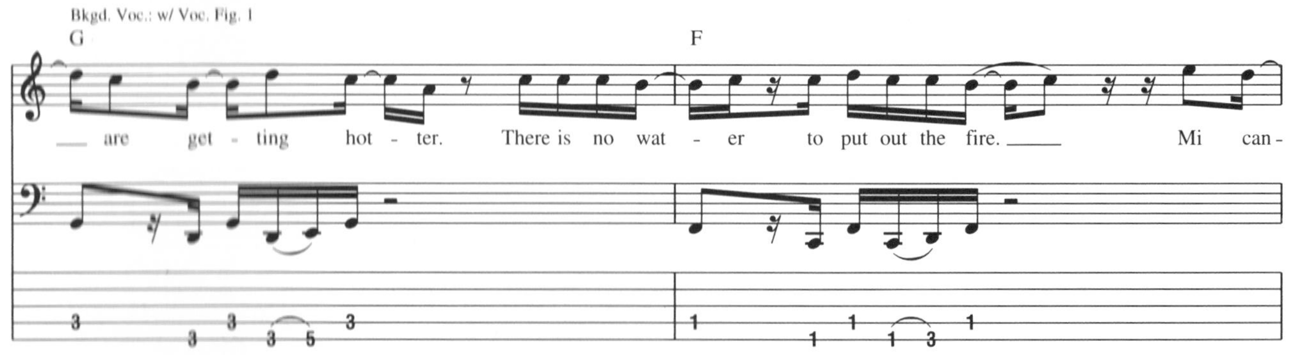
Bkgd. Voc.: w/ Voc. Fig. 1
G
F
are get - ting hot - ter. There is no wat - er to put out the fire. Mi can -

G E Am

- to __ es - per - an - za. Se mi-ra Ma-ri - a on __ the cor - ner thinking-ing of ways __

End Bass. Fig. 3

G F

__ to make _ it bet - ter. Then I looked _ up to __ the sky __ hop-ing of days __

Bridge

Bkgd. Voc.: w/ Voc. Fig. 2 (3 1/2 times)

G E Am

__ of par - a - dise. ________________

(A -

Spoken: (North Side.

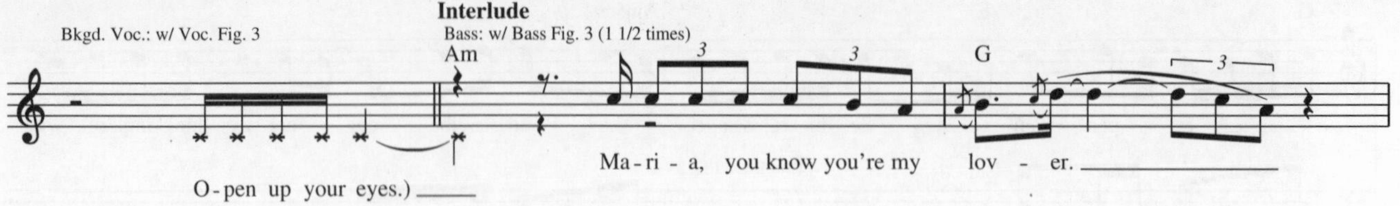
Interlude
Bkgd. Voc.: w/ Voc. Fig. 3
Bass: w/ Bass Fig. 3 (1 1/2 times)
Am
G
O-pen up your eyes.)
Ma-ri-a, you know you're my lov-er.

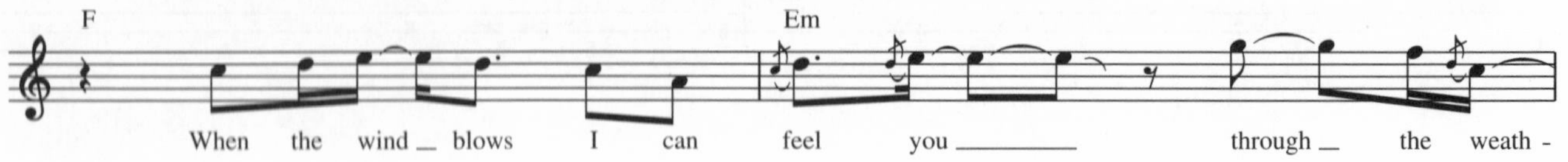
F
Em
When the wind blows I can feel you through the weath-

Am
G
-er. And e-ven when we are a-part

D.S. al Coda 2
Bass: w/ Bass Fill 4
F
E
it feels like we're to-geth-er. Ma-ri-

Coda 2
Outro
w/ Voc. ad lib.
Am
Play 4 times & fade

Bass Fill 4

Matchbox

Words and Music by Carl Lee Perkins

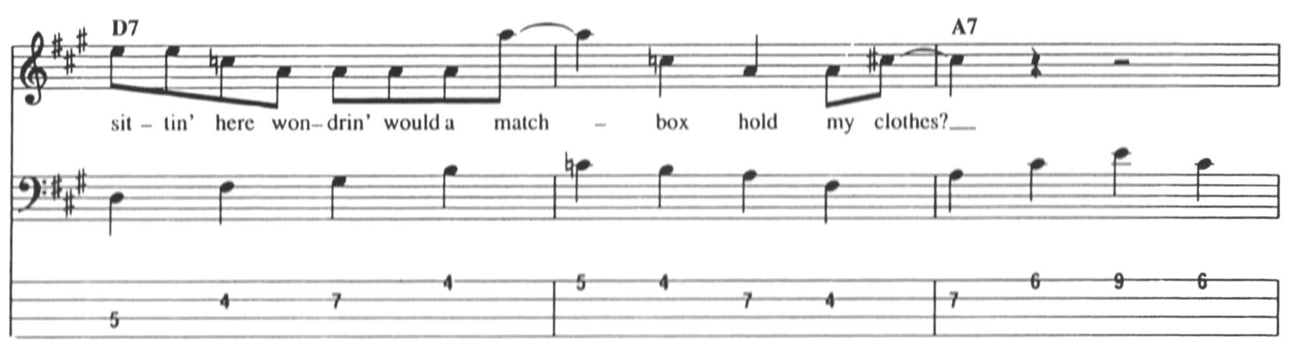

A
A
I'm an old poor boy a
7 6 9 6
7 5 7 5
7 6 9 6

long way from home.
I'm an old
7 6 9 6
7 6 9 6
7 5 7 5

D7
A
poor boy a long way from home.
5 4 7 4
5 4 7 4
7 6 9 6

3
Guess I'll nev-er be hap-py ev-'ry-thing I do is wrong.
7 4 5 6
7 6 9 6
7 5 4 7

1st Solo
A
A
Yeah!
7 5 7 5
7 5 7 5
7 5 7 5
7 5 7 5
7 5 7 5

D
A
7 5 7 5
5 4 7 4
5 4 7 4
7 5 7 5
7 5 7 5

E7
A
Well
7 7 7 7
7 7 5 5
7 5 7 5
7 5 7 5

Let me be your lit – tle dog 'til your big dog come.
7 0 9 6
7 6 9 6
7 6 9 6

D7
Let me be your lit – tle dog 'til your big dog

A7
E7
come. When the big dog gets here

A
show him what this lit – tle pup – py done. Well I'm sit –

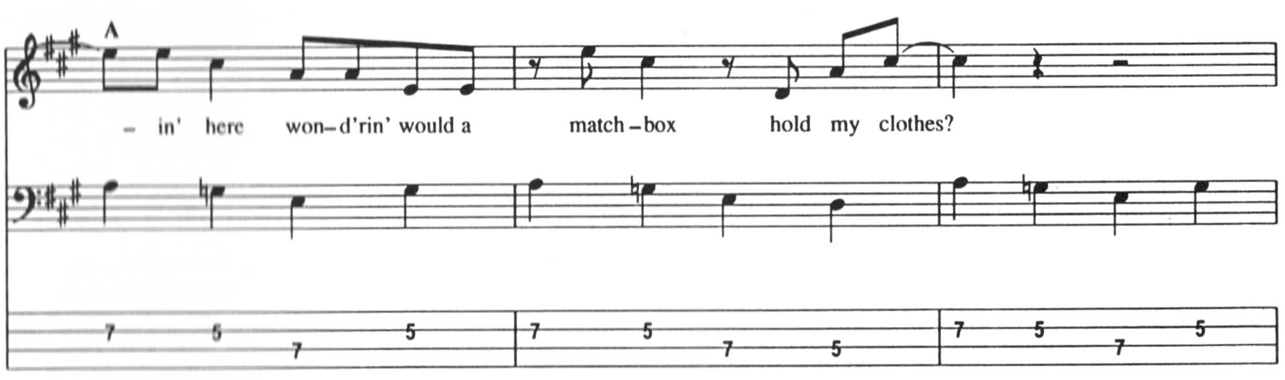
A
– in' here won–d'rin' would a match – box hold my clothes?

D
Yeah, sit – tin' here wond – d'rin' would a match – box hold my
A
E7
clothes? I ain't got no match – es
A
Got a long way to go. Let her go boy. Go go.
2nd Solo
A
D
A
E

A
Well I'm set – tin' here won – d'rin' would a match –
box hold my clothes?
Yeah I'm
D7
sit – tin' here won – d'rin' would a match – box hold my clothes?
A7
E7
I ain't got no match – es but I got a long way to go.
A

Message in a Bottle

Written and Composed by Sting

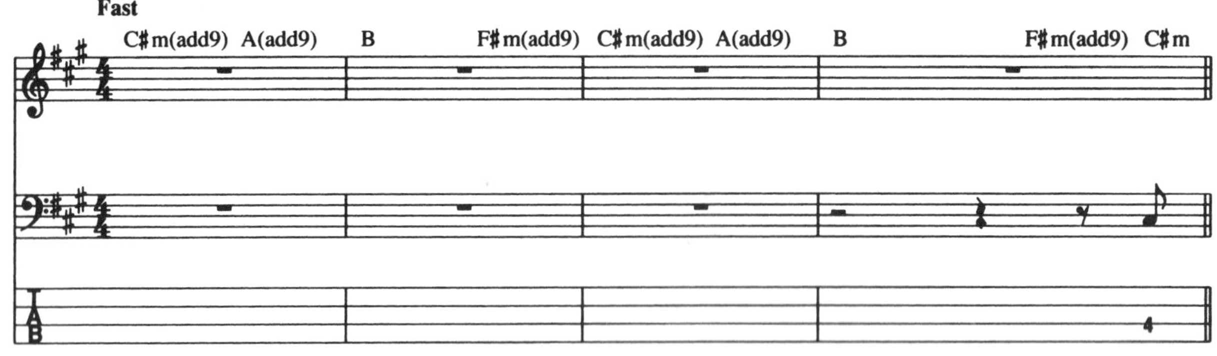
Fast
C#m(add9) A(add9) B F#m(add9) C#m(add9) A(add9) B F#m(add9) C#m

Verse
A B F#m C#m A B F#m C#m
Just a cast - a - way, an is - land lost at sea, oh.
A year has passed since I wrote my note
Walked out this morn - ing, I don't be - lieve what I saw,
2nd time tacet

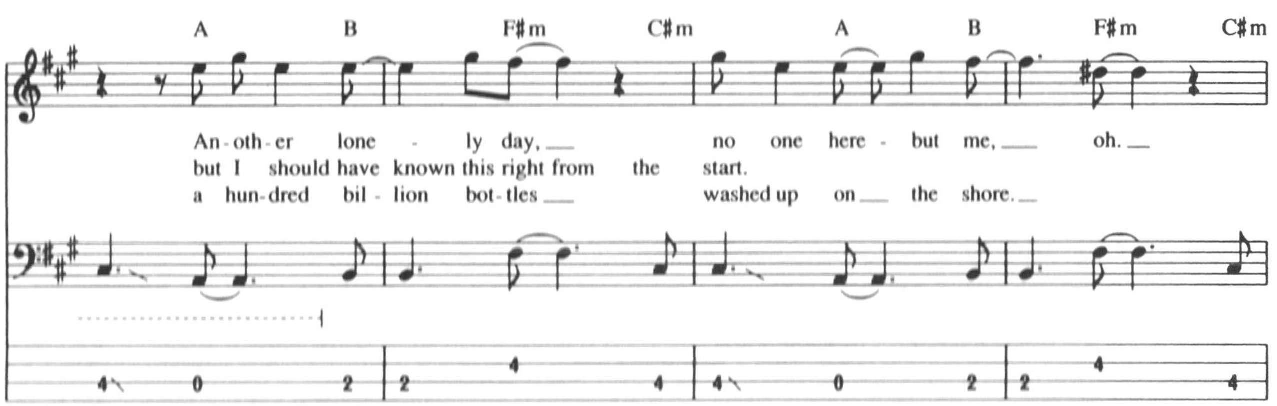
A B F#m C#m A B F#m C#m
An - oth - er lone - ly day, no one here - but me, oh.
but I should have known this right from the start.
a hun - dred bil - lion bot - tles washed up on the shore.

A B F#m C#m A B F#m C#m
More loneliness than any man could bear.
Only hope can keep me together.
Seems like I'm not alone in being alone.
A

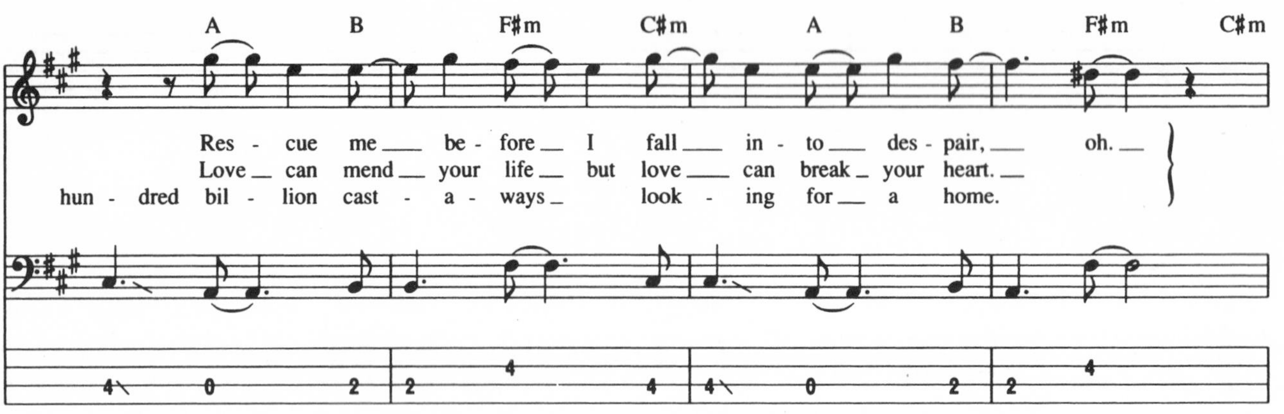
A B F#m C#m A B F#m C#m
Rescue me before I fall into despair, oh.
Love can mend your life but love can break your heart.
hundred billion castaways looking for a home.

Chorus
A D E A D E
I'll send an S. O. S. to the world. I'll send and S. O. S. to the world.

F#m D F#m D
I hope that someone gets my, I hope that someone gets my,

F#m
D
C#m
A
I hope that some - one gets my mes-sage in a bot - tle, yeah.
To Coda
Mes- sage in a bot - tle, yeah.
2nd time
1.
2.
Mes- sage in a bot - tle, yeah.
F#m

D.S. al Coda
Coda
C#m
A
mes-sage in a bot - tle,
C#m
A
C#m
A
mes-sage in a bot - tle,
C#m
A
C#m
A
mes-sage in a bot - tle, oh yeah.
F#m
G#m
A
B
F#m
Repeat and Fade
C#m
A
B
F#m
C#m
A
B
F#m
send - ing out an S. O. S. I'm
2nd time

(Bang Your Head)

Metal Health

Words and Music by Carols Cavazo, Kevin Dubrow, Frankie Banali and Tony Cavazo

C A C A G
A
A9 Bsus4/A
Well I'm an axe grind-er, pile— driv-er,
(2nd verse see additional lyrics)
Cmaj7/A Bsus4/A G A9
Ma-ma says that I'll nev-er, nev-er mind her.— Got no brains,—

Bsus4/A
Cmaj7/A
Bsus4/A
G
I'm in - sane
The teach - er says that I'm one big pain.
A9
Bsus4/A
Cmaj7/A
A9
Bsus4/A
I'm like a las - er six string raz - or
I got a mouth like an
A9
G
A9
Bsus4/A
al - li - ga - tor.
I want it loud - er,
more pow - er
C
D
G
I'm gon - na rock un - til it strikes the hour.
Bang yer

Chorus
A
C
G
C A C
head,
Met - al health will drive_ you mad_
A
G
D
A
C
G
Bang your head,
C A C
A
G
1. A
Met - al health will drive_ you mad._
Well I'm

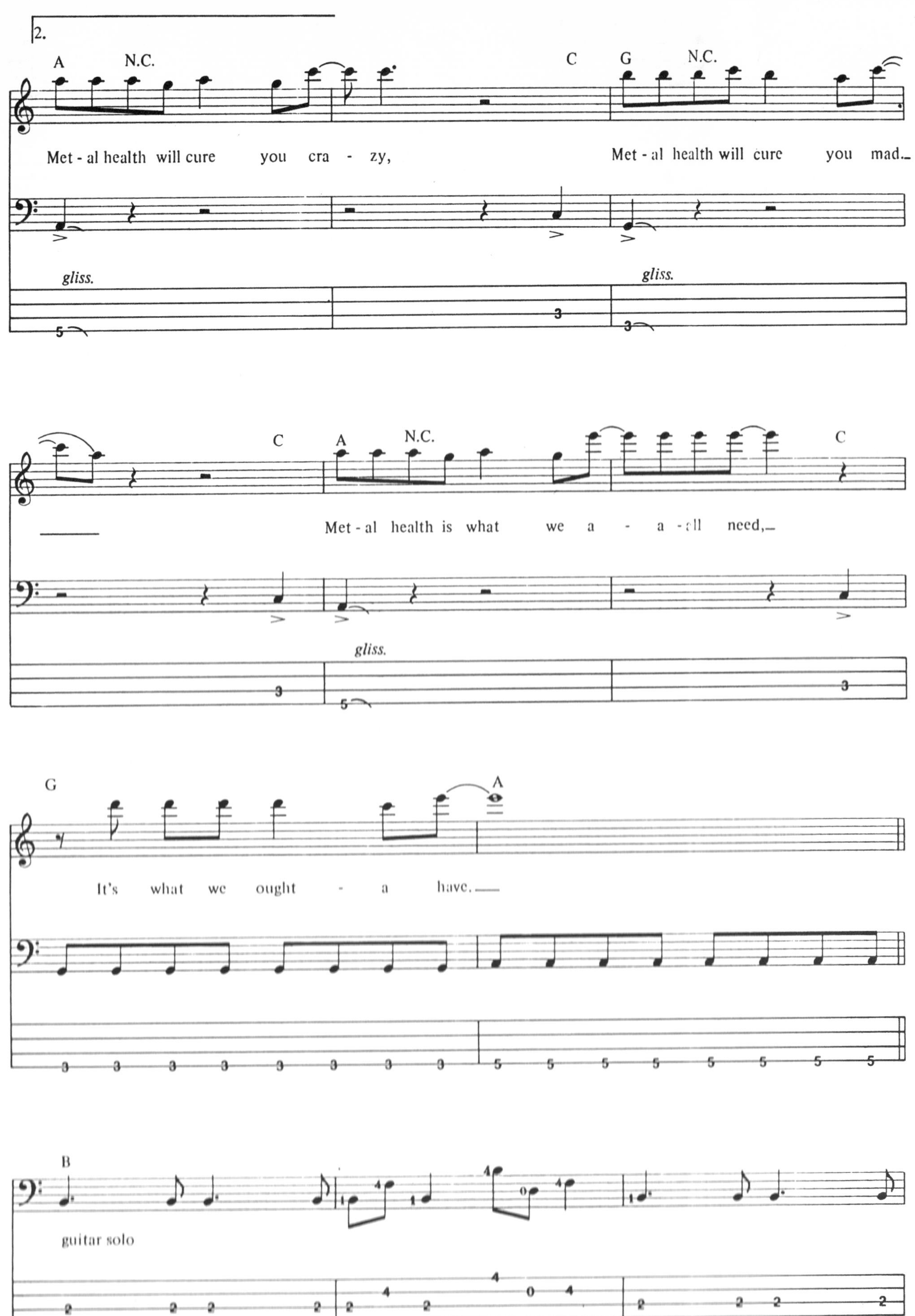
2.
A
N.C.
C
G
N.C.
Met - al health will cure you cra - zy,
Met - al health will cure you mad.
gliss.
gliss.
C
A
N.C.
C
Met - al health is what we a - a - ll need,
gliss.
G
A
It's what we ought - a have.
B
guitar solo

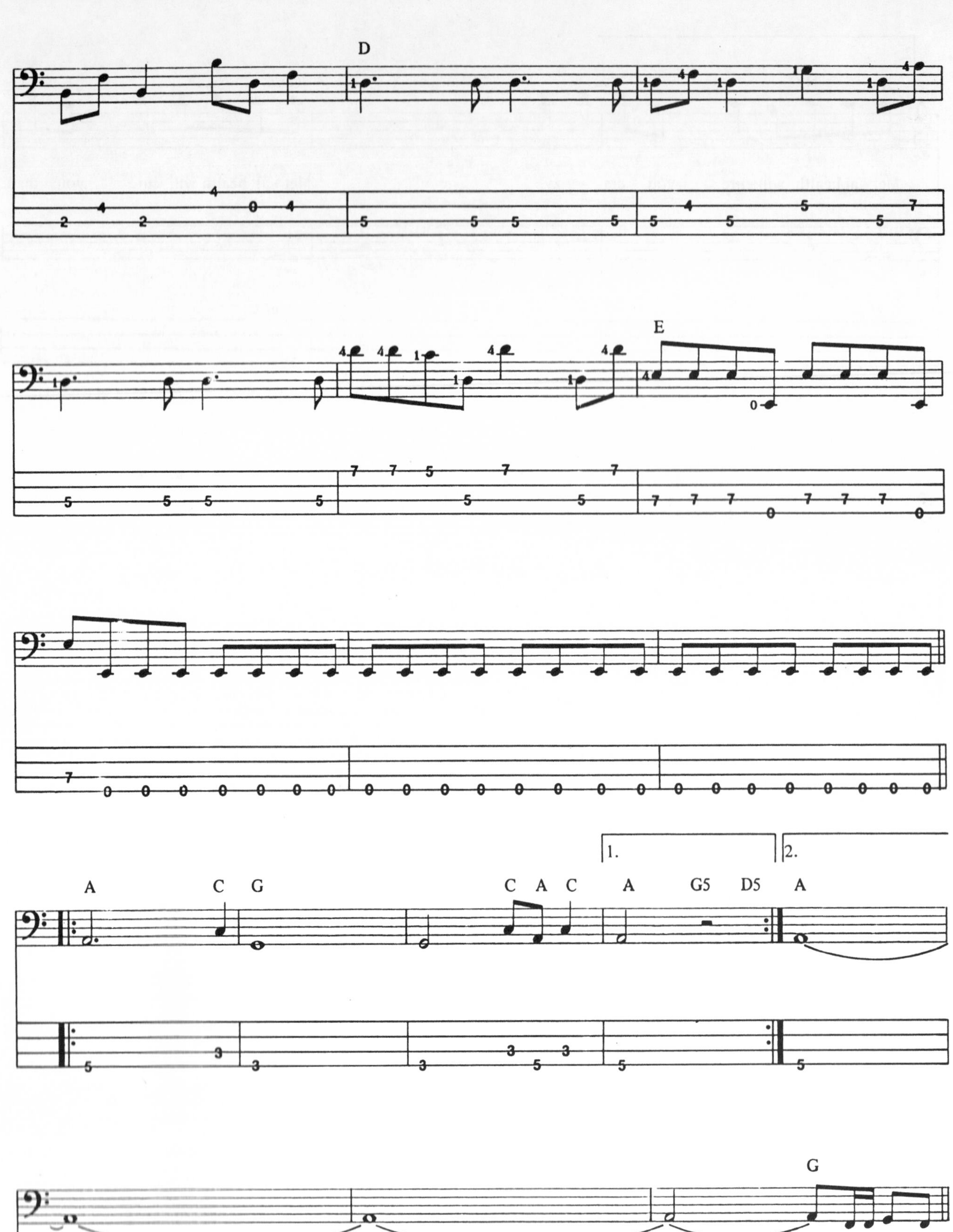
D
E
1.
2.
A
C
G
C
A
C
A
G5
D5
A
G

2. Well I'm frustrated, not outdated
I really wanna be overrated
I'm a finder and I'm a keeper
I'm not a loser and I ain't no weeper

I got the boys to make the noize
Won't ever let up, Hope it annoys you
Join the pack, fill the crack
Well now you're here, there's no way back

Mississippi Queen

Words and Music by Leslie West, Felix Pappalardi, Corky Laing and David Rea

Verse
D5 E5
G5 A5
she taught me ev - 'ry - thing.
1. Way down
2. This la -
G5 A5
around Vicks - burg, a - round Lou - i - si - an - a way,
- dy she asked me if I would be her man.
D5 E5
D5 E5
lived a Ca - jun la - dy called the
You know that I told her I'd do
A5 B5
Mis - sis - sip - pi Queen. You know she was a danc - er,
what I can to keep her look - in' pret - ty.
You know she was a danc - er,

G5 A5
N.C.(E5)
she moved bet - ter on wine. While the rest of them dudes was a'
Buy her dress - es that shine. While the rest of them dudes was a'
she moved bet - ter on wine, While the rest of them dudes was a'
1/2

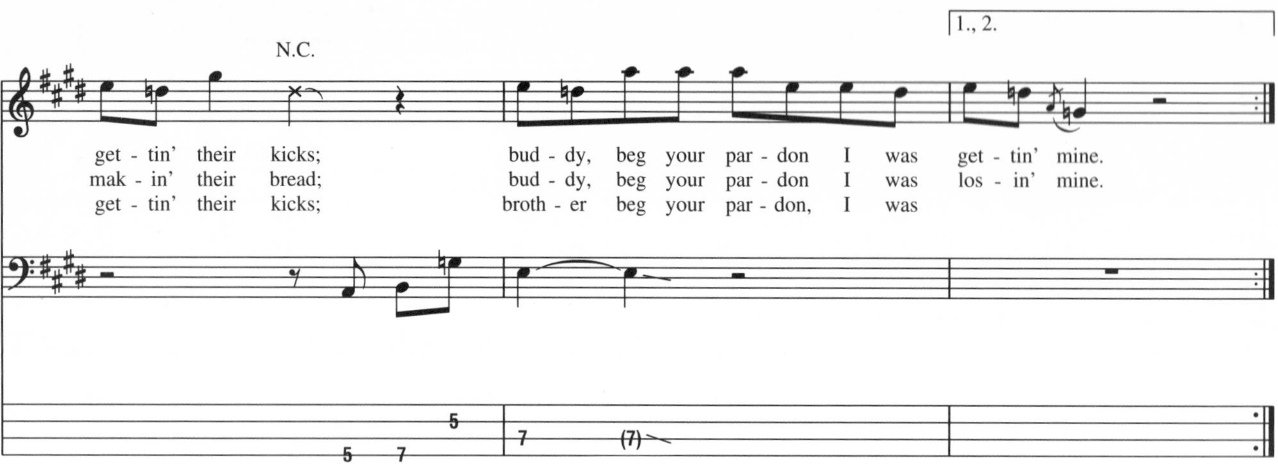
N.C.
1., 2.
get - tin' their kicks; bud - dy, beg your par - don I was get - tin' mine.
mak - in' their bread; bud - dy, beg your par - don I was los - in' mine.
get - tin' their kicks; broth - er beg your par - don, I was

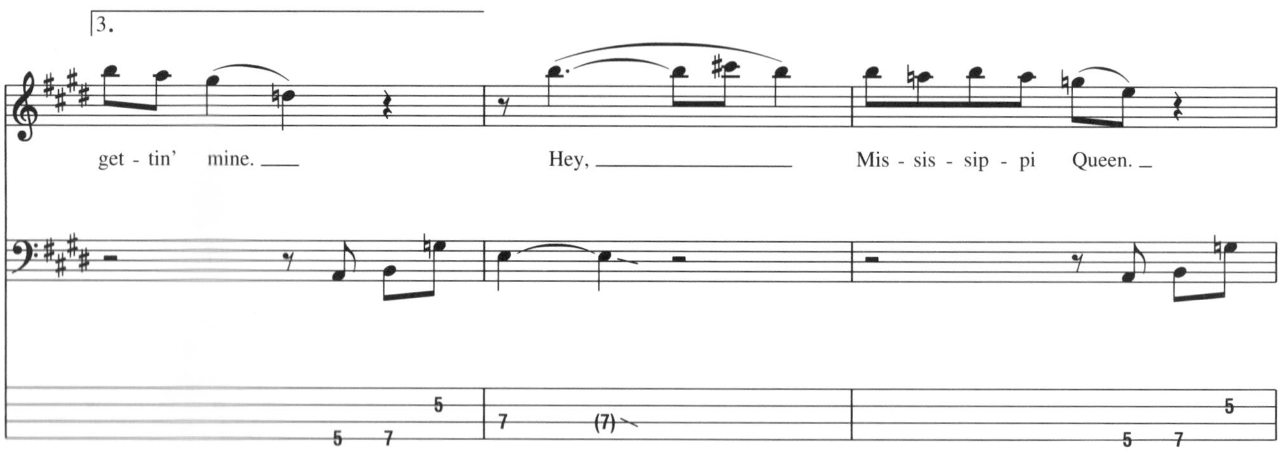
3.
get - tin' mine. Hey, Mis - sis - sip - pi Queen.

My Generation

Words and Music by Peter Townshend

Bass: w/ Bass Fig. 1, 1st time, simile
Bkgd. Voc.: w/ Voc. Fig. 1
N.C.(G5)
(G5/F)
G5
G/F
Things they do look aw - ful c - c - - cold.
I
not try - in' to cause a big s - s - sen - sa - tion,
I'm just
G5 N.C.(G5)
(G/F)
Bkgd. Voc.: w/ Voc. Fig. 1
G5
G/F
hope I die be - fore I get old.
talk - in' 'bout my g - g - g - gen-er-a - tion.
Yeah, my gen - er - a -
1.
Chorus
G Gsus4 G7 Gsus4 G Gsus4 G7 Gsus4
- tion. Said my gen - er - a - tion, ba - by.
Bass
2.
G7 Gsus4 G Gsus4 G7 Gsus4
Bass Solo
G5 N.C.
My gen - er - a - tion, ba - by.
full
G5 G6 G7 G6 G5 N.C.
1/4
1/4
G5 G6 G7 G6 G5 N.C.
full

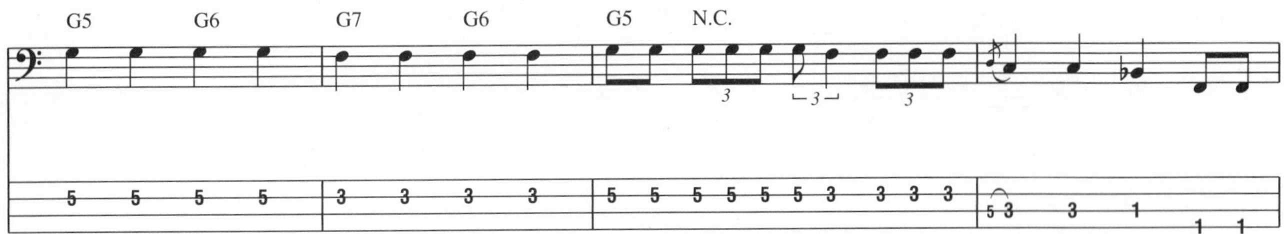
G5
G6
G7
G6
G5
N.C.

G6
G7
G6
G
Gsus4
G7
Gsus4
G
Gsus4

G7
Gsus4
Verse
A
N.C.
A
A/G
Voc. Fig. 2
End Voc. Fig. 2
3. Why don't you all ff fade a - way. Yeah,
(Talk - in' 'bout my gen - er - a - tion.)
Bass Fig. 3
End Bass Fig. 3

Bass: w/ Bass Fig. 3, 3 times
A
N.C.
Bkgd. Voc.: w/ Voc. Fig. 2
A
A/G
don't try and d - dig what we all s - s - s - s - s - say.

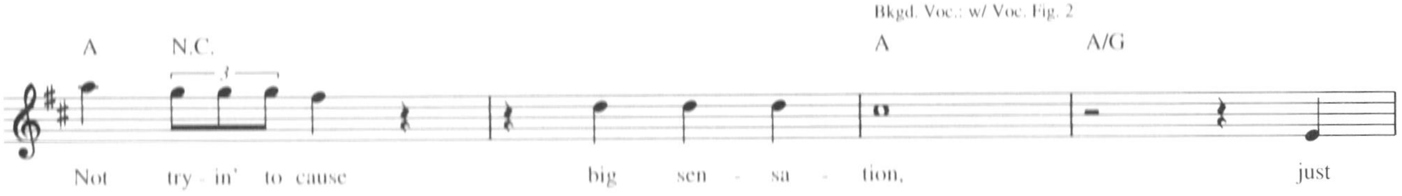
A
N.C.
Bkgd. Voc.: w/ Voc. Fig. 2
A
A/G
Not try - in' to cause big sen - sa - tion, just

A
N.C.
Bkgd. Voc.: w/ Voc. Fig. 2
A
A/G
talk - in' 'bout my g - gen - er - a - tion. Ba - by, my gen - er - a -

Chorus
A
Asus4
A
Asus4
- tion, this is my gen-er-a - tion, ba - by.
Bass
A Asus4 A Asus4 A Asus4
Bb5
My, my, ge - gen - er - a - tion. My, my, ooh, my, my. (1st time) My, my,
Verse
Bb5/Ab
Bb5 N.C.
Bb5 Bb6 Bb7 Bb6
Voc. Fig. 3
End Voc. Fig. 3
my, gen-er-a - tion. 4. Peo-ple try to put us d - down
(Talk-in' 'bout my gen - er - a - tion.)
Bass Fig. 4
End Bass Fig. 4
Bass: w/ Bass Fig. 4
Bkgd. Voc.: w/ Voc. Fig. 3
Bb5 N.C.
(Bb) (Bb/Ab) Ab5
just be - cause we g - g - g - get a - round.
Bass: w/ Bass Fill 1
Bkgd. Voc.: w/ Voc. Fig. 3
Bass: w/ Bass Fig. 4, last 3 meas.
Bkgd. Voc.: w/ Voc. Fig. 3
Bb5 N.C.
Bb Bbsus4 Bb Bbsus4
Things they do look aw - ful c - c - cold, yeah, I
Bass Fill 1
Bass

Chorus

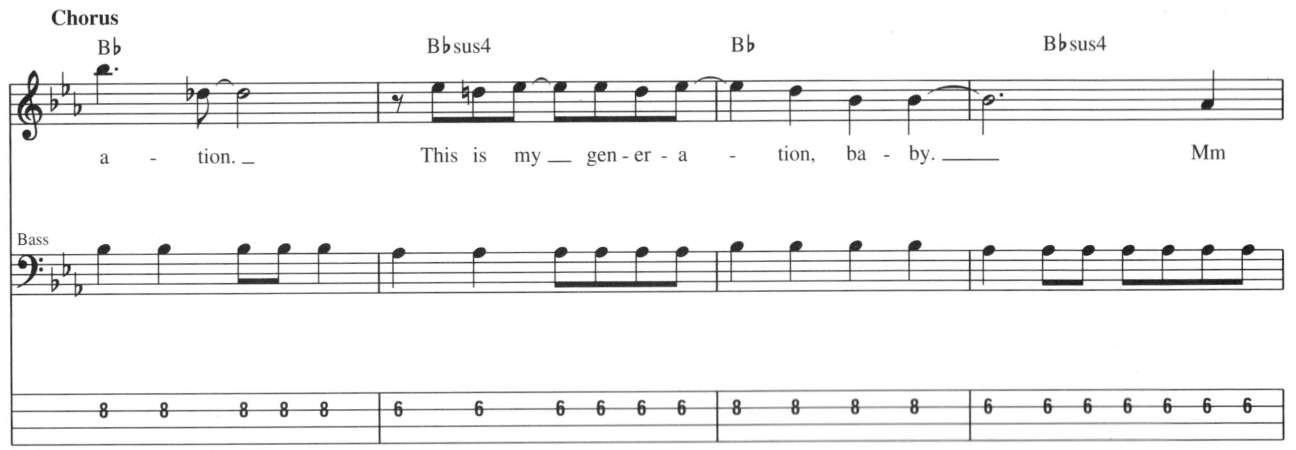

Guitar Solo

C
B♭/C
C
B♭/C
C
B♭/C
C
B♭/C
Outro
w/ Lead Voc. ad lib.
C
Talk - in' 'bout my gen - er - a - tion. Talk - in' 'bout my gen - er - a - tion.
Talk - in' 'bout my gen - er - a - tion. Talk - in' 'bout my gen - er - a - tion.
C
play 4 times
C
Talk - in' 'bout my gen - er - a - tion.

Mystery Train

Words and Music by Sam C. Phillips and Herman Parker Jr.

E
A/E
Six – teen coach – es long
Com – in' 'round the bend
Com – in' 'round the bend
7 7 7 7 7 7
E
A/E
E
A/E
E
A/E
Well that long
Well it took
Well it's bring –
7 7 7 7 7 7
B7
A7
black train got my
my ba – by but it
in' my ba – by 'cause she's
9 6 7 9 9 9 9 9
E
A/E
E
A/E
ba – by and gone
nev – er will a – gain No not a – gain
mine all all, mine She's mine all, all mine
7 7 7 7 7 7

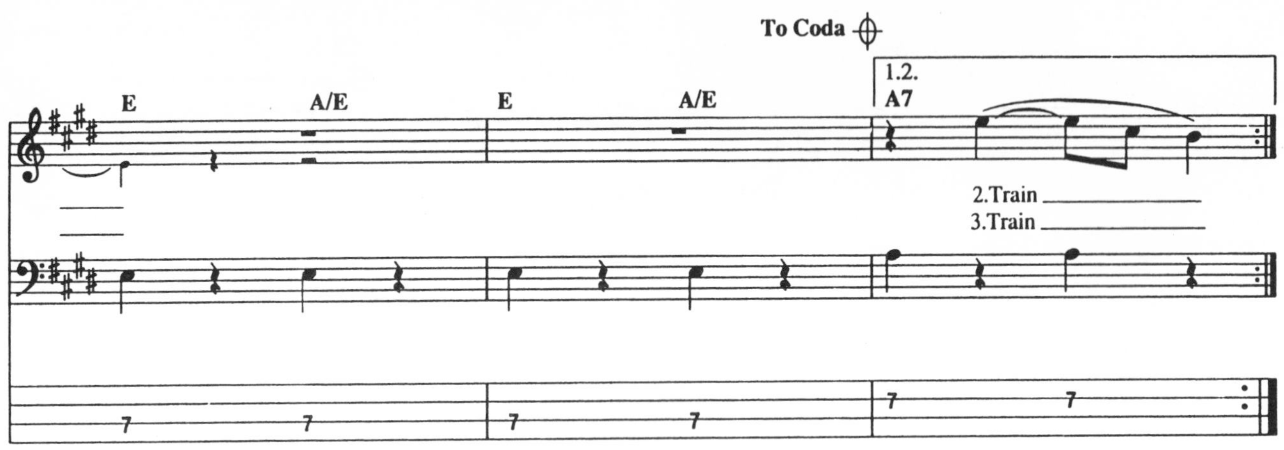

To Coda
1.2.
E
A/E
E
A/E
A7
2.Train
3.Train
7 7
7 7
7 7

3.
A7
E
7 7
7 7
7 7
7 7
7 7

B7
7 7
7 7
7 7
9 9
9 9

A7
E
7 7
7 7
7 6 7
7 6 7
7 6 7 6

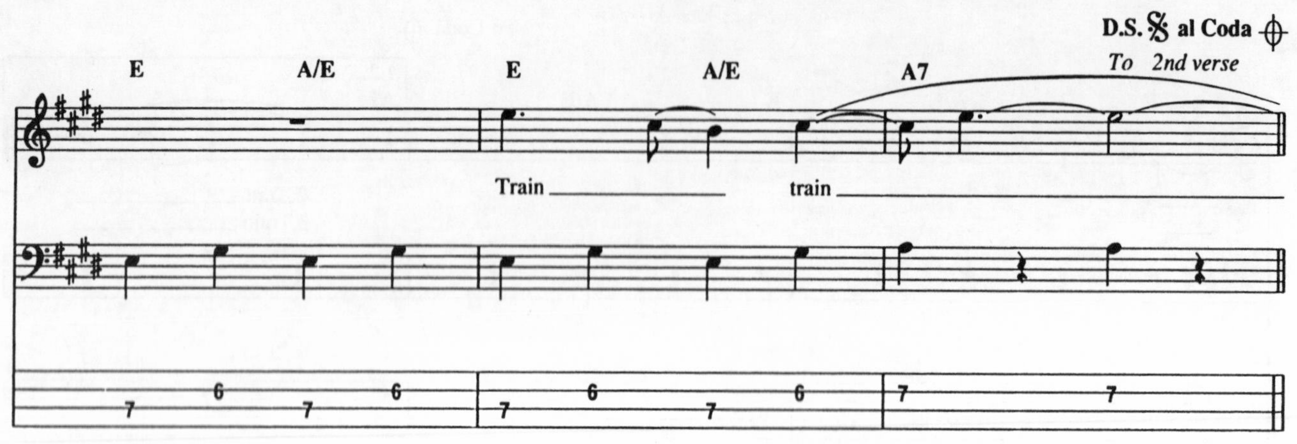
D.S. 𝄋 al Coda
To 2nd verse
E
A/E
E
A/E
A7
Train
train

Coda
Ooh
wo!

E

New Year's Day

Words by Bono
Music by U2

G5
F

A5

G5
F

Am

B Verse
Am
All is qui -
C
- et on New Years
Em
Day.
Am
A world in white
C
gets un - der
Em
way.
Am
Oo, I want to
C
be with you, be with you

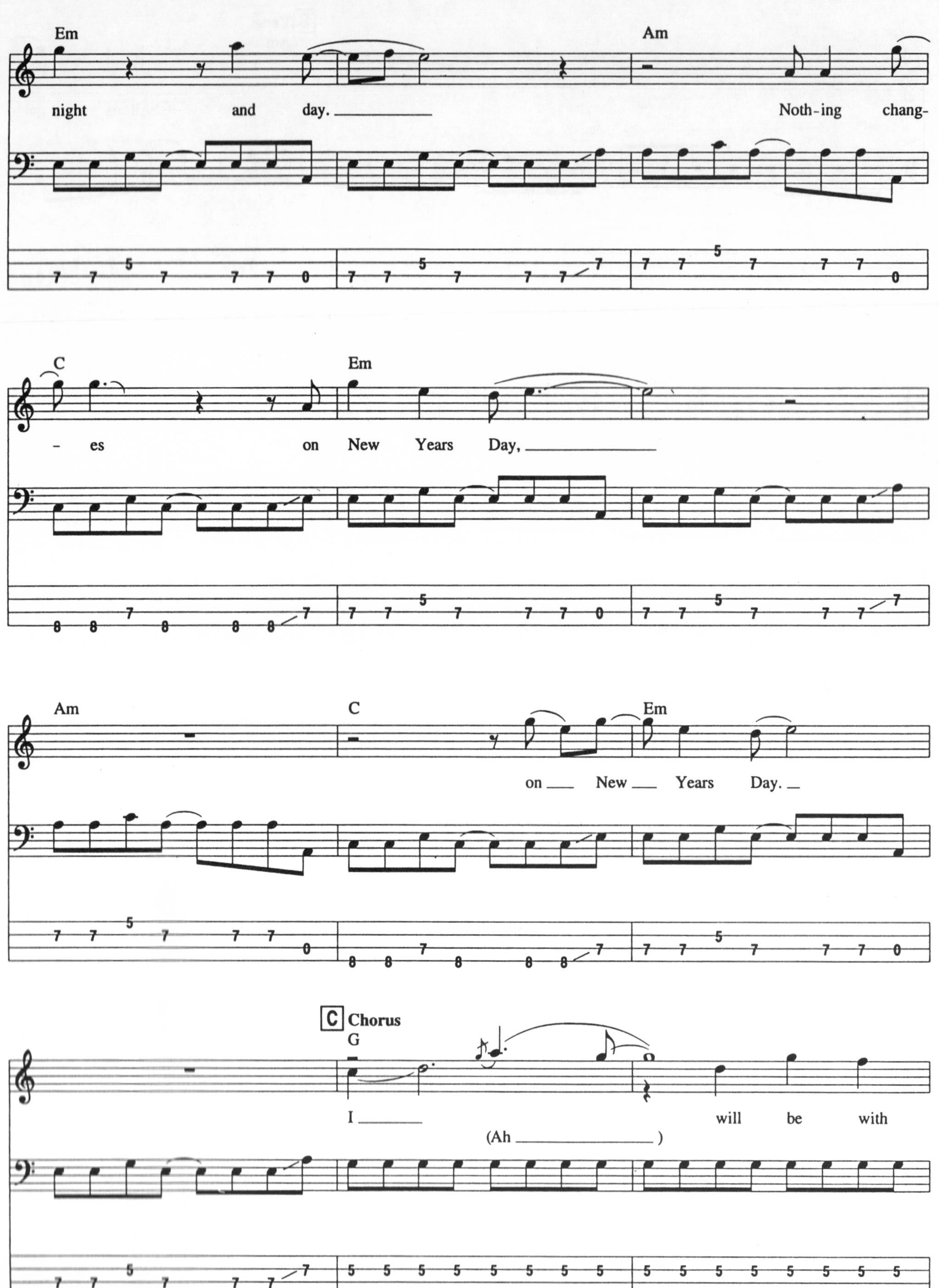
Em
Am
night and day.
Noth-ing chang-
C
Em
- es on New Years Day,
Am
C
Em
on New Years Day.
C Chorus
G
I will be with
(Ah)

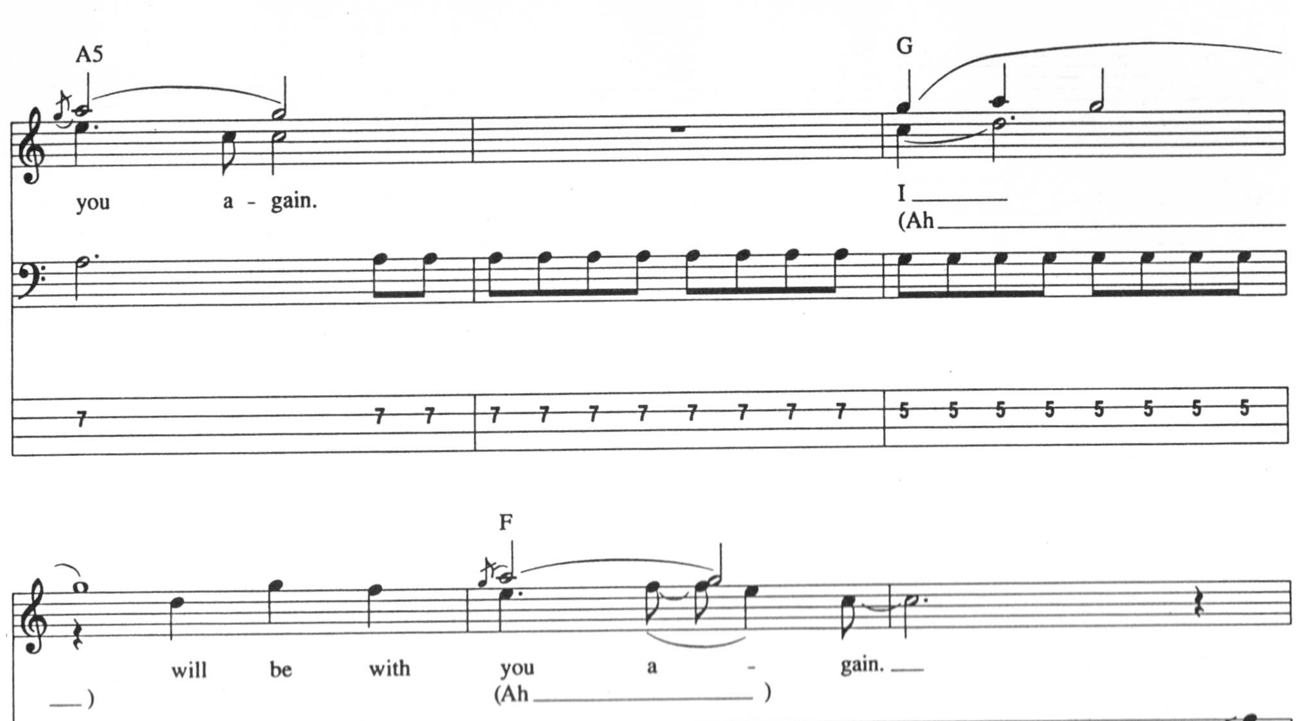
A5
G
you a - gain.
I
(Ah
F
will be with you a - gain.
)
(Ah)
7 7 7 7 7 7 7 7 7 7 7
5 5 5 5 5 5 5 5
5 5 5 5 5 5 5 5
3 3 3 3 3 3 3 3
3 3 3 3 3 3 3 7

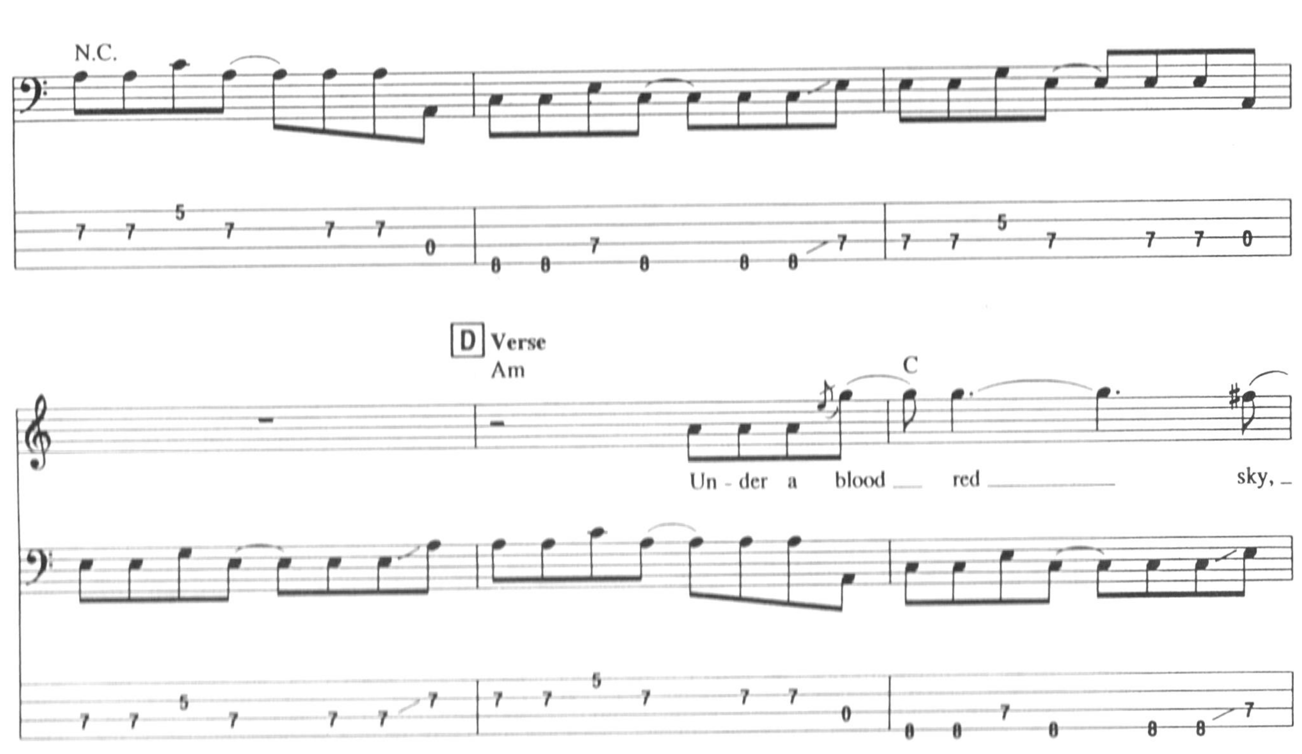
N.C.
D Verse
Am
C
Un - der a blood red sky,

Em
Am
a crowd has gath -
C
Em
ered,
black and
white.
Am
C
Em
Arms _ en - twined, _
the
cho - sen
few. _
Am
C
The news - pa - per
says,

Em
G
says
say it's true,
it's true,
A5
and we can break through.
Though
G
torn in two,
we can
F
be one.
E Chorus
G
I,
I will be -
(Ah,)
5 7 0

A5
G
gin a - gain.
(Ah,)
I,
(Ah,
F
I will be - gin a - gain.
)
(Ah,)
F Interlude
Am
C
Em
Am
C
Yeah,
ho,
wo.

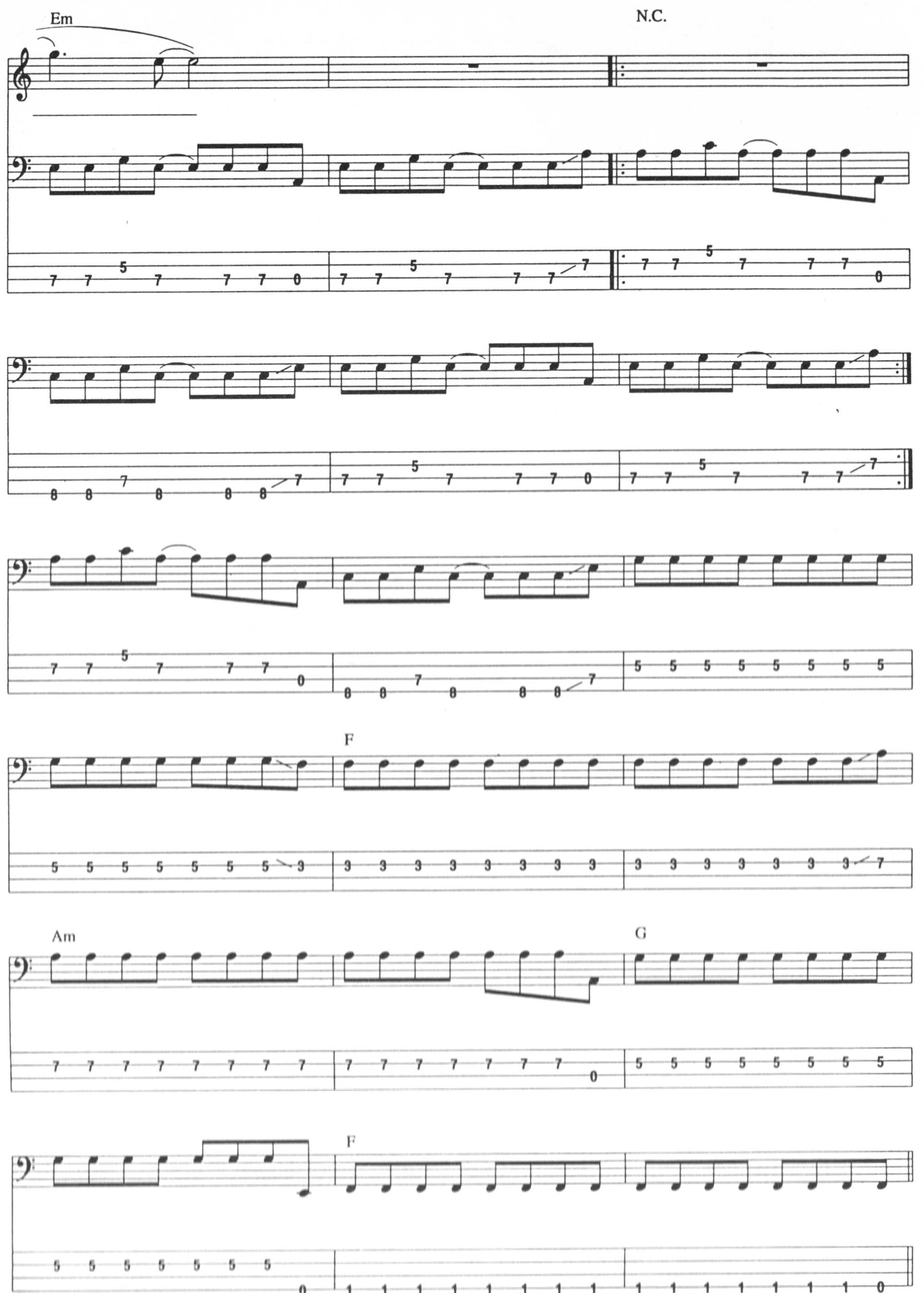
Em
N.C.
F
Am
G
F

G Guitar Solo
Am
C
Em
Am
Am
C
Em
Ah, ah, wa da oh, oo da da do da da.
H Chorus
G
I,
will be with
(Ah,)

Am
G
you a - gain.
I,
(Ah,
)
(Ah,
)
F
will be with you a - gain.
(Ah,
)
G
Am
I,
will be with you a - gain.
(Ah,
)
(ah,
)
G
I,
will be with
(Ah,
)
F
Am
you a - gain.
(Ah,
)

No Excuses

Written by Jerry Cantrell

Tune down 1/2 step:
④ = Eb ② = Db
③ = Ab ① = Gb

Moderate Rock ♩ = 114

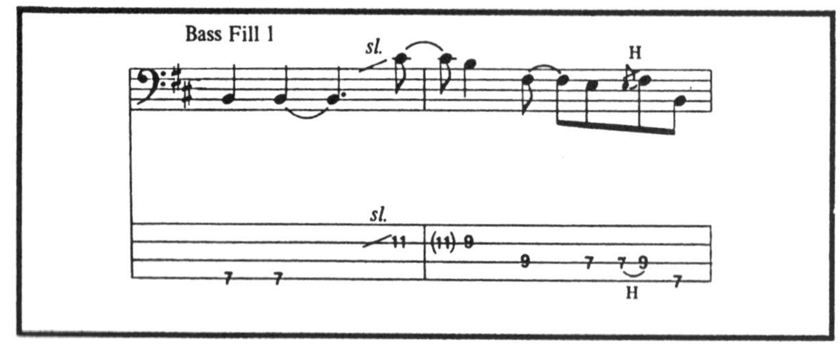

sl.
3rd time to Coda
Chorus
G6
Aadd2
Badd4
Ev - 'ry day it's some - thing...
2nd time substitute Bass Fill 2
E
H
Bass Fill 2

Badd4
sl.
H
sl.
sl.
H
sl.
sl.
Guitar solo
G6
Aadd2
Badd4
Aadd2
G6
Aadd2
H
E
D.S. al Coda
H
Coda
Chorus
G6
Aadd2
Ev - 'ry day it's some - thing...

Badd4
G6
Aadd2
E
Badd4
sl.
Badd4
(Drums out)
poco rit.
2

One Way Rider

Words and Music by Bill Monroe

Fast Country Rock

C
3 3 3 3 3 3 3 3 3 3 3 3 3 3 1 0

3 3 3 3 3 3 3 3 3 3 3 3 3 3 1 0

Now You're off and run – nin', run just like you're scared
Once up – on a vic – tim, cir – cum – stan – ces duc
3 3 3 3 3 3 3 3

run just like a gray dog run just like a deer
can it take a hold on ev' – ry – thing you do?
3 3 3 3 3 3 1 0

some – thing in the bush – es star – in' out at you
first we fol – low los – ers, next we fol – low fools
3 3 3 3 3 3 3 3

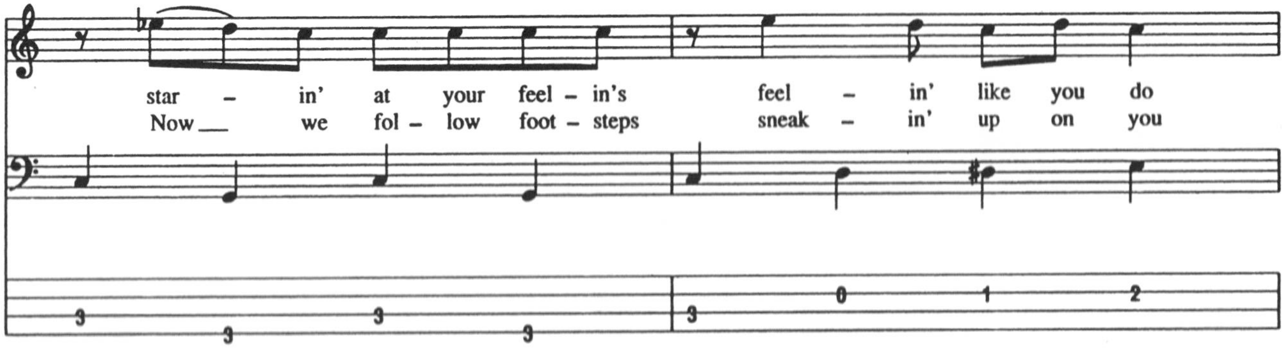
star – in' at your feel – in's feel – in' like you do
Now we fol – low foot – steps sneak – in' up on you
3 3 3 3 3 0 1 2

F
One Way Rid – er One way down the
3 3 3 3 2 3 3 1 0

C
road. Ba – by I'm
3 3 3 3 3 3 3 0 2

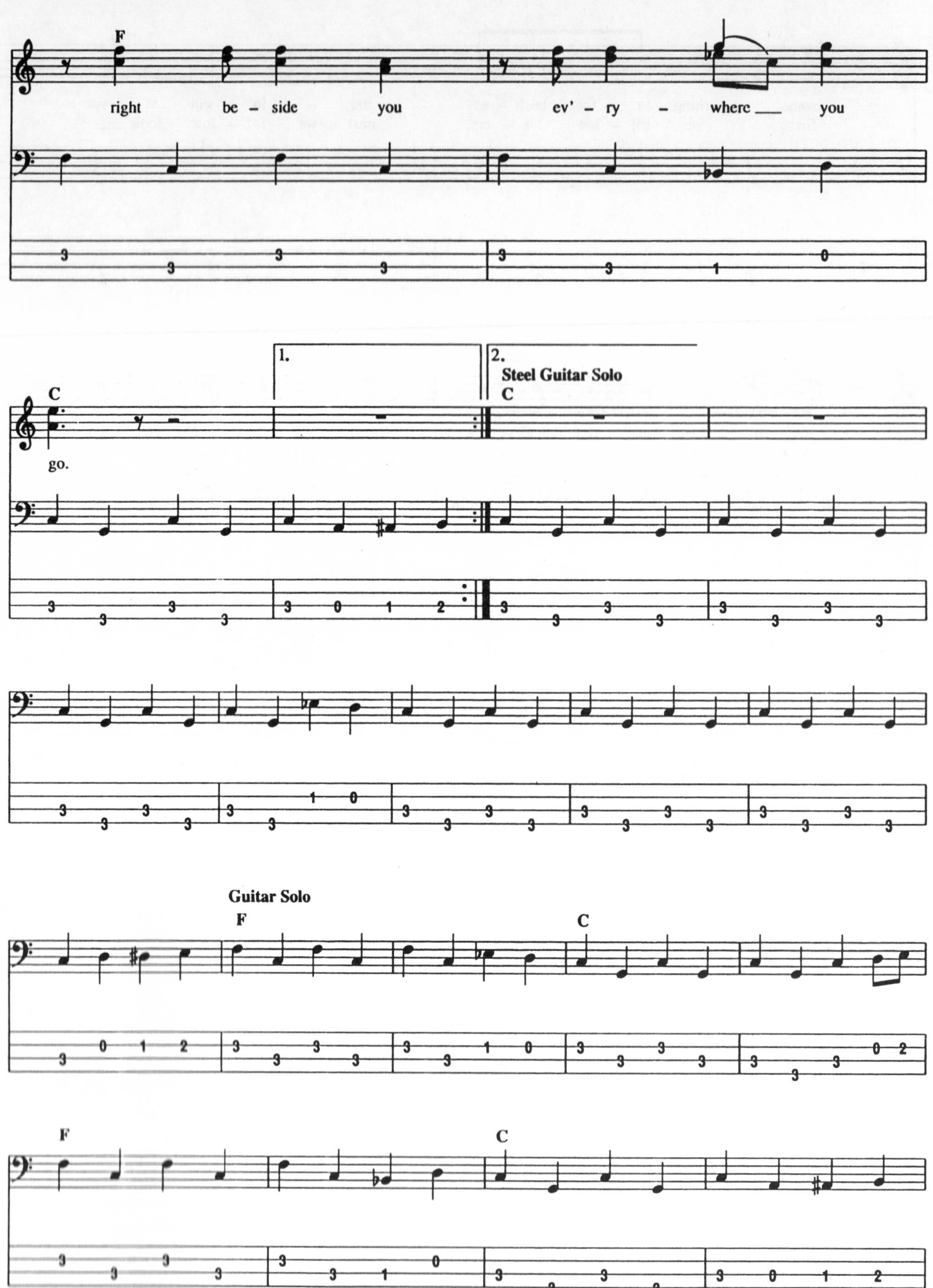
F
right be – side you ev' – ry – where ___ you
C
go.
1.
2.
Steel Guitar Solo
C
Guitar Solo
F
C
F
C

(C)
Lov – ers save these se – crets. Trust not un – to fools.

Don't go look for trou – ble. It will come for you.

Find some long lost pas – sion. Find broke – en line.

Here with me a mo – ment, real – ly gone this

F
C
time. One Way Rid – er One way down the road.
F
Ba – by I'm right be–side you ev – 'ry where – you
C
F
go. Yeah I'm a One Way Rid – er.
C
One way down the road. Ba – by I'm

F
C
Right be – side_ you ev – 'ry where you go.
1st Guitar Solo
C
1st Fiddle Solo
F
C
F
C
1st Steel Guitar Solo
F
C

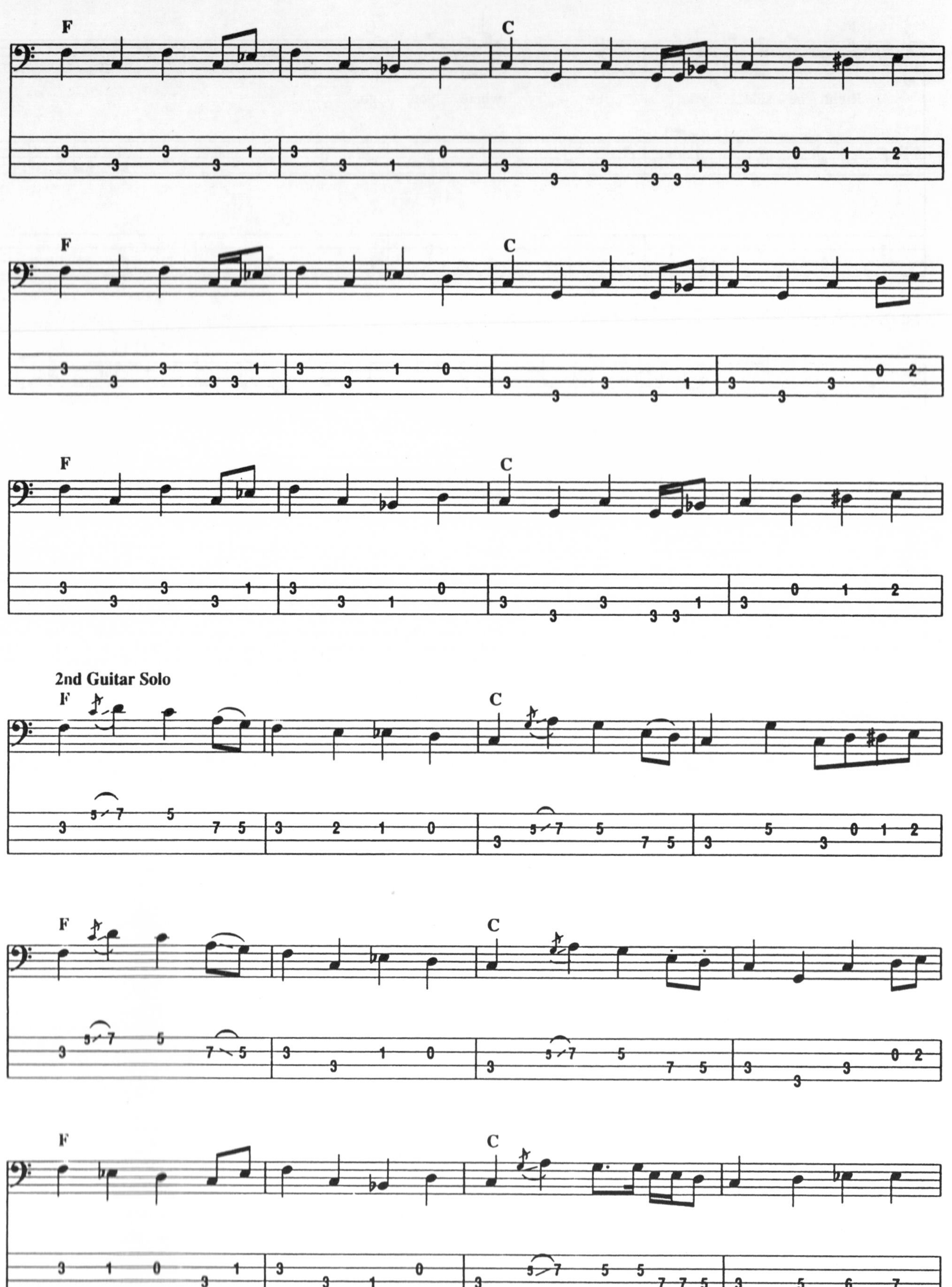
F
C
F
C
F
C
2nd Guitar Solo
F
C
F
C
F
C

2nd Fiddle Solo
F
C
F
C
F
C
F
C
2nd Guitar Solo
F
C
F
C

F
C
F
C
F
C
F
C
F
C
F
C
Fade

Over the Mountain

Words and Music by Ozzy Osbourne, Randy Rhoads, Bob Daisley and Lee Kerslake

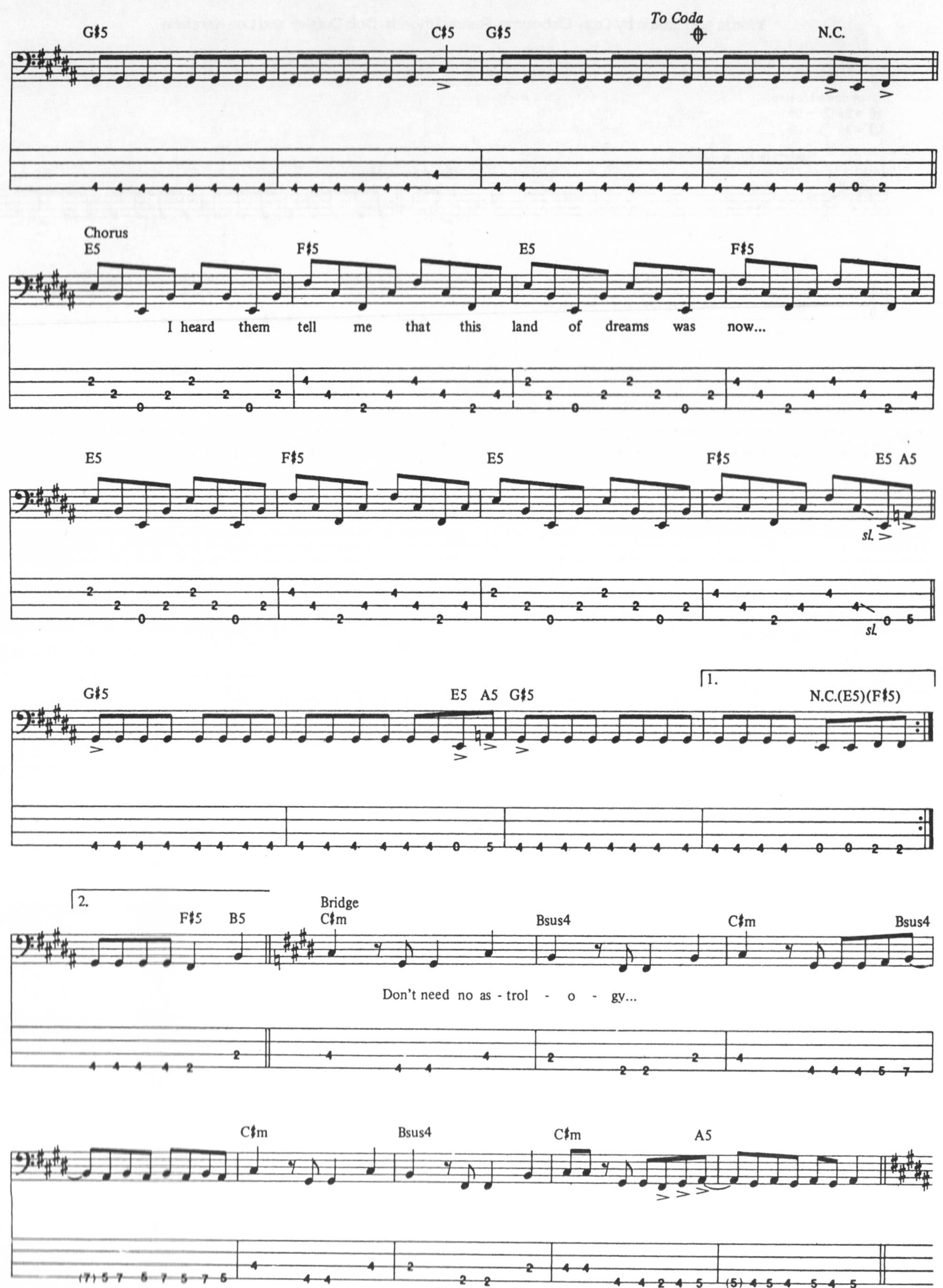
G♯5
C♯5
G♯5
To Coda
N.C.
Chorus
E5
F♯5
I heard them tell me that this land of dreams was now...
E5 A5
sl.
1.
N.C.(E5)(F♯5)
2.
F♯5
B5
Bridge
C♯m
Bsus4
Don't need no as - trol - o - gy...
A5

Interlude
D♯m
G♯5
D♯m
G♯5
D♯m
G♯5
sl.
N.C.(B5)
Guitar solo
N.C.(G♯°)
(C♯5)
(A5)
(B5)
(C♯5)
(E5)
(F♯5)
(G♯5)
E5
E5 A5 G♯5
D.S. al Coda
N.C.(E5)(F♯5)

Coda
F♯5
B5
Bridge
C♯m
Bsus4
C♯m
Bsus4
Don't need no as-trol - o - gy...
C♯m
Bsus4
C♯m
A5
Interlude
D♯m
G♯5
D♯m
G♯5
D♯m
G♯5
sl.
D♯m
N.C.(B5)
Outro
N.C.(G♯5)
(E5)
(F♯5)
(G♯5)
(E5)
(F♯5)
G♯5
(F♯5)
E5
D♯5
C♯5
E5
A5
G♯5

Oye Como Va

Words and Music by Tito Puente

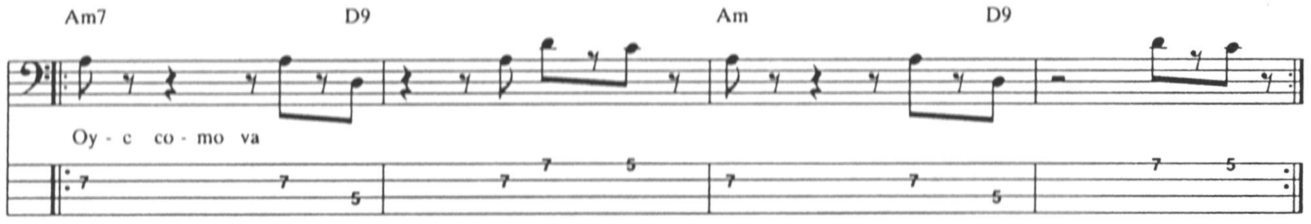

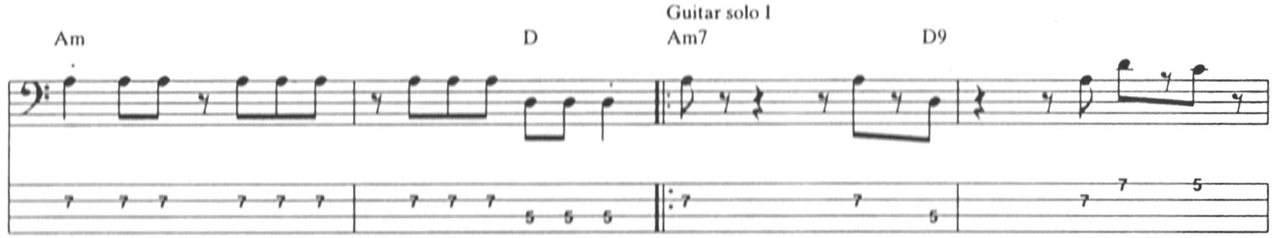

1.2.
Am7
D9
3.
Am
Am(maj7)
Am6
Organ solo
*Play 6 times
*w/slight variations on repeats.
Am/D
D
Oy - e co - mo va...
D7(no3rd)
Guitar solo II
D/A

Paperback Writer

Words and Music by John Lennon and Paul McCartney

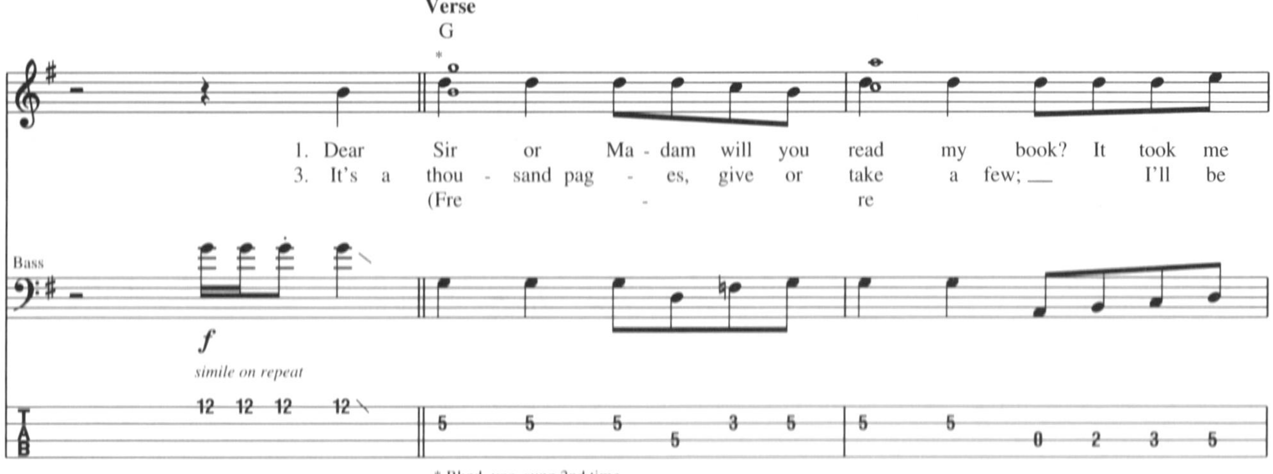

Bass: w/ Bass Fill 1, 2nd time

man named Lear and I need a job ___ so I
like the style, ___ I can change it 'round ___ and I
re Jac - que.)

want to be a pa - per - back

C

writ - er, ___ pa - per - back

G

writ - er. ___

To Coda ⊕

2. It's the
4. If you

Verse

G

dir - ty sto - ry of a dir - ty man, ___ and his cling - ing wife ___ does - n't

un - der - stand. His son is work - ing for the Dai - ly Mail; ___ it's a

C
stead - y job but he wants to be a pa - per - back writ - er, pa - per - back
D.C. al Coda
Coda
Verse
G
writ - er.
G
real - ly like it you can have the rights, it could
(Fre - re
make a mil - lion for you o - ver - night. If you must re - turn if you can
Jac - que. Fre -
send it here, but I need a break and I want to be a pa - per - back
re Jac - que.)

C
writ - er,
pa - per - back writ - er.

Outro

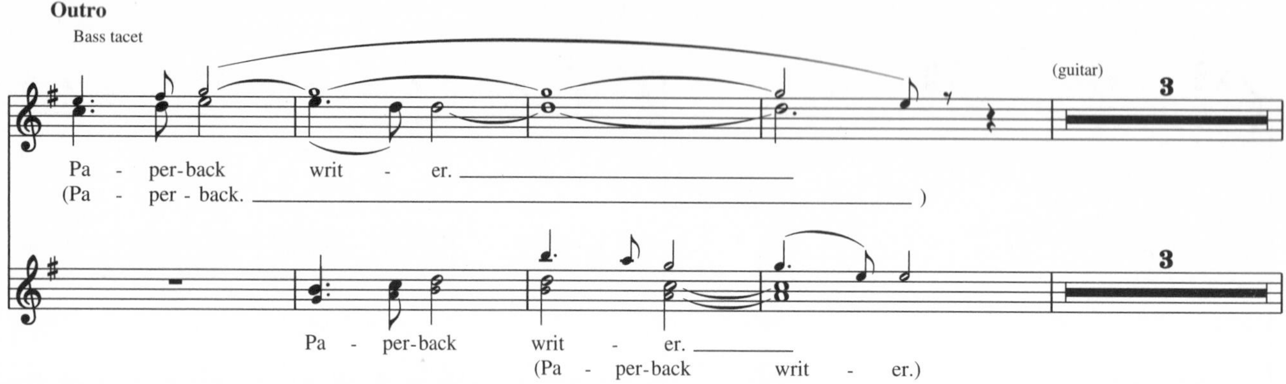
Bass tacet
(guitar)
3
Pa - per-back writ - er.
(Pa - per - back.)
3
Pa - per-back writ - er.
(Pa - per-back writ - er.)

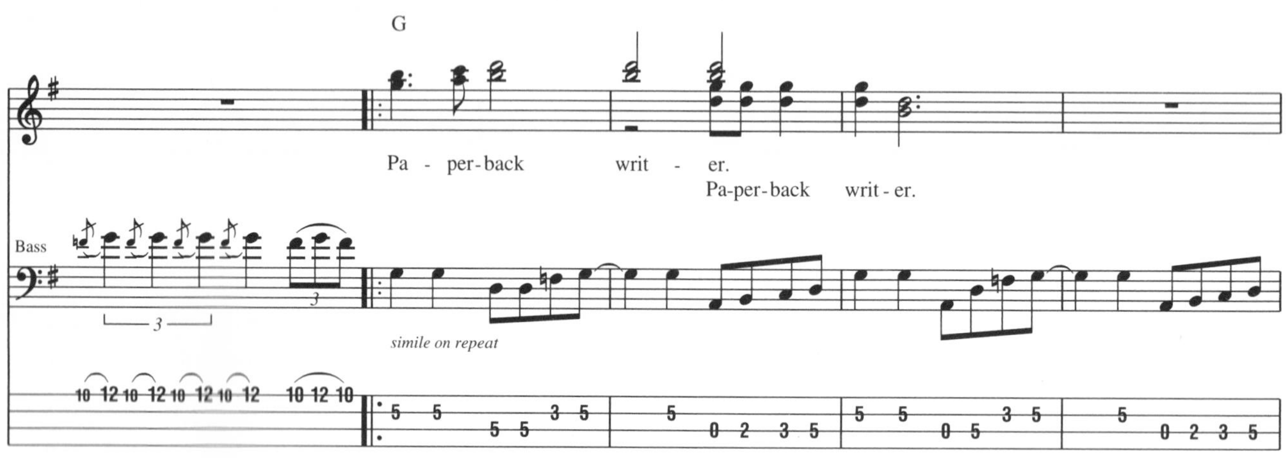
G
Pa - per-back writ - er.
Pa-per-back writ - er.
Bass
simile on repeat

Repeat and Fade
Pa - per-back writ - er.
Pa - per-back writ - er.

Paranoid

Words and Music by Anthony Iommi, John Osbourne, William Ward and Terence Butler

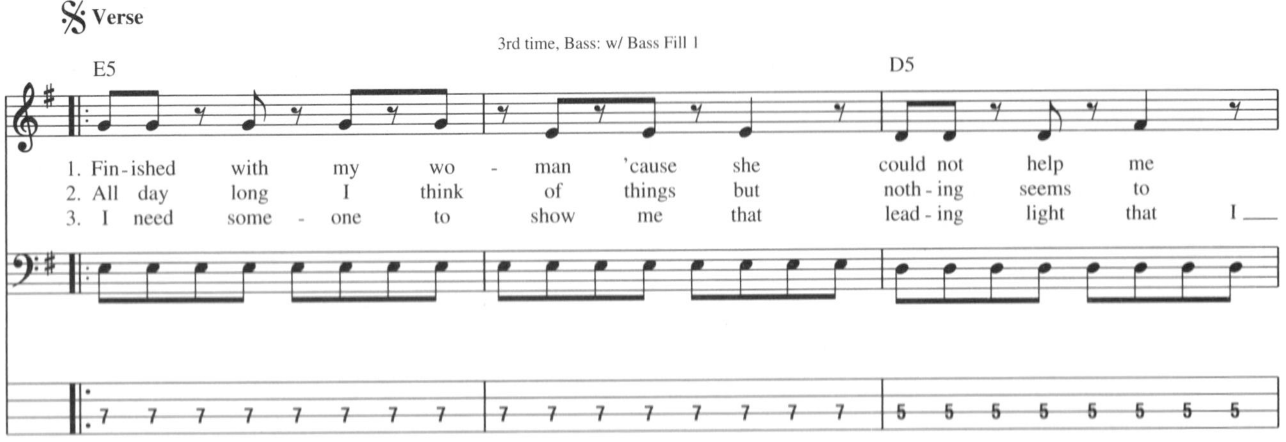

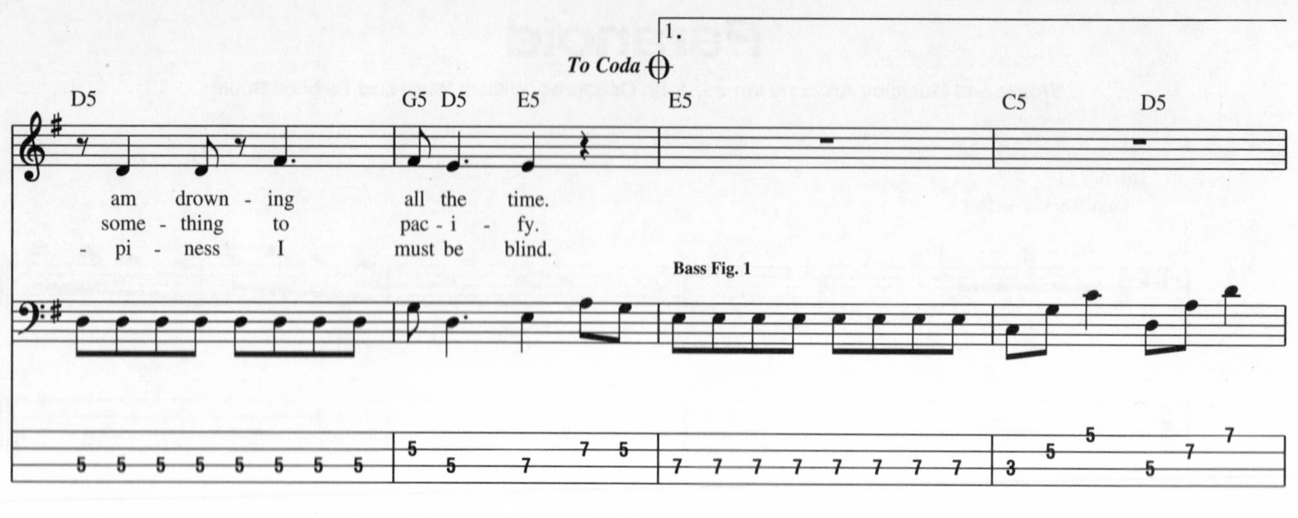

1.
To Coda
D5
G5 D5
E5
E5
C5
D5
am drown - ing all the time.
some - thing to pac - i - fy.
- pi - ness I must be blind.
Bass Fig. 1

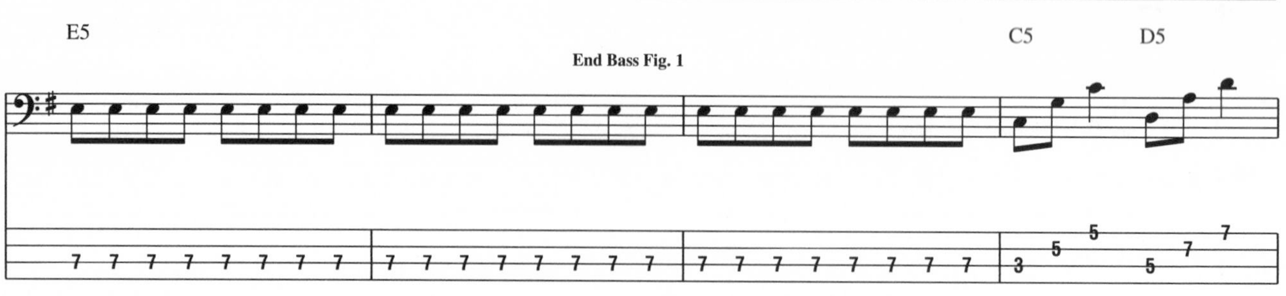

E5
End Bass Fig. 1
C5
D5

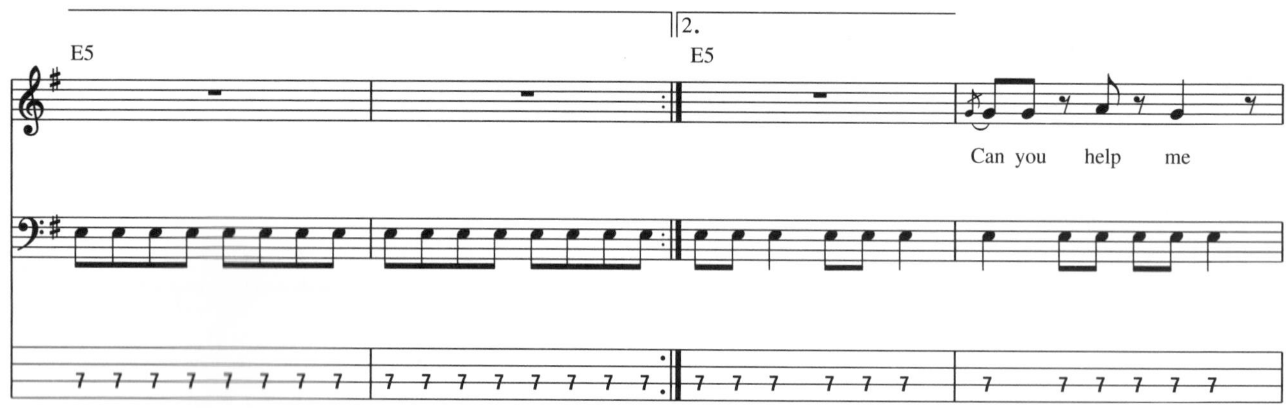

E5
2.
E5
Can you help me

D5
E5
cut you from my brain.

D5
E5
Wo
yeah.
Bass Fig. 2
1.
2.
D.S. al Coda
G5 D5 E5
End Bass Fig. 2
Coda
Guitar Solo
1., 3.
2., 4.
Verse
2nd time, Bass: w/ Bass Fill 1
4. Make a joke and I will sigh and
5. And so as you hear these words tell - ing

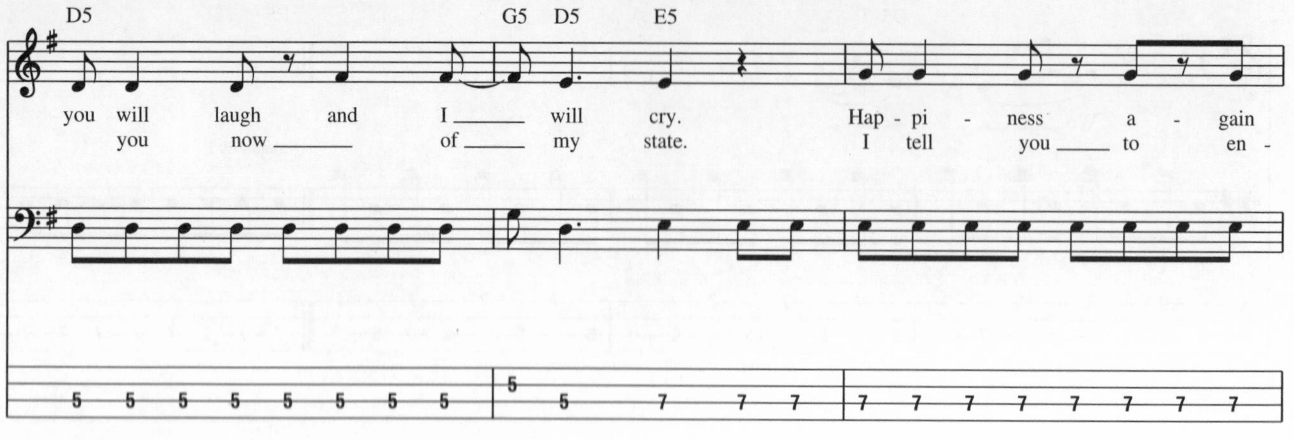
D5
G5 D5 E5
you will laugh and I ___ will cry. Hap - pi - ness a - gain
you now ___ of ___ my state. I tell you ___ to en -
5 5 5 5 5 5 5 5
5
5 7 7 7
7 7 7 7 7 7 7 7

2nd time, Bass: w/ Bass Fill 1
D5
G5 D5 E5
I feel ___ and love to me ___ is so un - real.
joy life ___ I wish I could ___ but it's too late.
7 7 7 7 7 7 7 7
5 5 5 5 5 5 5 5
5
5 7 7 5

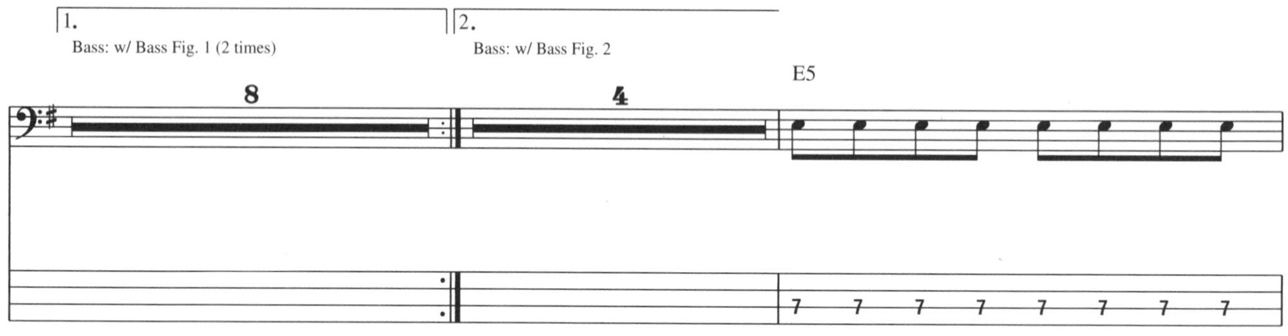
1.
Bass: w/ Bass Fig. 1 (2 times)
8
2.
Bass: w/ Bass Fig. 2
4
E5
7 7 7 7 7 7 7 7

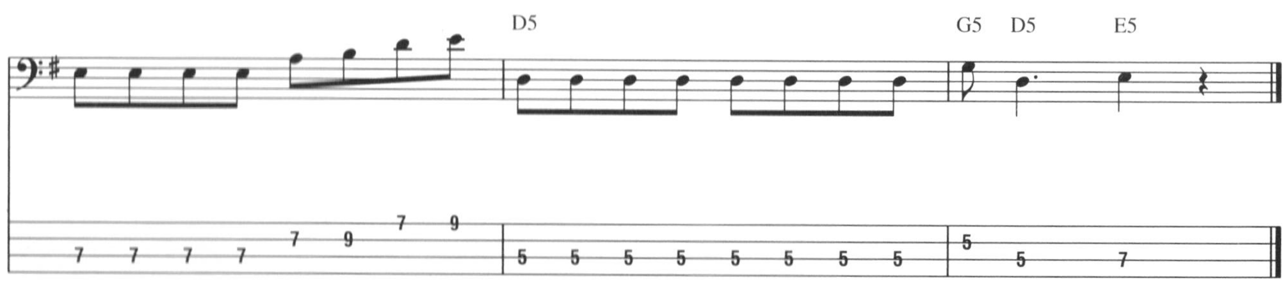
D5
G5 D5 E5
7 7 7 7 7 9 7 9
5 5 5 5 5 5 5 5
5
5 7

Peg

Words and Music by Walter Becker and Donald Fagen

Intro

Moderate Jazz-Rock ♩ = 117

Gmaj9 F♯7♯9 Fadd9 E7♯9 E♭add9 D7♭9

Bass

mf

T A B: 3 | 2 | 1 3⁄12 14 | 13 | 11 | 10

Cmaj6 Bm7♯5 Cmaj7 Gadd9

𝄋 **Verse/ Guitar Solo**

Cmaj7 Gadd9

1. I've seen your pic - ture,
pin - shot,
3. Guitar Solo; vocal tacet

Cmaj7 Gadd9 Cmaj7 Gadd9 Cmaj7 Gadd9

your name in lights a - bove it. This is your
I keep it with your let - ter. Done up in

Fmaj7 Cadd9 Fmaj7 Cadd9 Cmaj7 Gadd9

big de - but, __ it's like a dream come __ true. __
blue - print - blue, __ it sure looks good on __ you, __

Cmaj7 Gadd9 Gmaj7 Dadd9 Fmaj7 Cadd9
So won't you smile for the cam - 'ra: I know they're gon - na
and when you smile for the cam - 'ra, I know I'll love you
Cmaj7 Gadd9
1. Cmaj7 Gadd9
2. Cmaj7 Gadd9
love it, Peg. 2., 4. I like your
bet - ter.
Chorus
Cmaj7 Bm7♯5 A7sus4 E7sus4 Cmaj7 Bm7♯5
Peg, it will come back to you. Peg, it will come
(Peg. Back to you. Peg.
Bass Fig. 1
T P T T P T T T T P T P P T T P T T T T P T T P T T T T P
A7sus4 E7sus4 A C G F♯7
back to you. Then the shut - ter falls, you see it
Back to you. Ah, shut - ter falls
T P P T T P T T T P T P T T T T T P T P T P T T T T T T

To Coda
Bm7
E7#9
Am7
D9sus4
Cmaj7
Gadd9
all in three D. It's your fav - 'rite for-eign mo-vie.
all in three D. for - eign mo - vie.)
End Bass Fig. 1
T T P T P T T P T T T T T P T P T T P T
Interlude
Cmaj7
Gadd9
F#m7
Bm7
Em7
Bm7
Cmaj7
Gmaj9
F#7#9
D.S. al Coda
(take repeat)
Fadd9
E7#9
Ebadd9
D7#9
Cmaj7
Bm7#5
Cmaj7
Gadd9
Coda
Outro
Bass: w/ Bass Fig. 1
Cmaj7
Bm7#5
A7sus4
E7sus4
Cmaj7
Bm7#5
A7sus4
E7sus4
mo-vie it will come back to you, Peg, it will come back to you.
(Peg, Back to you, Peg, Back to you.
Play 4 Times and Fade
A
C
G
F#7
Bm7
E5#9
Am7
D9sus4
then the shut-ter falls you see it all in three D. It's your fav-'rite for-eign
Ah, shut-ter falls, all in three D. for-eign mo - vie)

Peggy Sue

Words and Music by Jerry Allison, Norman Petty and Buddy Holly

Verse
A D A D A
Peg - gy Sue, Peg - gy Sue, oh, how my heart yearns for you oh,
D A D A
Peg - gy, my Pa-heg - gy Sue. Oh well, I
E D A D A E
love you gal, yes I love you Peg - gy Sue.
Bridge
A F A
Peg - gy Sue, Peg - gy Sue, pret-ty, pret-ty, pret-ty, pret-ty Peg - gy Sue. Oh, oh
2nd time
D A D A
Peg - gy, my Peg - gy Sue. Oh well, I

To Coda
E
D
A
D
A
E
love you gal, and I need you Peg - gy Sue.
Verse
A
D
A
D
A
I love you, Peg - gy Sue, with a love so rare and true oh,
D
A
D
A
Peg - gy, my Peg - gy Sue. Oh well, I
E
D
A
D
A
E
love you gal, I want you Peg - gy Sue.
Guitar Solo
A
D
A
D
A
D
A
D
A
D
A
D
A

D.S. al Coda
E D A D A E

Coda
Verse
A D A D A
I love you, Peg - gy Sue, with a love so rare and true, oh

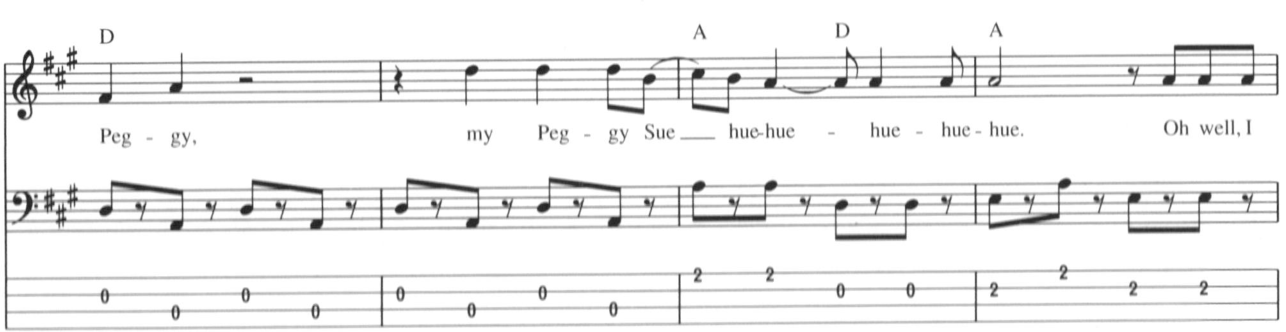
D A D A
Peg - gy, my Peg - gy Sue hue-hue - hue - hue - hue. Oh well, I

E D A D A
love you gal, and I want you Peg - gy Sue. Oh well, I

E D A D A
love you gal, and I want you Peg - gy Sue.

Photograph

Words and Music by Steve Clark, Joe Elliott, Robert John Lange, Rick Savage and Pete Willis

E B A E B/E
ly, one I wan-na touch. I see your face ev-'ry time
ev-'ry man feel like a child. You got some kind a hold
A/E D/E E B/E A/E D/E
I dream on ev-'ry page, ev-'ry mag - a - zine.
on me, your all wrapped up in mys - ter - y.
So wild,
E B/E A/E D/E E B A
so free, so far from me, you're all I want, my fan - ta-sy.

C G/B D A D A G A G/B
Oh, look what you've done to this rock 'n' roll clown.
C G/B D A G/B A G A
Oh, look what you've done.
Chorus
G/B C D Em G/B C Em D
Pho - to-graph, I don't want your pho - to-graph. I don't need your

G/B
C
D
Em
G/B
C
pho - to-graph, all I've got is a pho - to-graph,
but it's not e-nough!
1.
2.
G/B
C
Em
D
E
B
I'd be your
to-graph.
You've gone straight to my head.
A
Asus4
E
B
A
Asus4
E
B
A
Asus4
Solo Guitar
E
B
A
Aaua4
E
B
A
Asus4

E B A Aaua4 E B
A Asus4 E B A
D.S. al Coda
Coda
G/B C No Chord C5 D5 E5
to-graph. I wan-na touch you!
G/B C D Em G/B C Em D
Repeat and fade

Pinball Wizard

Words and Music by Pete Townshend

Asus4
A
G6sus4
G6
H
H
H
H
F♯7sus4
F♯
B
A
D
E
f
. . .sure plays a mean pin - ball.
B
A
D
E
He's a
Chorus
E
F♯
B
E
F♯
B
etc.
E
F♯
B
sl.
sl.
sl.
pin - ball wiz - ard, there has to be a twist.
sl.
sl.
sl.
G
D
sl.
sl.
sl.
sl.
D
Csus2
D
Csus2
D
Csus2
D
mf

3rd Verse
Bsus4
B(add4)
etc.
Asus4
Ain't got no dis - trac - tions, can't hear no buz - zers and bells,. . .
A
H
G6sus4
G6
F♯7sus4
F♯
B A D E
. . .sure plays a mean pin - ball.
Chorus
E F♯ B
etc.
thought I was the Bal - ly ta - ble king,. . .
G
D
sl

Dsus4
6
D
E - ven
4th Verse
Dsus4
D
etc.
Csus4
on my fa - v'rite ta - ble,
he can beat my best. . .
C
Bb sus4
Bb
Asus4
A
D
C
F
. . . sure plays a mean pin - ball!
Bb
Begin fade
Fade out

Port of Entry

By Wayne Shorter

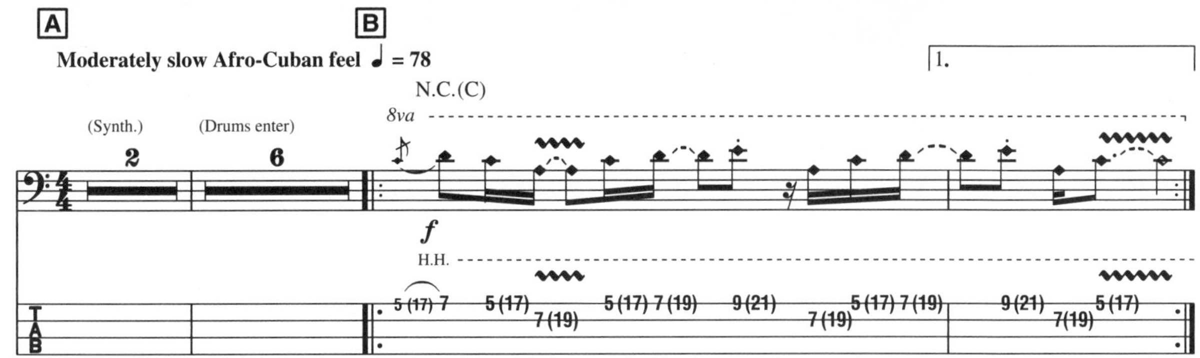

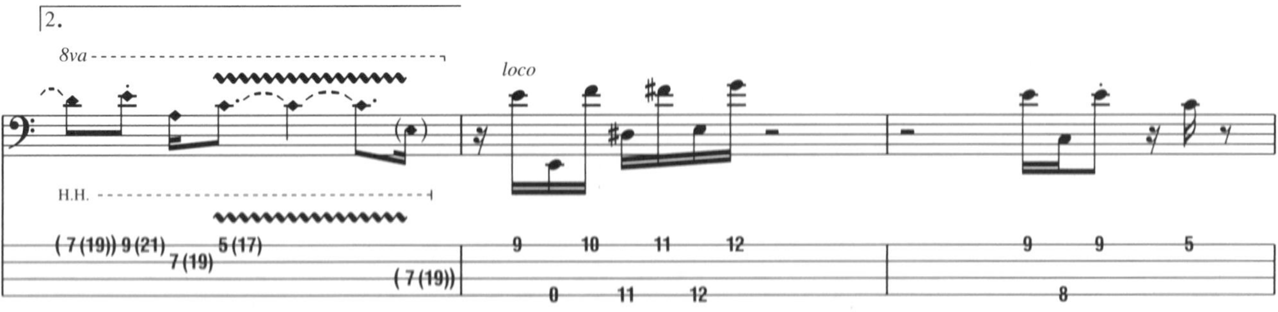

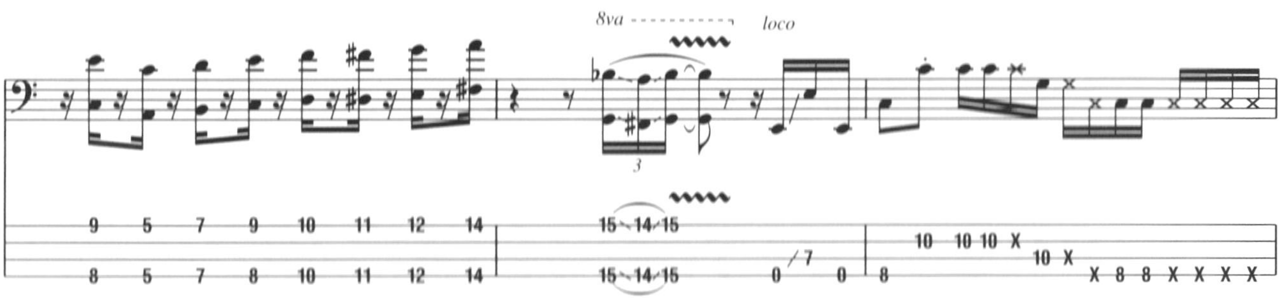

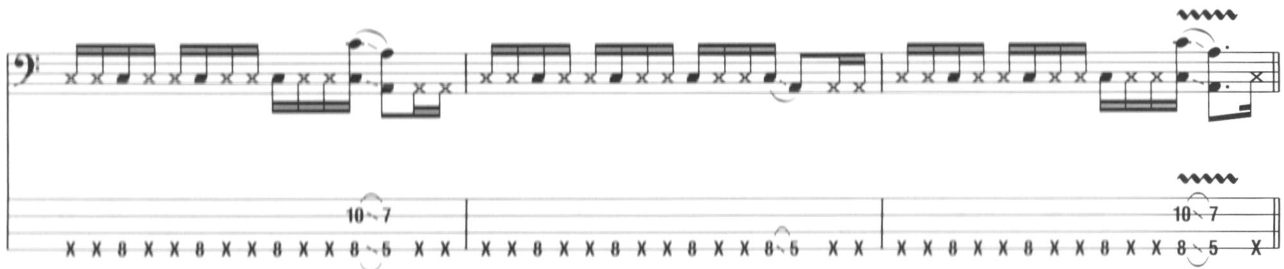

C
C
Play 5 times

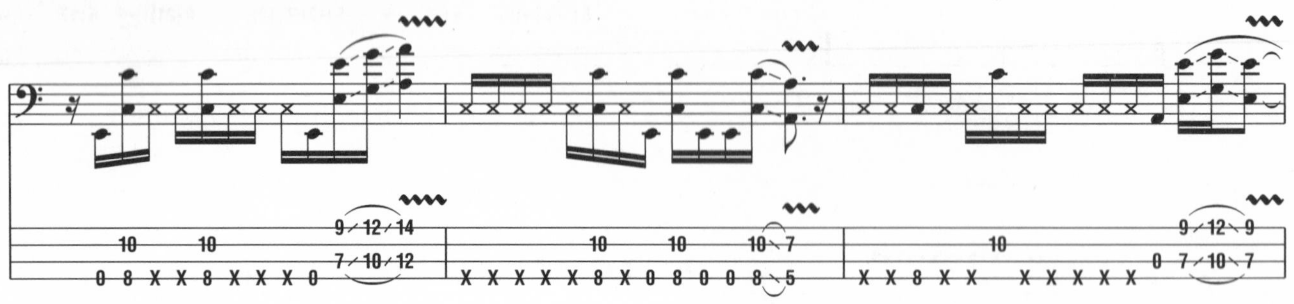

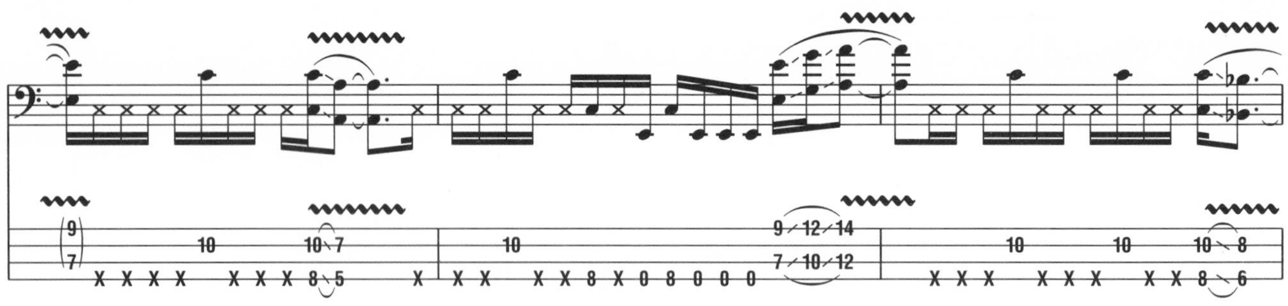

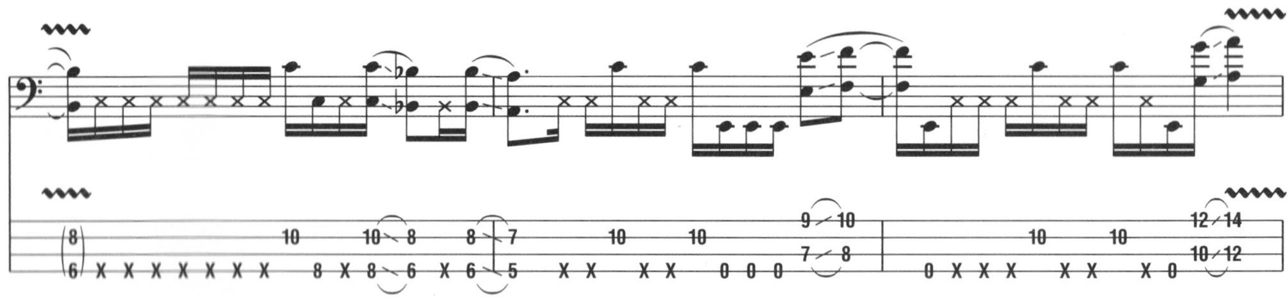

15ma
loco
Harm.

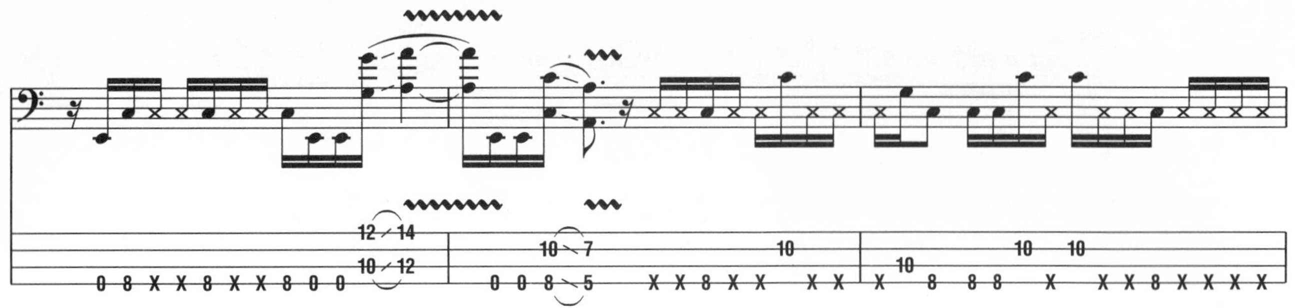

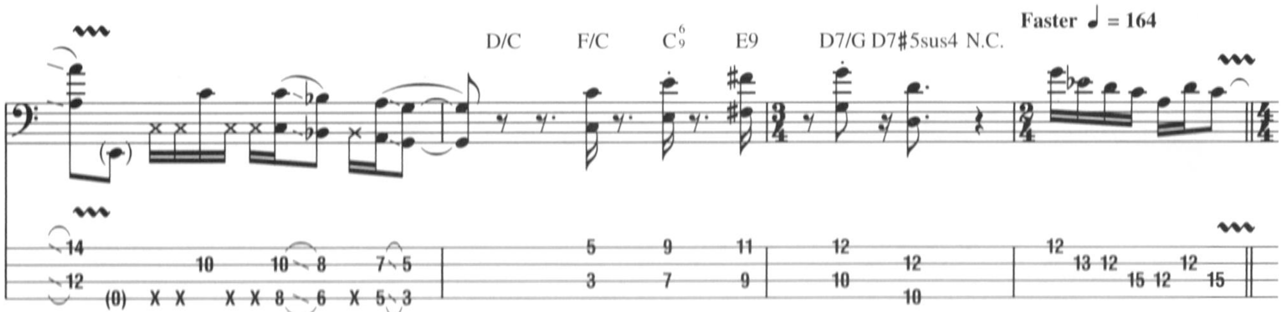
Faster ♩ = 164
D/C
F/C
C6/9
E9
D7/G
D7♯5sus4
N.C.

D
C
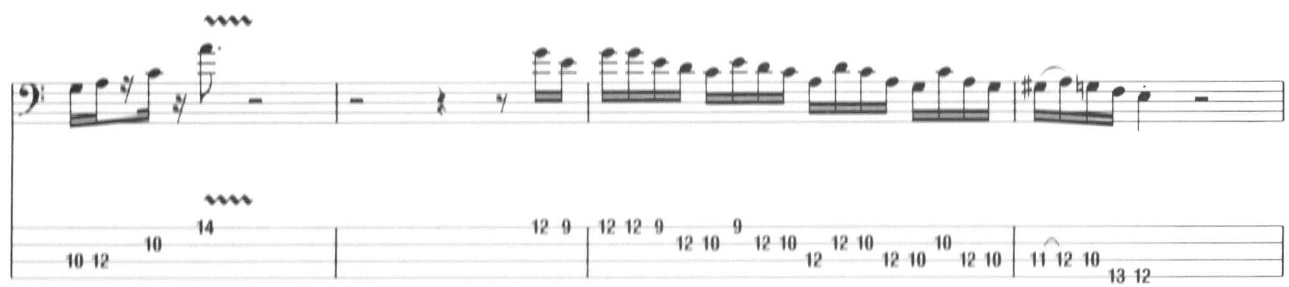

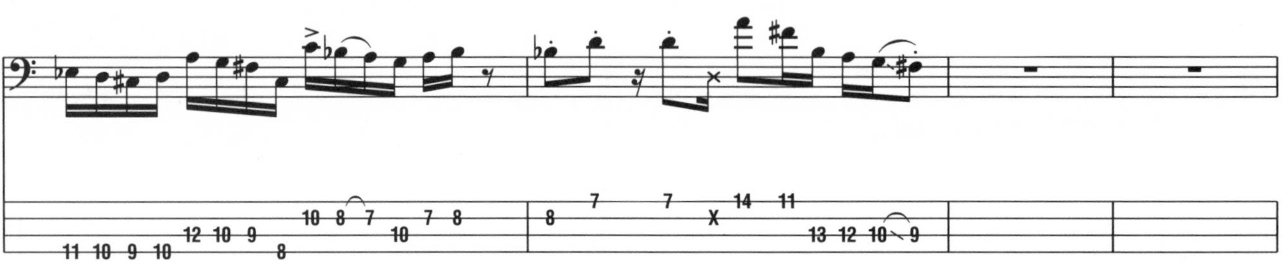

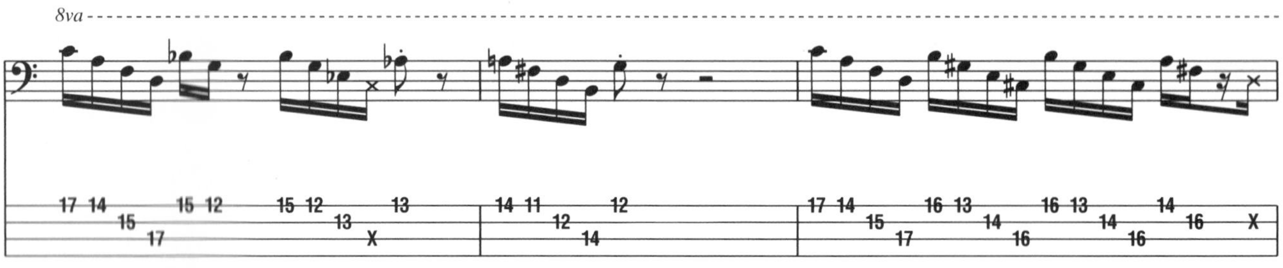
8va

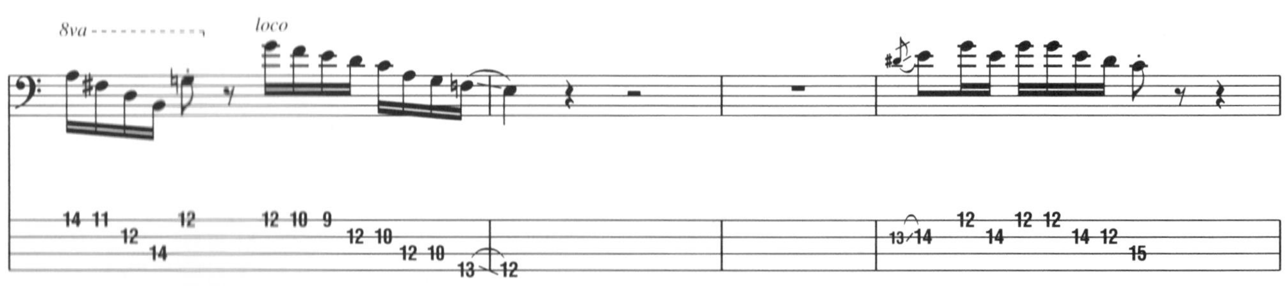
8va
loco

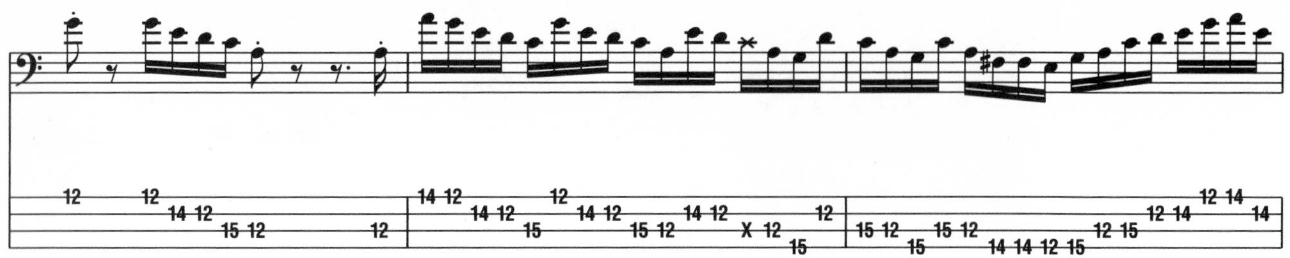
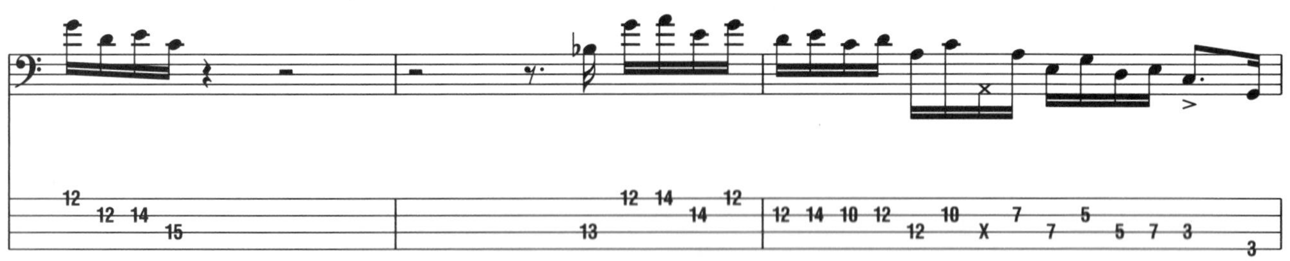

8va
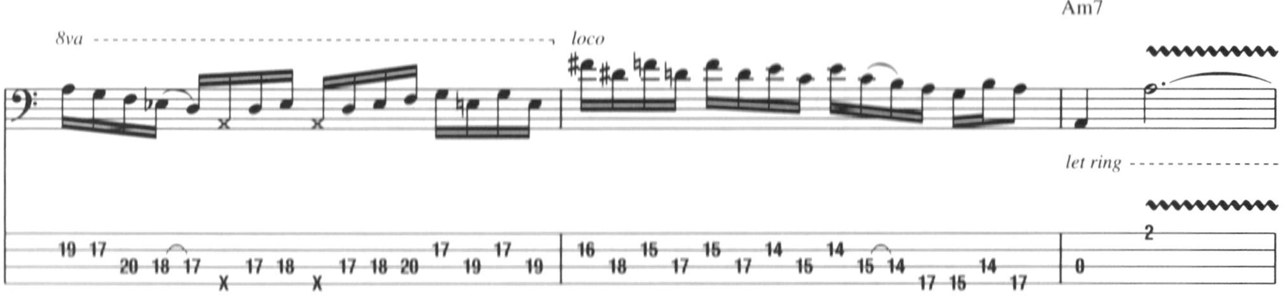
8va
loco
Am7
let ring

E
N.C.(F)
Dm7
let ring
let ring

G
C
8va

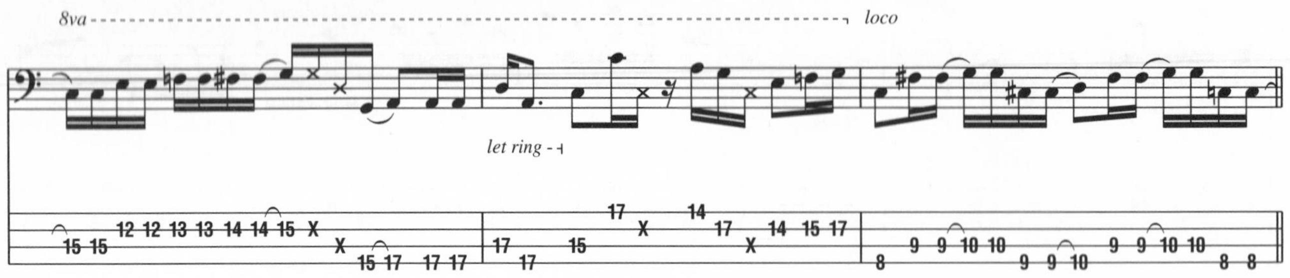
8va
loco
let ring

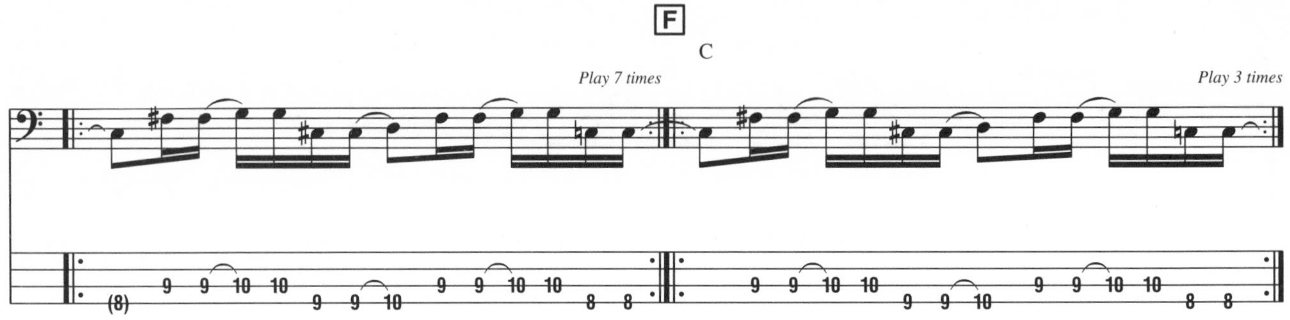
F
C
Play 7 times
Play 3 times

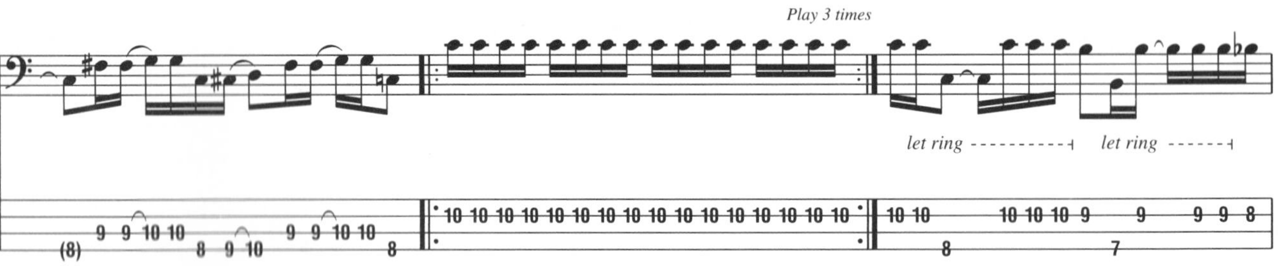
Play 3 times
let ring
let ring

let ring
let ring
let ring

8va
8va
8va
8va
loco
8va

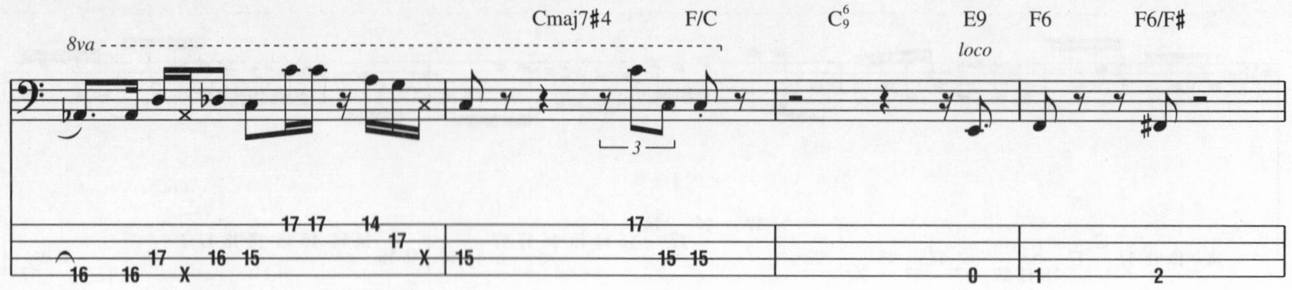
Cmaj7♯4
F/C
C^6_9
E9
F6
F6/F♯
8va
loco
3

G
C
(applause approx. 6 secs.)

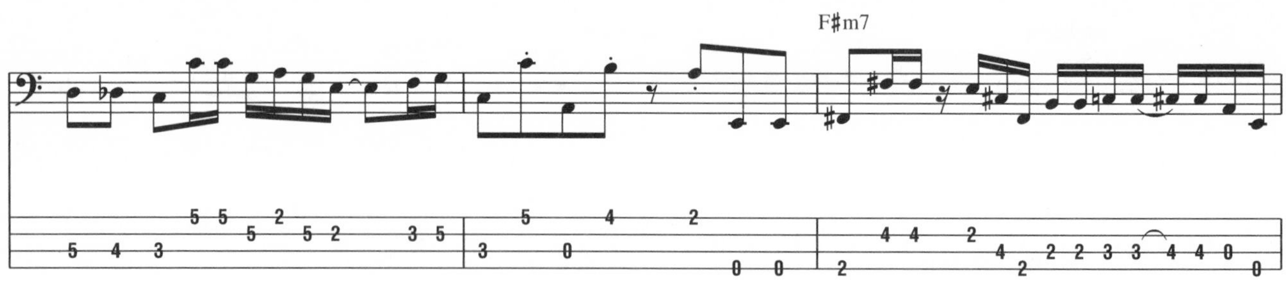
F♯m7

A6
G/D
Cmaj7/D
D/E
Amaj9

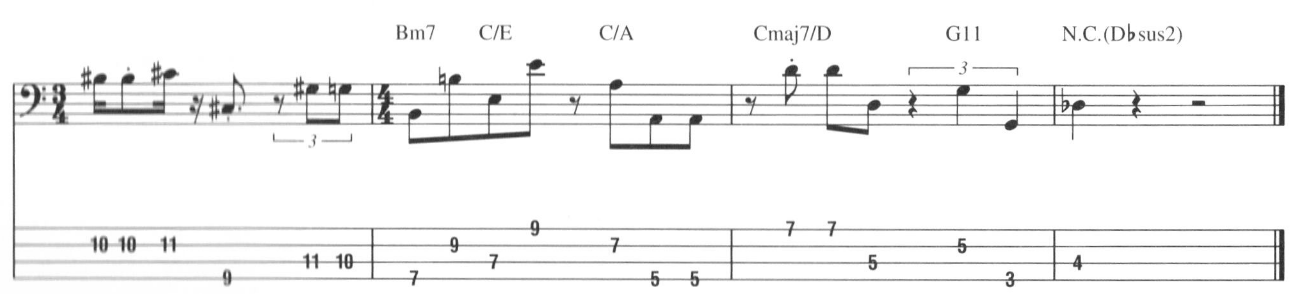
Bm7
C/E
C/A
Cmaj7/D
G11
N.C.(D♭sus2)
3
3

Pour Some Sugar on Me

Words and Music by Steve Clark, Phil Collen, Joe Elliott, Robert John Lange and Rick Savage

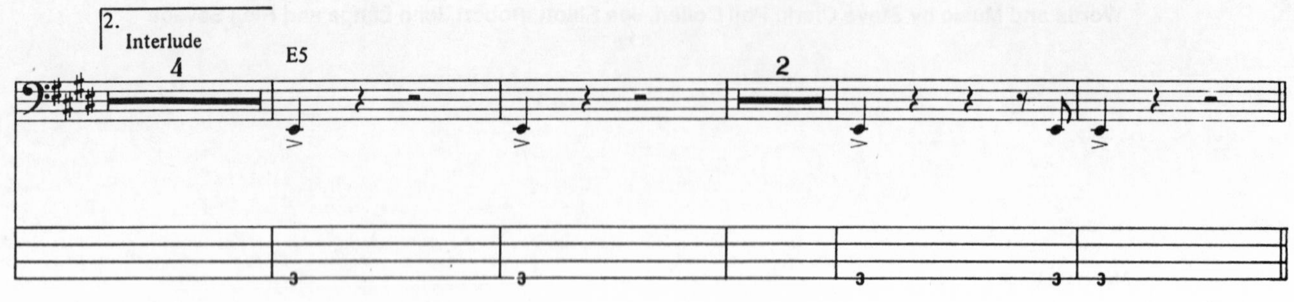
2.
Interlude
4
E5
2
3
3
3
3
3

3rd Verse
4
E5
D.S. al Coda
3
3
3
3

Coda
E5
A
B
Play 5 times
E5
A
B
3 3
0 0
0
2 2
2 2
3 3
0 0
0
2 2

Pride (In The Name Of Love)

Words by Bono
Music by U2

F♯
B
E
One man come, he to jus - ti - fy,
A
F♯
C Chorus
B
one man to o - ver throw.
In the name of love.
E
A
F♯
What more in the name of love.
In the name
B
E
A
of love.
What more in the name of love.
D Verse
F♯
B
E
One man caught in a barbed wire fence,

A
F♯
B
one man he re - sist.
One man washed on an
E
A
F♯
emp-ty beach,
one man be - trayed with a kiss.
In the name
E Chorus
B
E
A
of love.
What more
in the name of love.
F♯
B
E
In the name
of love.
What more
A
F♯
F Interlude
B
in the name of love.
Look out for me.

D
E
(lyric ad lib.)
Come back to
5 5 5 3 4 5 5 4 5 5 5 5
0 0 7 5 6 7 6 6 7 7
0 0 7 5 6 7 7 5 6 7 0
B
D
E
me.
2 2 2 0 1 2 2 0 1 2 2
5 5 5 3 4 5 5 4 5 5
0 0 7 5 6 7 5 6 7 7
B
E
0 0 7 5 6 7 7 5 6 7 0
2 2 2 2 0 1 2 0 1 2 2
0 0 (7) 7 7 7 0 0 2 0 0 0 0
A
F♯
B
5 5 5 5 5 5 5 5 5 5 5
2 2 2 (2) 2 2 2 2 2
2 2 2 2 2 0 1 2 2 0 1 2 2
E
A
F♯
Hmmm
0 0 7 0 0 0 0 0 0
5 5 5 (5) 5 5 5 5 5
2 2 2 4 4 2 2 4 4
B
E
A
hmmm hmmm hmmm hmmm hmmm hmmm hmmm hmmm hmmm hmmm.
2 2 4 4 2 2 2 4 4
0 0 0 0 0 0 0 0 0
5 7 7 7 5 5 5 5 5

G Verse
F♯
B
E
Ear-ly morn-ing, A - pril four,
A
F♯
B
shots ring out in the Mem-phis sky.
Free at last, they
E
A
F♯
took your life, they could not take your pride.
In the name
H Chorus
B
E
A
of love, What more in the name of love.
F♯
B
E
In the name of love.
What more

A
F♯
B
in the name of love.
In the name of love.
E
A
F♯
What more in the name of love.
In the name
B
E
A
of love.
What more in the name of love.
F♯
B
E
Oh, oh oh, oh, oh, oh, oh.
Oo, oo, oo, oo.
A
F♯
Repeat 3 Times and Fade
oh, oh, oh, oh, oh. Oh,
oo, oo, oo.

Pride and Joy

Written by Stevie Ray Vaughan

B 1st Verse

B7
E7
Well you've heard a - bout love giv - in' sight to the blind.

A7
My ba - by's lov - in' cause the sun to shine. She's my sweet lit - tle thing.

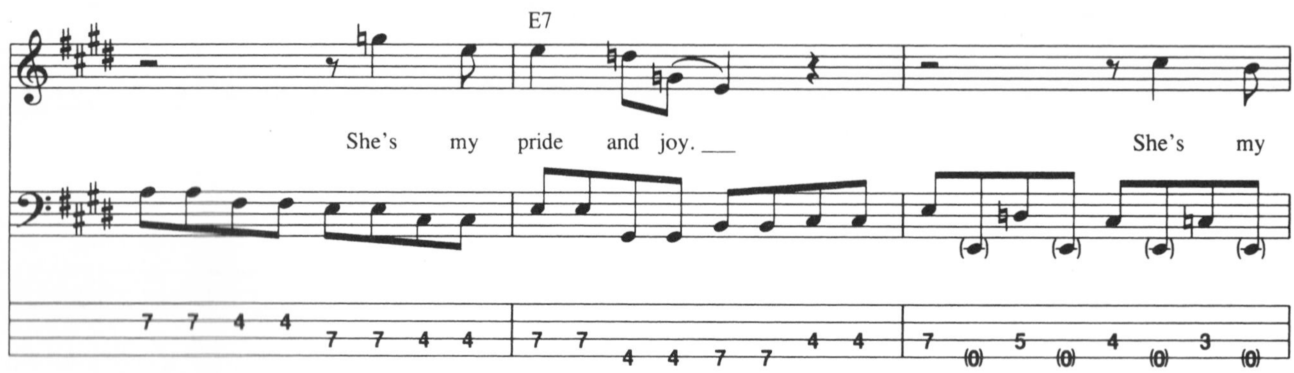
E7
She's my pride and joy. She's my

B7
A7
E7
sweet lit - tle ba - by, I'm her lit - tle lov - er boy.

C 2nd Verse
B7
E7
Yeah, I love my ba - by my heart and __ soul. ___
A7
Love like ours won't nev - er grow __ old. She's my sweet lit- tle thing. _
E7
She's my pride and joy. ___ She's my
B7
A7
E7
sweet lit - tle ba - by I'm ___ her ___ lit - tle lov - er boy. ________

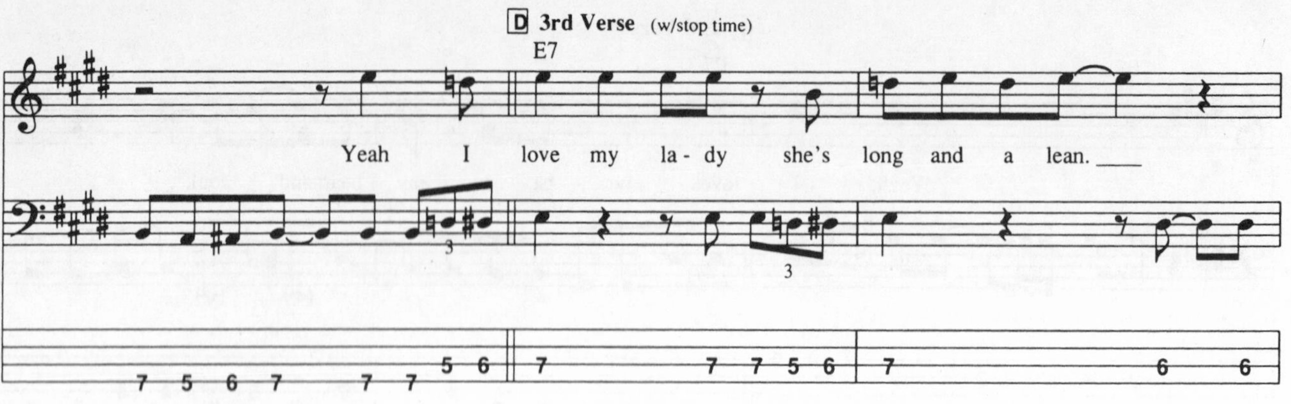
D 3rd Verse (w/stop time)
E7
Yeah I love my la - dy she's long and a lean.
7 5 6 7 7 7 5 6 7 7 7 5 6 7 6 6

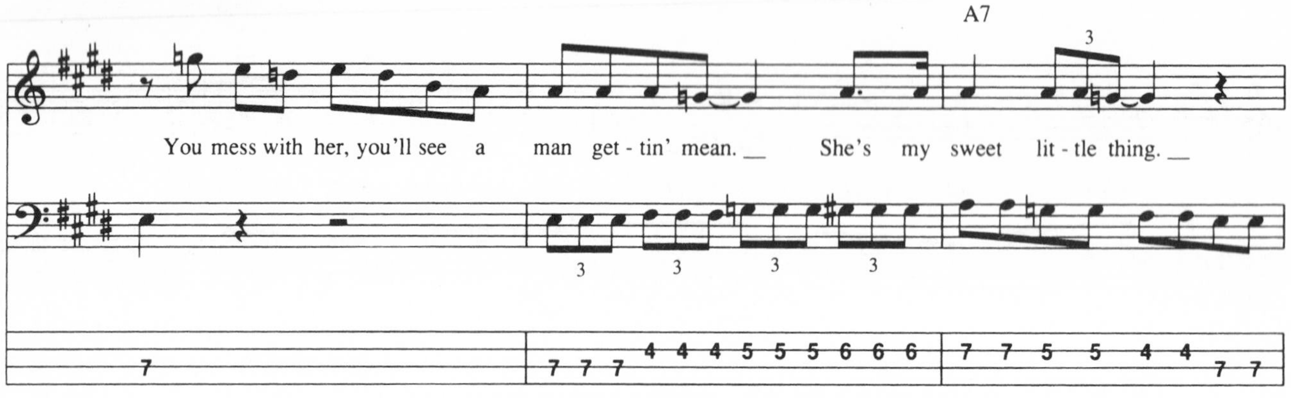
A7
You mess with her, you'll see a man get - tin' mean. She's my sweet lit - tle thing.
7 7 7 7 4 4 4 5 5 5 6 6 6 7 7 5 5 4 4 7 7

E7
She's my pride and joy. She's my
5 5 4 4 5 (0) 6 (0) 7 7 4 4 7 7 4 4 7 7 5 5 4 4 3 3

B7
A7
E7
sweet lit - tle ba - by, I'm her lit - tle lov - er boy.
7 7 6 9 7 9 6 6 5 7 (0) 4 4 5 5 6 6 7 0 4 0 7 7 4 7

E Guitar Solo
E7
B7
E7
A7
E7
B7
A7
E7
B7
E7
A7

F 4th Verse w/stops

B7
A7
E7
sweet lit - tle ba - by I'm ___ her ___ lit - tle lov - er boy. ________
G 5th Verse
B7
E7
Yeah, I love my ba - by, my heart and ___ soul. ___
A7
Love like ours won't nev - er grow ___ old. She's my sweet lit - tle thing. ___
E7
She's my pride and joy. ___ She's my

B7
A7
E7
sweet lit - tle ba - by, I'm ___ her ___ lit - tle lov - er boy. _______

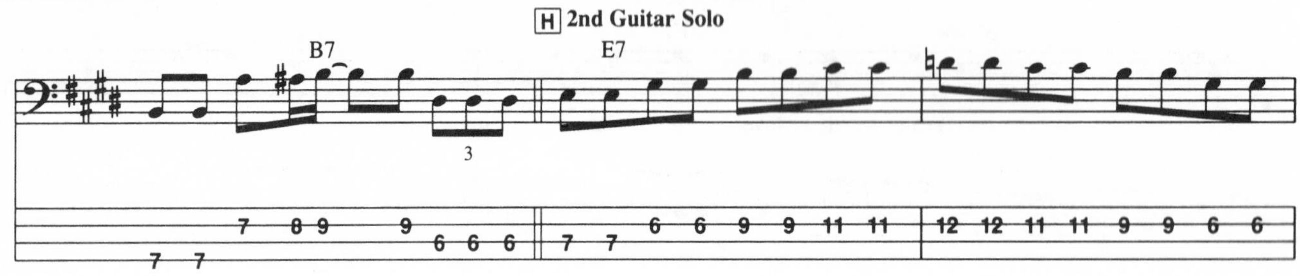
H 2nd Guitar Solo
B7
E7

A7

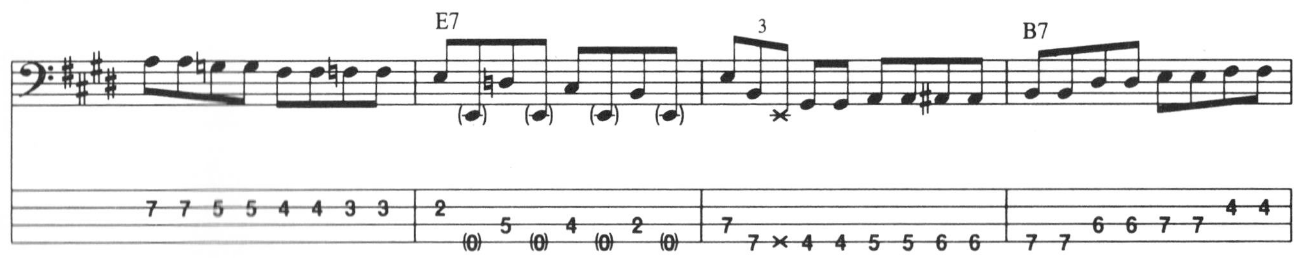
E7
B7

A7
E7
B7
E7

Pure Massacre

Words by Daniel Johns
Music by Daniel Johns and Ben Gillies

D5 F5 D5 F5 D5 C5 D5 F5 D5 F5 G5 A5
It's hap - pen - in' ev - 'ry day.
Bass Fig. 2A
(end Bass Fig. 2A)
sl.

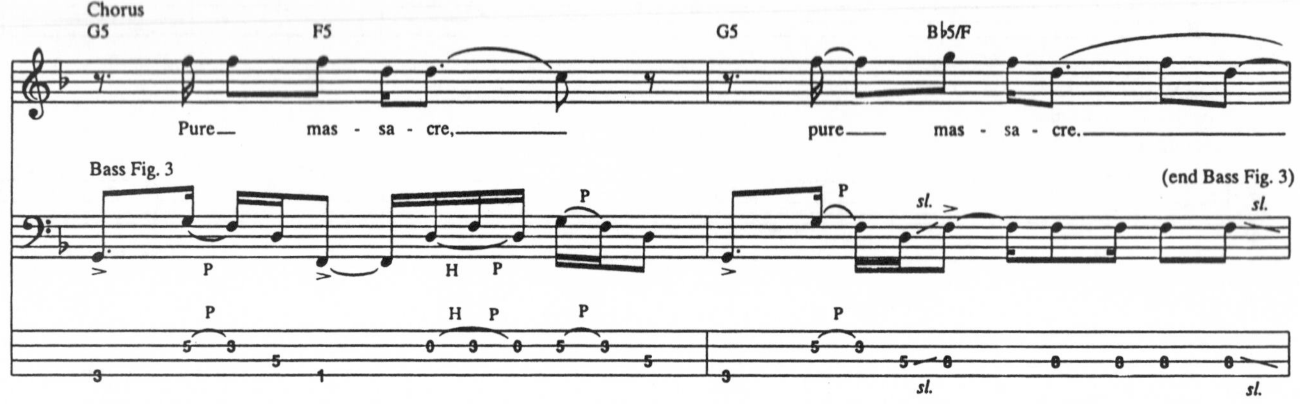
Chorus
G5 F5 G5 B♭5/F
Pure mas - sa - cre, pure mas - sa - cre.
Bass Fig. 3
(end Bass Fig. 3)
P H P sl.

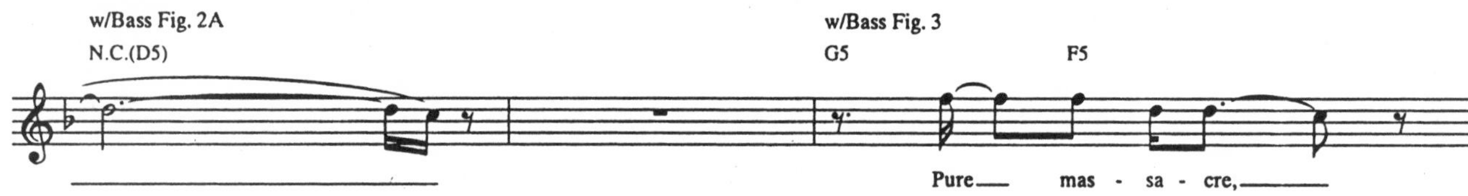
w/Bass Fig. 2A
N.C.(D5)
w/Bass Fig. 3
G5 F5
Pure mas - sa - cre,

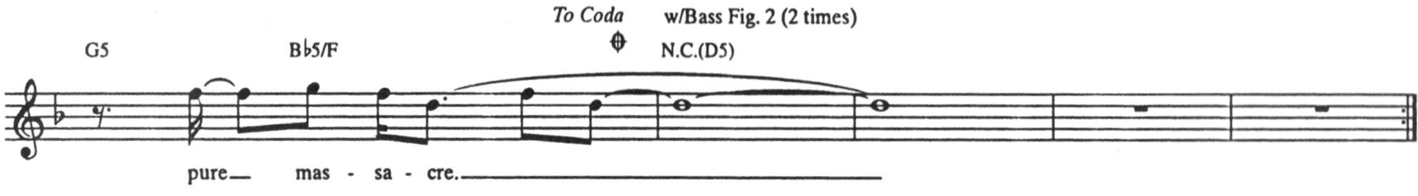
G5 B♭5/F
To Coda
w/Bass Fig. 2 (2 times)
N.C.(D5)
pure mas - sa - cre.

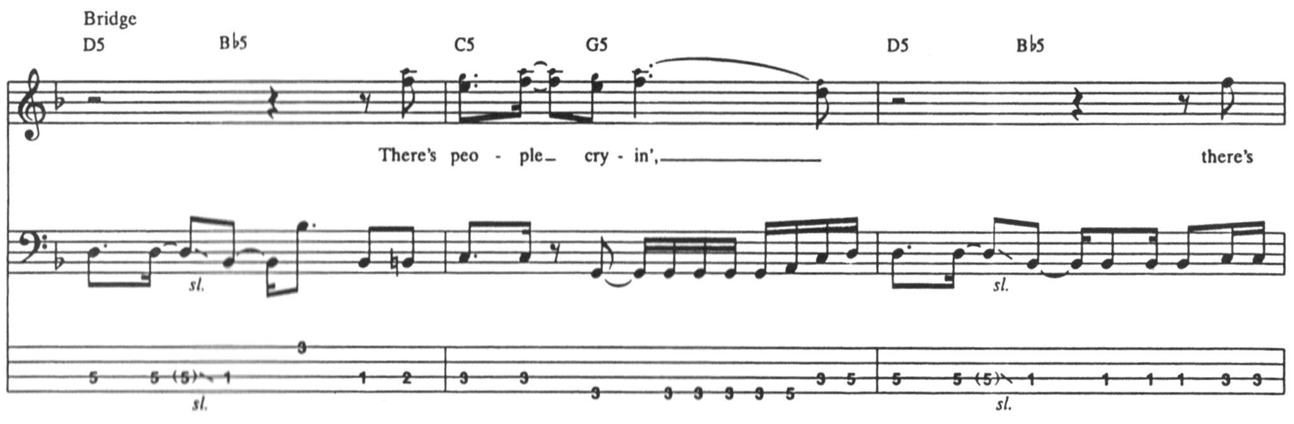
Bridge
D5 B♭5 C5 G5 D5 B♭5
There's peo - ple cry - in', there's
sl.

C5
G5
D5
B♭5
peo - ple dy - in'.
(Dy - in'.
But
But
sl.
some - one's tak - en
some - one's tak - en
it all.
it all.)
w/Bass Fig. 2 (4 times)
D5 F5 D5 F5 D5 C5 D5 F5 D5 F5 G5 A5 D5 F5 D5 F5 D5 C5
D5 F5 D5 F5 G5 A5 D5 F5 D5 F5 D5 C5 D5 F5 D5 F5 G5 A5
Yeah.
w/Bass Fig. 2 (2 times)
D.S. al Coda
N.C.(D5)

Additional Lyrics

3.4. Machine guns pumpin', hearts thumpin',
Death is all around there.
People cryin' for freedom,
No one hears a sound. *(To Chorus)*

Purple Haze

Words and Music by Jimi Hendrix

N.C.(E5)
Verse
E7#9
S'cuse me while I kiss the sky.
2. Pur-ple haze

G
A
E7#9
G
A
all a - round.
Don't know if I'm com - in' up or down.

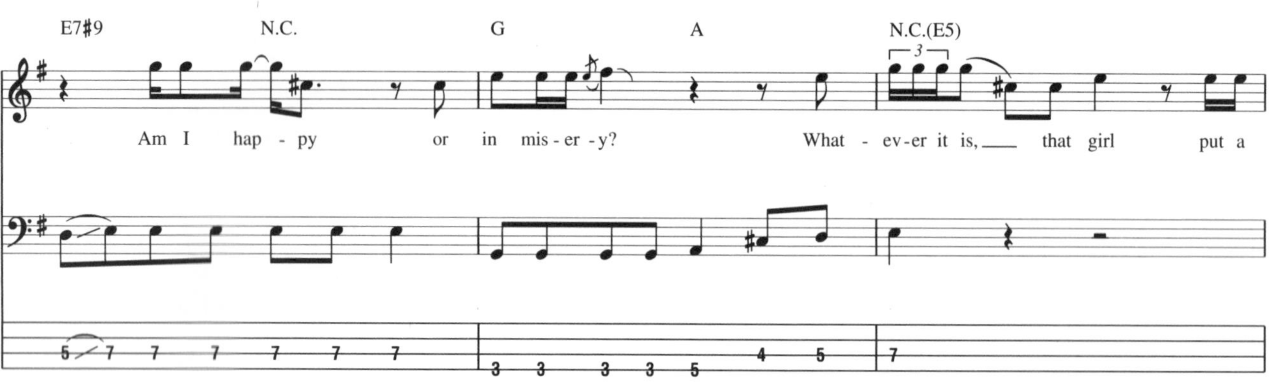
E7#9
N.C.
G
A
N.C.(E5)
Am I hap - py or in mis - er - y?
What - ev - er it is, that girl put a

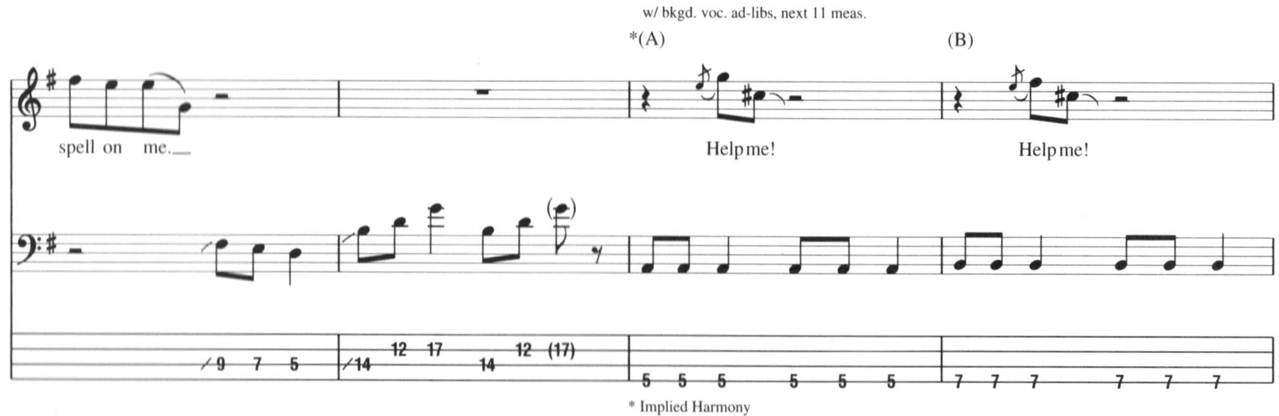
w/ bkgd. voc. ad-libs, next 11 meas.
*(A)
(B)
spell on me.
Help me!
Help me!
* Implied Harmony

Guitar Solo
w/ voc. ad-lib., next 8 meas.
(D)
N.C.(E7#9)
(D5)
(E7#9)
Oh, no, no!
(F#5)
(D5)
(E7#9)
(F#5)
(D5)
(E7#9)
Interlude
(F#5)
(D5)
N.C.(E5)
Ooh!
Ah!
Ooh!
sim.
Ah!
Ooh!
Ah!
Ooh!
* tongue click

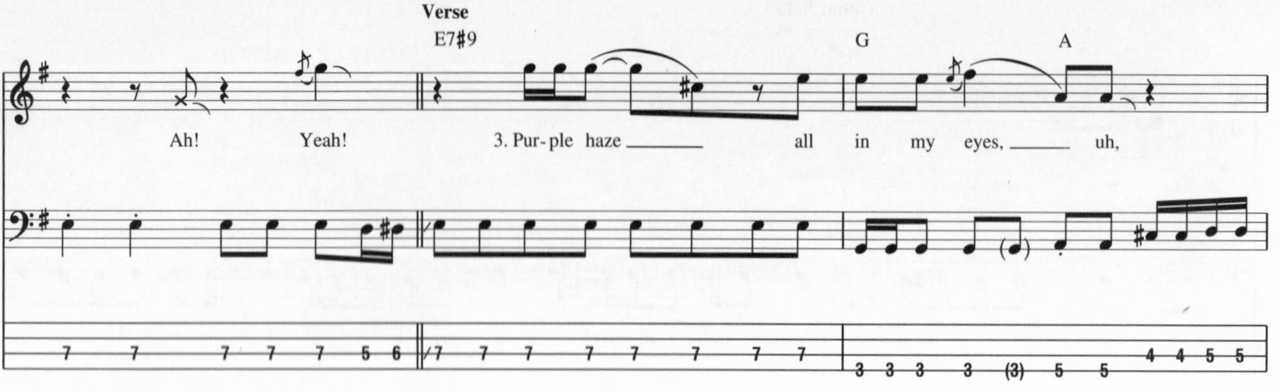
Verse
E7#9
G
A
Ah! Yeah! 3. Pur-ple haze all in my eyes, uh,
7 7 7 7 7 5 6
7 7 7 7 7 7 7 7
3 3 3 3 (3) 5 5 4 4 5 5

E7#9
G
A
E7#9
don't know if it's day or night. You got me blow-ing,
7 7 7 7 7 7 7
3 3 3 3 5 5 4 5
7 7 7 (7) 7 7 7 7 7

G
A
N.C.(E5)
blow-ing my mind. Is it to-mor-row or just the end of time?
3 3 3 3 5 4 5
7
9 7 5

Outro
Bsus4
D5/E
D
D#
Ooh. Help me. Ahh, yeah.
14 12 17 14 12 17
5 5 5 5 5 7
7 7 7 7 7 7
5 (5) 7 5 5 5 6

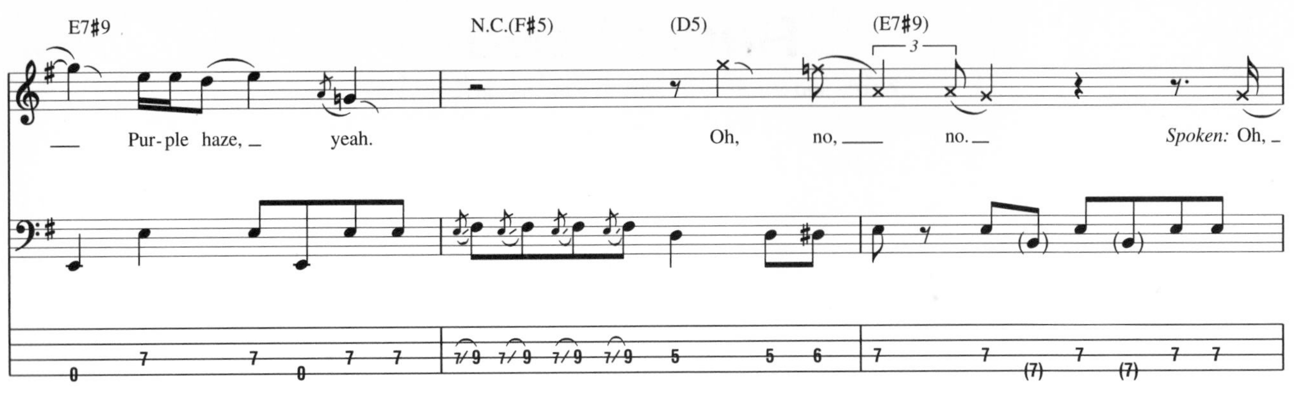

E7#9
N.C.(F#5)
(D5)
(E7#9)
Purple haze, yeah.
Oh, no, no.
Spoken: Oh,

(F#)
(D5)
(E7#9)
(F#5)
(D5)
help me. Tell me baby, tell me! I can't go on like this.
(Purple haze.)

(E7#9)
(F#5)
(D5)
(E7#9)
(F#5)
(D5)
You're makin' me blow my mind. Mama. No, no. No. No,
(Purple haze.)
(Purple haze.)

Begin Fade
Fade Out
(E7#9)
(F#5)
(D5)
(E7#9)
(F#5)
(D5)
it's painful baby...
(Purple haze.)
Purple haze.

Radar Love

Words and Music by George Kooymans and Barry Hay

- by call - in', says, "I need you here."
road has got me hyp - no - tized,
And it's a
and I'm
half past four and I'm shift - in' gear.
spin-nin' in - to a new sun - rise.
Pre-Chorus
E5
B5
F#5
Voc. Fig. 1
1. When she is lone - ly and the long - ing gets too much,
2. When I get lone - ly and I'm for sure I've had e - nough,
(Oo,
she sends a ca -
she sends a com -
oo.
Bass Fig. 2
B5
A5/B
B5/C#
C#5
B5/C#
- ble com - ing in from a - bove.
fort com - ing in from a - bove.
Don't need a phone at all.
We don't need no let - ter at all.
Ah.)
Chorus
D
A5
E5
F#5
End Voc. Fig. 1
1. We've got a thing, and that's a - called ra - dar love.
2. We've got a thing, that's called ra - dar love.
End Bass Fig. 2
Bass Fig. 3

D
A5
E5
1.
N.C.
We've got a wave in the air.
We've got a light in the sky.
Ra - dar
End Bass Fig. 3
Bass Fig. 3A
End Bass Fig. 3A
Interlude
Bass: w/ Bass Fig. 1
(F#m7)
Bass: w/ Bass Fig. 1A (3 times)
love.
2. The
2.
Interlude
N.C.
Play 8 times
F#m7
Ra - dar
love.
(Sing 1st time only)
Play 24 times
C#5
Breakdown
N.C.
(drums)
Play 4 times

E5

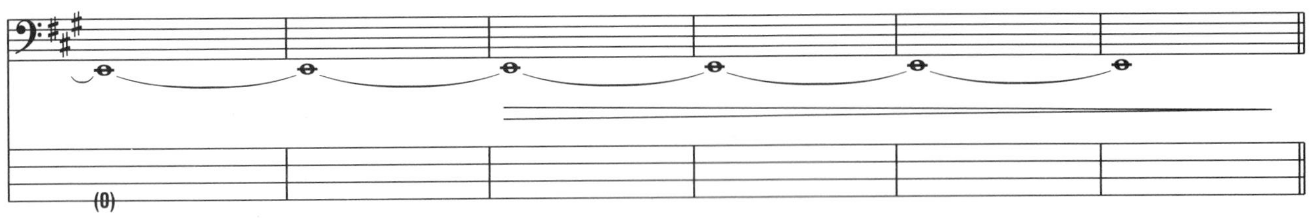

Interlude

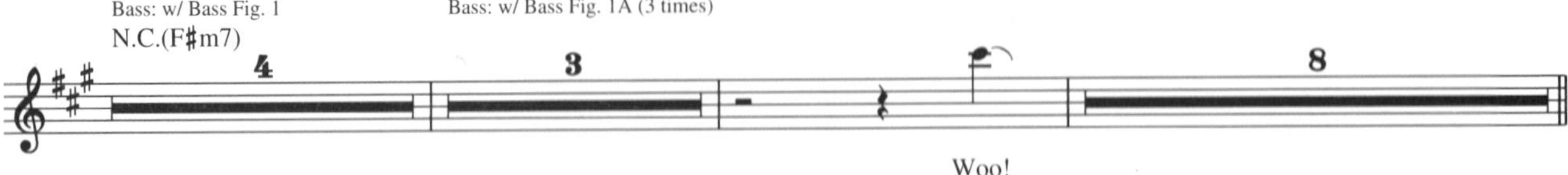
Bass: w/ Bass Fig. 1
Bass: w/ Bass Fig. 1A (3 times)
N.C.(F#m7)
Woo!

Verse

Bass: w/ Bass Fig. 1A (8 times)
N.C. (F#m7)
3. No more speed, I'm al - most there. Got - ta keep cool now,

got - ta take care. Last car to pass, here I go!

And the line of cars drove down real slow, whoa.

And the ra - di - o played that for - got - ten song.

Bren - da Lee, it's com - in' on strong. And the news man sang his

same song. Oh, one more ra - dar lov - er gone.

Pre-Chorus

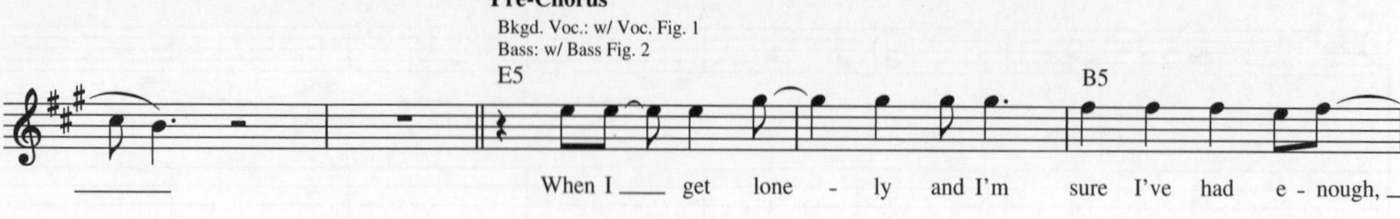

Chorus

Interlude

Outro

Riding With the King

Words and Music by John Hiatt

5-string bass:
(low to high) B–E–A–D–G

Intro
Moderate Blues ♩ = 102
A7
(guitar)
3
Bass
B7
mf

Verse
B7
1. I dreamed I had a good job and I

* Eric Clapton-full size notes, B.B. King-cue size notes.

E7
got well - paid. _ I blew it all at the pen-ny ar - cade.

B7
Our hard earned dol-lars on a cup-id doll. _ No pret-ty chick is gon-na

* Cue notes are female harmony (next 2 meas.)
Eric Clapton upstem notes.
B.B. King downstem notes.

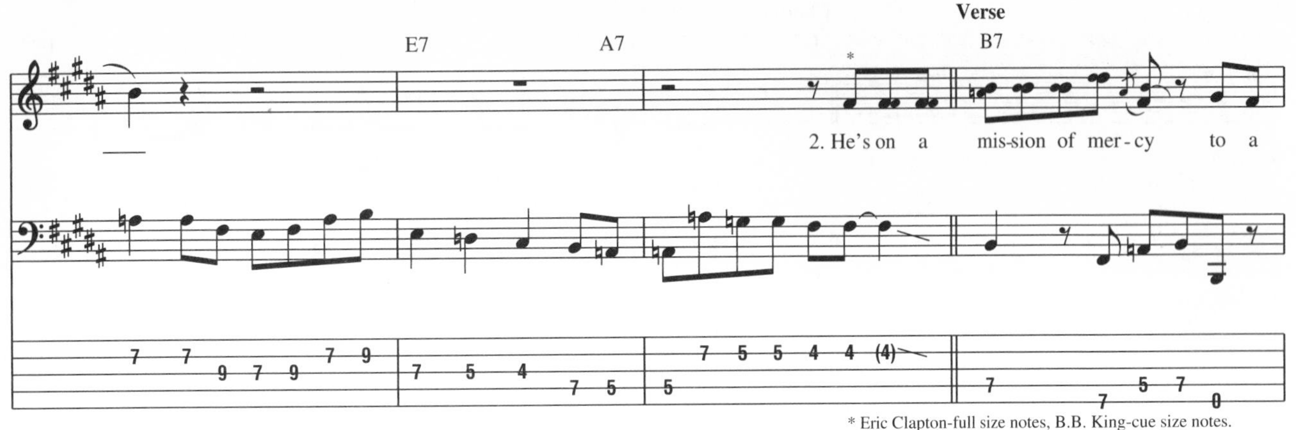
Verse
E7
A7
B7
2. He's on a mis-sion of mer-cy to a

* Eric Clapton-full size notes, B.B. King-cue size notes.

E7

new fron - tier. He's gon-na check us all out, out of here.

B7

Up to that man-sion on {the hill, / on the hill,} where you can get your pre -

E7 B7

scrip - tion filled

B.B. King, Spoken: Any kind of pill, folks, ha, ha, ha, ha.

Chorus
G7
F♯7 F7 E7
Get on a T. W. A. to the Prom-ised Land.
(Ev - 'ry - bod -
G7
Ev - 'ry - bod - y, clap your hands.
- y. Clap your hands.)
And don't you girls love the
A7
way that it seems.
Don't you know we're rid - in' with The
(Rid - in' with The
* Cue notes are female harmony (next 2 meas.)
Eric Clapton - upstem notes
B.B. King - downstem notes
B7
E7
A7
King? We're rid-in' with The King.
King?
Spoken: Yeah, you're ridin' with The King.
Don't you know we're rid - in' with The
You're rid - in' with The
* as before.

B7
E7
A7
King? ___
King.) ___

Bridge

D7
B7
A tux - e - do and a shin - y Three - thir - ty - five. ___
B.B. King, Spoken: That's me.
* Female harmony cues (till end).

D7
You can see it in his face, the blues is his life. ___
Ha, ha, ha.

B7
G7
To-night, ev - 'ry-bod-y's get-tin' their an-gel wings._

Recitation
A7
B7
And don't you know we're rid - in' with The King?
B.B. King, Spoken: I
stepped out of Mississippi when I was ten years old, with a suit cut sharp as a razor, and a heart made of gold. I had a guitar
B7
Outro-Guitar Solos
E
A7
B7
Well, don't you know we're rid - in' with The King?
hang-in' just about waist high, and I'm gonna play this thing until the day I die.
Ha, ha, ha, ha.
E7
A7
B7
Don't you know you're rid - in' with The King?
(Don't you know you're rid - in' with The King?
B.B. King, Spoken: You're ridin' with me daddy.

E7
A7
Don't __ you know you're rid - in' with The
Don't you know you're rid - in' with The
You're in good hands, you're ridin' with me.
B7
E7
A7
King? ________
King? ________
You're rid-in', you're rid - in' with The
You're rid - in' with The
Yes, yes, you're ridin' with The King.
I wanted to say B.B. King, but you know who King is.
B7
E7
King. ________
King. ________
You're
You're
Yes, you're ridin' with The King.
Yes, you are, you're ridin' with The King.
A7
B7
rid - in', you're rid - in' with The King. ________
rid - in', you're rid - in' with The King.
Rid - in' with The
You're ridin' with The King.
I'm a good chauffer too.

E7
A7
B7
King.
Rid - in' with The
King.
Don't you know you're rid - in' with The
King?
All of you girls, come on, you're ridin' with me.
That's alright Eric, you can ride with me
Begin fade
E7
A7
Rid - in' with The
King.
Rid - in' with The
You're rid - in', you're rid - in', you're rid - in' with The
too if you feel like it.
Yes, you're ridin' with The King.
B7
E7
King.
King.
Rid - in' with the
King.
You're ridin' with The King.
I'm a good chauffer.
A7
B7
Fade out
Don't you know you're rid - in' with The
King?
Rid - in' with The King.)

Rock and Roll All Nite

Words and Music by Paul Stanley and Gene Simmons

Tune Down 1/2 Step:
① = G♭ ③ = A♭
② = D♭ ④ = E♭

Bass: w/ Fill 1, 2nd time
E
D
E
The par-ty's just be - gun; we'll let you in. You drive us wild; we'll drive you cra -
Ba - by, ba - by, that's quite a lot. And you drive us wild; we'll drive you cra -
0 3 0 2 0 0 7
0 5 0 4 2 4 5
5 4 2 0 0 7
7 5 5 4 4 2

Pre- Chorus
Dsus4
D Dsus4 D F
G
- zy.
- zy.
You keep on shout - in' you keep on shout - in'.
0 0 1
1 1 1 1 1 1 1 3
3 3 3 3 3 3 3 3

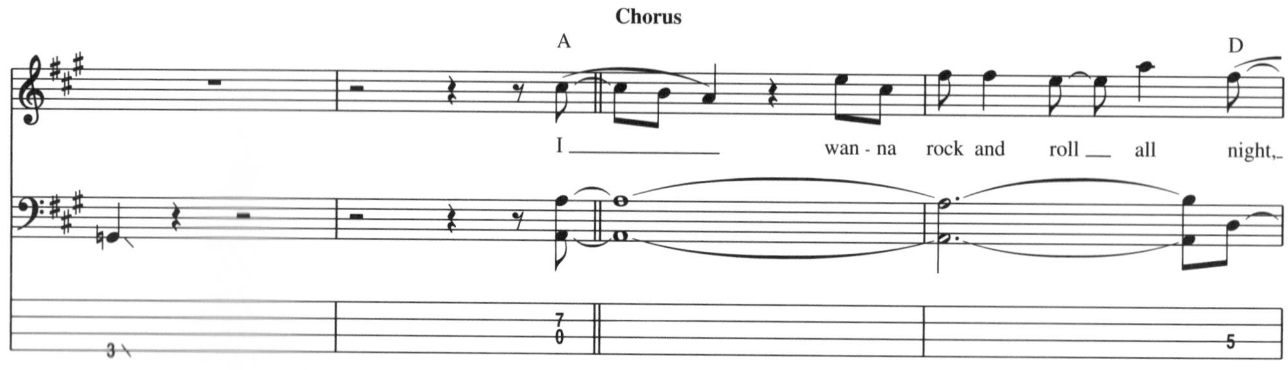
Chorus
A
D
I wan - na rock and roll all night,
3
7
0
5

Fill 1
Bass
(7) 0 5 0 4 2
1 1 1 1 1 1 1 3

E
A
D
and par - ty ev - er - y day.
I wan - na rock and roll all night
(5) 0 4 0 2 0 0 7
0 5 0 4 2
7
0
5

E
A
and par - ty ev - er - y day.
I wan - na rock and roll all night
(5) 0 4 0 2 0 0 7
0 5 0 4 2
7
0

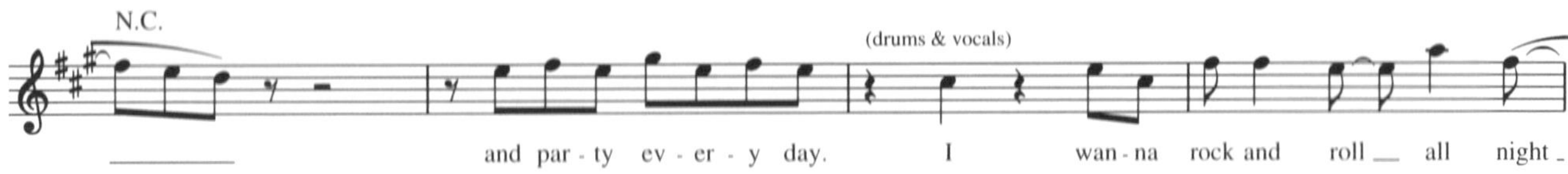
N.C.
(drums & vocals)
and par - ty ev - er - y day.
I wan - na rock and roll all night

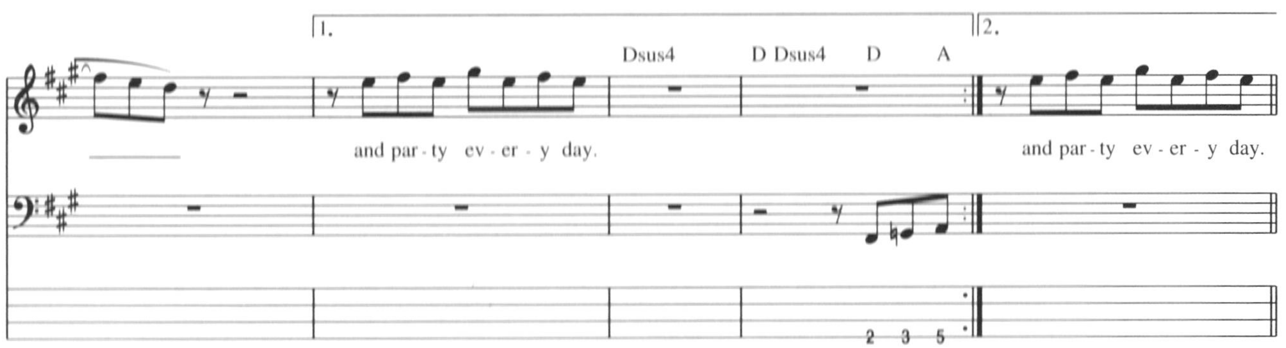
1.
2.
Dsus4
D Dsus4
D
A
and par - ty ev - er - y day.
and par - ty ev - er - y day.
2 3 5

Play 5 Times and Fade
A
D
E
I wan - na rock and roll all night
and par - ty ev - er - y day.
7
0
5
0 4 0 2 0 0 7
0 5 0 4 2 2 0

Rock and Roll Hoochie Koo

Words and Music by Rick Derringer

A5
C5
D5
C5
N.C.
group called the Jok-ers, they were lay-in' it down. To
A5
C5
D5
C5
N.C.
know I'm nev-er gon-na lose that funk-y sound.
Chorus
F5
G5
A5
Voc. Fig. 1
N.C.
Rock and roll hooch - ie koo.
(Rock and roll hooch - ie koo.
F5
F6
F5
C5
G5
End Voc. Fig. 1
A5
N.C.
Lord - y ma - ma light my fuse.
Light my fuse.

F5 G5 A5 N.C. F5 F6 C5 G5
Rock and roll hooch-ie koo.
Drop on out an' spread the news.
Rock and roll hooch-ie koo.)
A5 N.C.
2. Mos-
1/4
Verse
A C5 D5 C5 N.C.
qui-toes start-ed buz-zin' 'bout this time of year. I'm
3. Hope you all know what I'm talk-in' a-bout. The way you
simile on repeat
A5 C5 D5 C5 N.C.
go-in' 'round back, said she'd meet me there. We were
wig-gle that thing real-ly knocks me out. Get-tin'

A5
C5
D5
C5
N.C.
rol-lin' in the grass, it was be-hind the barn.
high all the time, hope you all are too.
Well, my
Come
A5
C5
D5
C5
N.C.
ears start-ed ring - in' like a fire a - larm.
on a lit - tle clos-er, I'm gon-na do it to you.
Chorus
F5
G5
Bkgd. Voc.: w/ Voc. Fig. 1
A5
N.C.
F5
C5
G5
Rock and roll hooch-ie koo.
Lord - y, ma - ma light my fuse.
A5
N.C.
F5
G5
Bkgd. Voc.: w/ Voc. Fig. 1
A5
N.C.
Rock and roll hooch-ie koo.

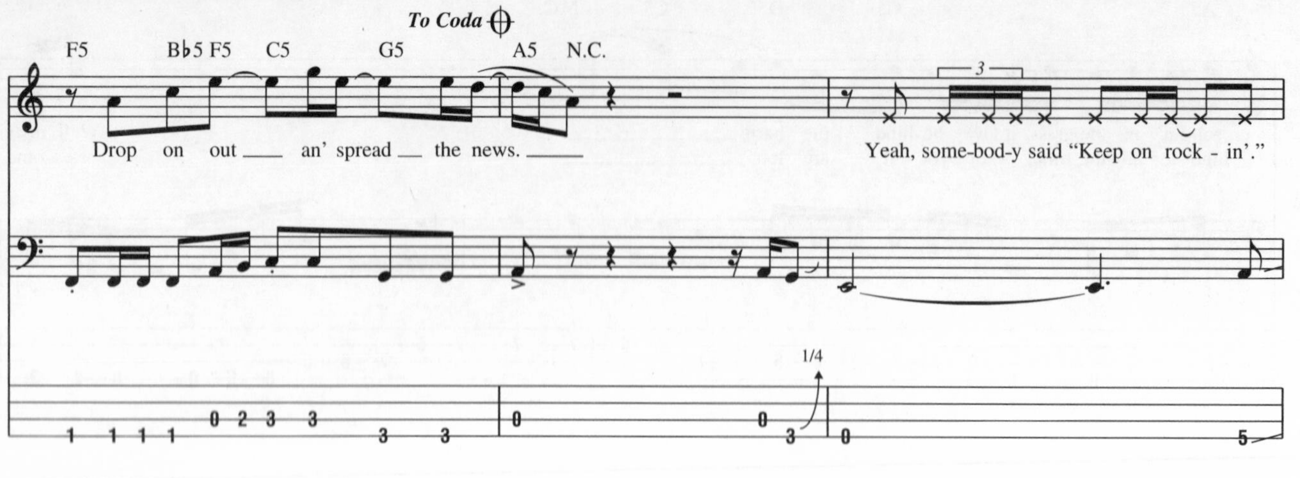

To Coda
F5
B♭5 F5
C5
G5
A5
N.C.
Drop on out an' spread the news.
Yeah, some-bod-y said "Keep on rock - in'."
1/4

Guitar Solo

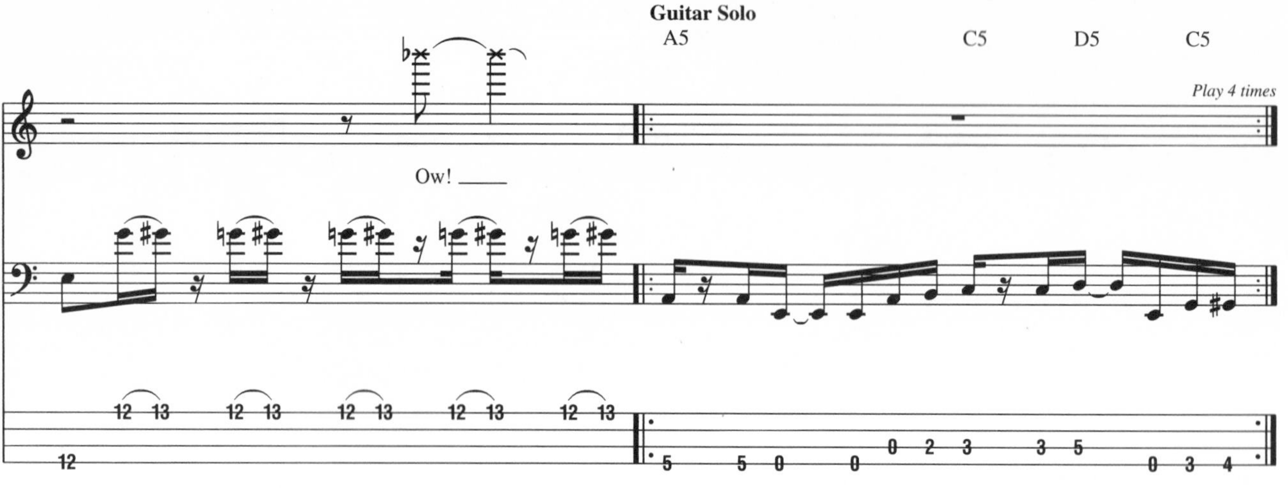

A5
C5
D5
C5
Play 4 times
Ow!

A5
C5
D5
C5
A5
C5
D5
C5

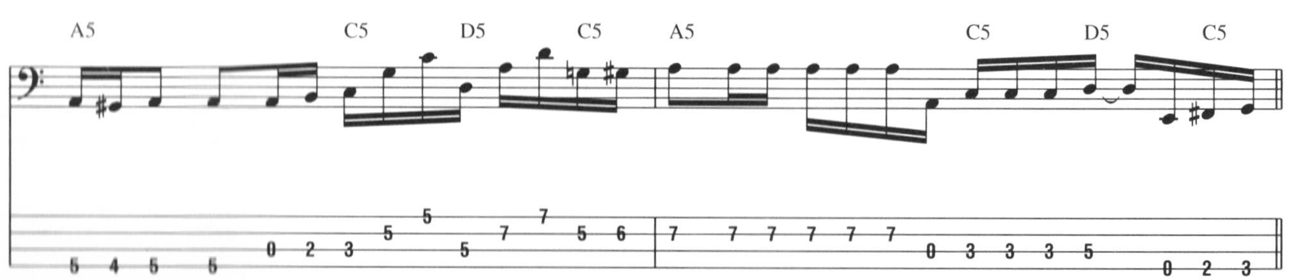

A5
C5
D5
C5
A5
C5
D5
C5

4th time, D.S. al Coda

Play 4 times
Play 4 times
A5
C
D
A5
C
D

Coda
Outro-Chorus
Bkgd. Voc.: w/ Voc. Fig. 1 (6 times)
A5 N.C.
F
G
A5
Woo! Rock and roll hooch-ie koo.

F5
C5
G5
A5
Lord - y ma - ma, light my fuse.

F
G
A5
Rock and roll hooch-ie koo.

F5
C5
G5
A5
Drop on out an' spread the news.
F
G
A5
Man, I'm tired of pay - in' dues.
F5
C5
G5
A5
Done said good - bye to all my blues.
Free Time
F5
G5
rit.
A5
Lord - y, ma - ma, light my fuse.
Woo!
Ow!
rit.

Rock Me Baby

Words and Music by B.B. King and Joe Bihari

N.C.(Am)
Verse
A
E
1. Rock me ba - by,
A
N.C.(Am)
rock me all ___ night long. _
Rock me all night long. _
D
N.C.(Am)
Rock me ba - by,
rock me all ___ night long. ________
E
D
Want you to rock me
like my back ain't got no bone. _

N.C.(Am)
Verse
A
E
2. Roll me ma - ma,
A
N.C.(Am)
like a wag - on wheel.
D
N.C.(Am)
Roll me ba - by,
like a roll - in' wag - on wheel.
E
D
Rock and roll.
When ya rock me ma - ma,
no I could - n't make me feel.

N.C.(Am)
Verse
A
E
3. Rock me ba - by,
A
N.C.(Am)
rock me slow, _
rock me ma-ma, 'til I ____ can't rock no more. ____
D
N.C.(Am)
Rock me ba - by,
rock me all ____ night _ long. ____
E
D
Whoo! ____
Want you to rock me,
like my back ain't got no bone. _

Guitar Solo
N.C.(Am)
A
E
Yeah, rock me, whoo!
A
E
A
E
A
D
N.C.(Am)
E
D
N.C.(Am)
A
E

A
E
A
E
A

D
A
E

A
E
D

N.C.(Am)

Verse
A
E
A
E
A
E
4. Rock me ma-ma, rock me slow, _ rock me ba-by 'til I _______ can't

A
D
rock no more.
Rock me ba - by,
rock me all night long.

N.C.(Am)
E
Rock me all night long.
Want you to rock me ba - by,

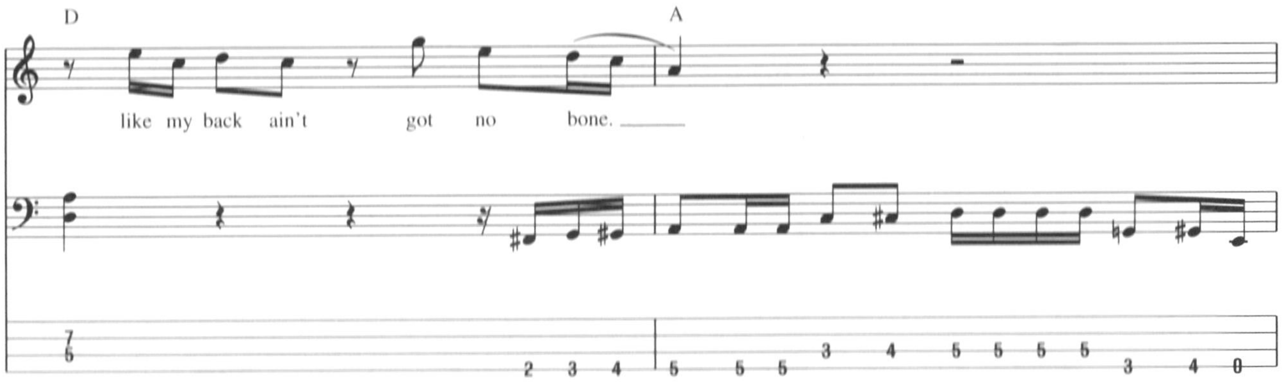
D
A
like my back ain't got no bone.

Yeah!

Rock of Ages

Words and Music by Steve Clark, Robert John Lange and Joe Elliott

A5 G5 A5 G5 E7 G5 A5 E7
What do you want? What do you want? I want rock 'n' roll Yes I do!
Long live rock 'n' roll! Let's go, let's strike a light, we're gon-na blow like dy-na-mite!
A5 G5
I don't care if it takes all night, gon-na set this town a-light! C-'mon, what do you want?

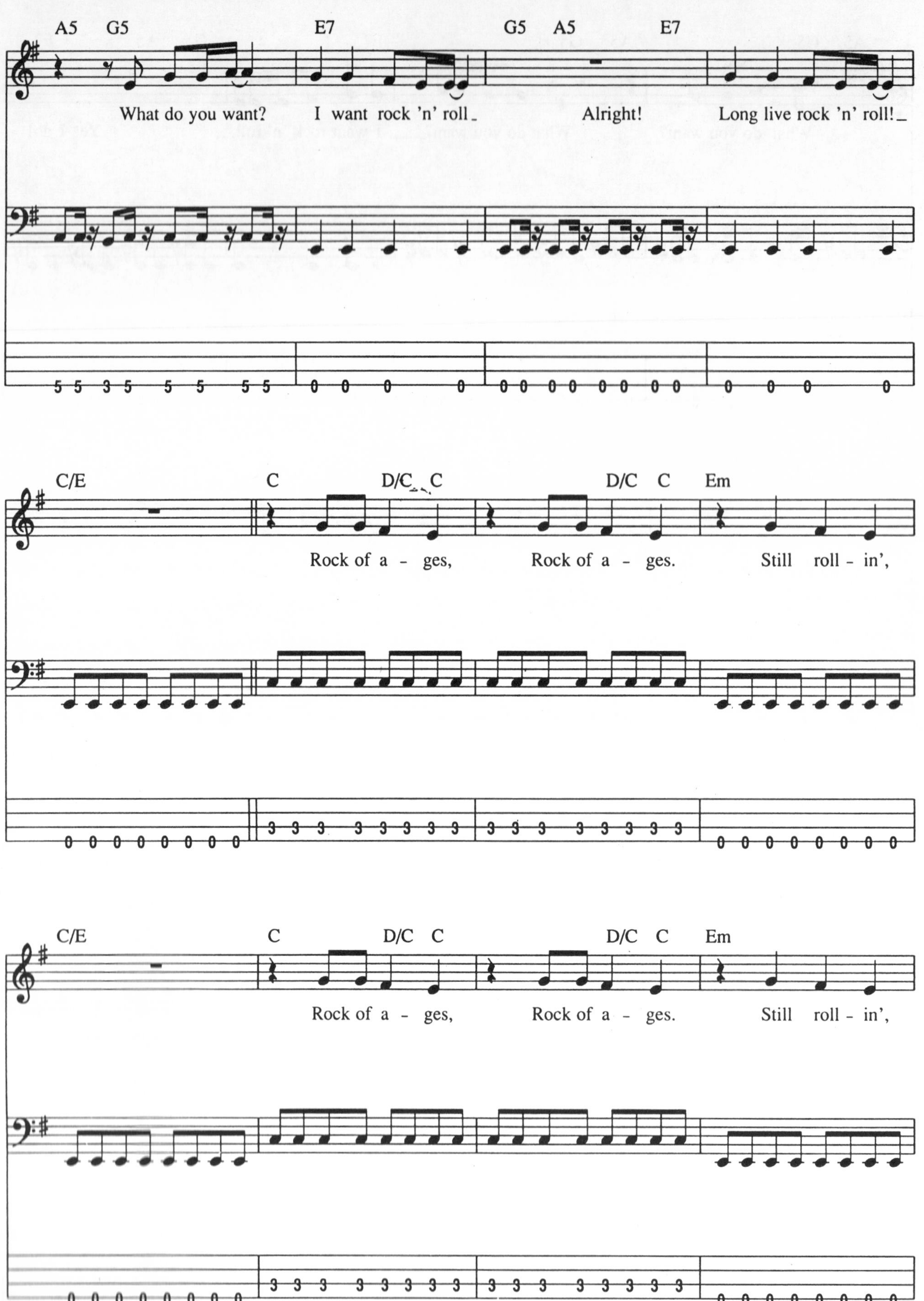
A5 G5
What do you want?
E7
I want rock 'n' roll
G5 A5
Alright!
E7
Long live rock 'n' roll!
C/E
C
D/C C
Rock of a - ges,
D/C C
Rock of a - ges.
Em
Still roll - in',
C/E
C
D/C C
Rock of a - ges,
D/C C
Rock of a - ges.
Em
Still roll - in',

A5
C
rock 'n' roll - in'. We got the pow - er! Got the glo - ry! Just say you need it,
To Coda
E
D
B
A
and if you need it say: yeah, Oh yeah!
E5
Listen to me: I'm burn - in', burn - in'. I got the fe - ver. I know for sure.

There ain't no cure, so feel it, don't fight it. go with the flow! gim-me
gim-me gim-me gim-me gim-me one more for the road!
A5 G5
What do you want?
A5 G5 A5 E7 G5 A5 E7
What do you want? I want rock 'n' roll. You betcha! Long love rock 'n' roll!

Solo Guitar
E5
E5
A5
G5
A5
G5 A5
E5
D.S. al Coda
E
D
B
A
D
E
Yeah!
Say yeah!
We're gonna burn this damn place
E
D
B
A
D
E
A
down,
down to the ground!

Roll Over Beethoven

Words and Music by Chuck Berry

Uptempo Rock (♩= 178)

*Optional bass line.

like a spin-nin' top,
She got a
F7
C
cra - zy part - ner you ought-a see 'em reel an' rock.
G7
Long as she's got a dime the mu-sic won't ev - er stop!
C
solo
T
A
B

(C7)
F7
C
G7
C
G7
C
Well, ear - ly in the morn-in' and I'm

giv - in' you my warn - in' don't you step on my new suede shoes.
3 3 3 3 3 3 3 3
3 3 0 0 1 1 2 2
F7
C
Hey, did - dle, did - dle I'm a play - in' my fid - dle I ain't got noth - in' to
3 3 3 3 3 3 3 3
3 3 3 3 3 3 3 3
G7
lose. Roll o - ver Bee - tho - ven and tell Tchai - kow - sky the news
3 3 3 3 3 3 3 3
5 5 5 5 5 5 5 5
5 5 5 5 5 5 5 5
C
Roll o - ver Bee - tho - ven
3 3 3 3 3 3 3 3
3 3 3 3 3 3 3 3

Roll o - ver Bee - tho - ven
Roll o - ver Bee - tho -
F7
- ven
C
Roll o - ver Bee - tho - ven
G7
Roll o - ver Bee - tho - ven,
And
C
tell Tchai - kow - sky the news.
T
A
B
3 3 3 3 3 3 3 3
3 3 1 1 0 0 3 3
1 1 1 1 1 1 1 1
3 3 3 3 3 3 3 3
3 3 3 3 3 3 3 3
5 5 5 5 5 5 5 5
5 5 5 5 5 5 2 4
5
3

Route 66

By Bobby Troup

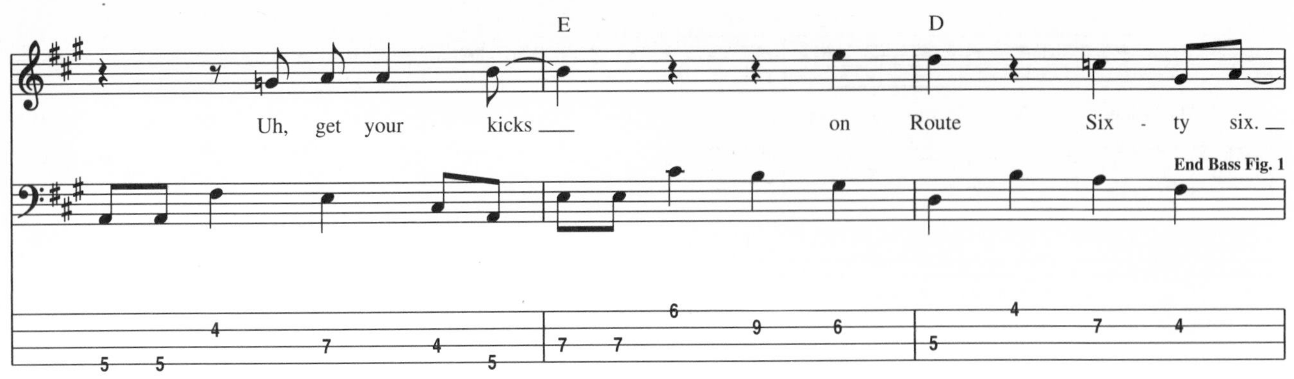
E
D
Uh, get your kicks __ on Route Six - ty six. __
End Bass Fig. 1

1.
2.
A
A
__ 2. Well, it winds __ __ Well,

Bridge
A
it goes through St. Lou - is, down to Mis - sou - ri. O - kla - ho - ma Cit - y looks oh __

D
__ so pret - ty. You'll see Am - a - ril - lo, and

A
E7
Gal - lup, New Mex - i - co. Flag - staff, Ar - i - zo - na, don't
for - get Ta - co - ma, King-man, Bar - stow, San Ber - na - di - no. 3., 4. Won't you
Verse
Bass: w/ Bass Fig. 1, simile
A
D
A
get hip to this kind - ly tip.
D
A
Yeah, go take that Cal - i - for - nia trip.
To Coda
E
D
Uh, get your kicks on Route Six - ty six.
Guitar Solo
A
A
Bass
D
A

D.S. al Coda
E
D
A
Well,

Coda
A
E
Well, get your kicks on

D
A
E
Route Six - ty six.
Well, get your kicks on

D
A
Route Six - ty six.

Roxanne

Written and Composed by Sting

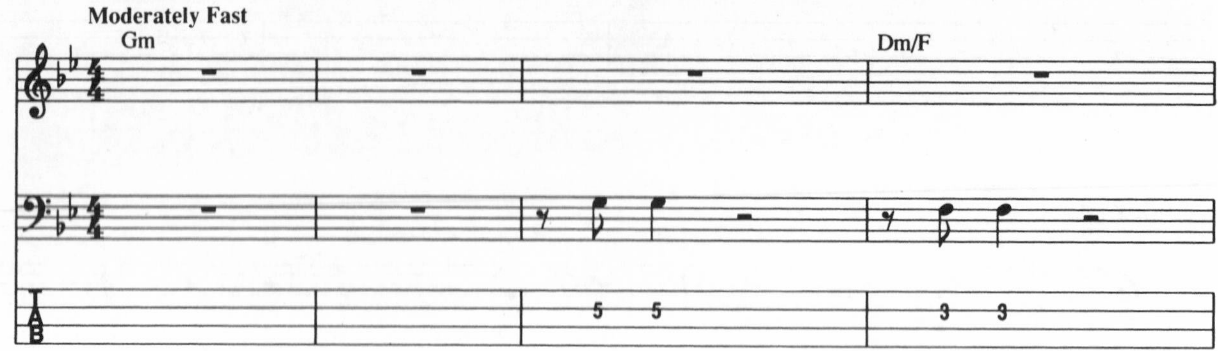

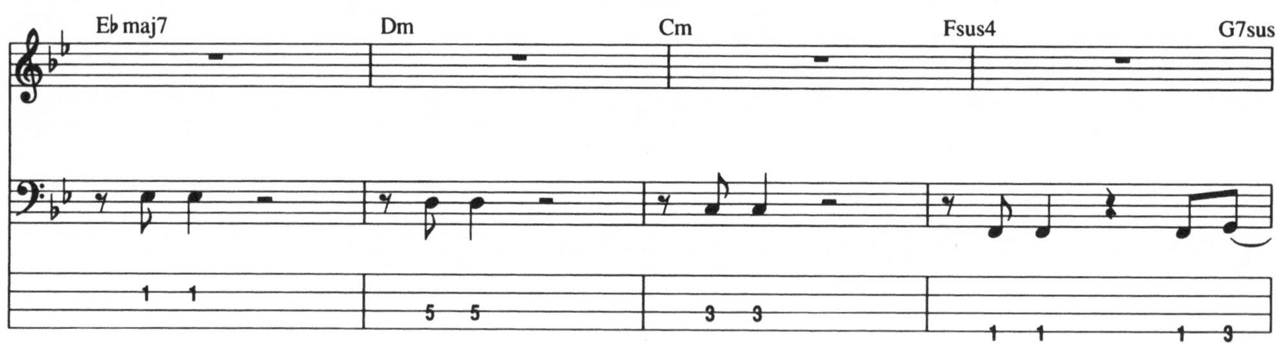

E♭maj7
Dm
Cm
Fsus4
G7sus4
— put on the red light. —
Those days are o - ver.
You don't have to
would-n't talk down to ya. —
I have to
tell you just how I feel.
I — won't
sell your bod-y to the night. —
Gm
Dm/F
Rox - anne, —
you don't have to
share you with an - oth-er boy. —
I know my mind is made up
so
wear that dress — to - night,
walk the streets for mon-ey.
You don't care
put a - way your make - up. —
Told you once, I won't tell you a - gain. It's a crime
— if it's wrong or if it's right.
— the way...
Rox - anne, —
you don't have to

Gsus4
Cm
Fsus4
G7sus4
put on your red light. Rox - anne, you don't have to
To Coda
Cm Bb
Eb F
put on the red light. Rox-anne. Rox-anne..
Bkgd. (Put on your red light.)
2nd time
F Gm
Cm Bb
Rox-anne. Rox-anne.
(Put on the red light.) (Put on the red light.)
Eb F
G7sus
Rox-anne. Oh.
(Put on the red light.) (Put on your red light.)

D.S. al Coda
Gm
Gm/F
Gm
Gm/F
(3)
1 3
3 1
1 3
3 1

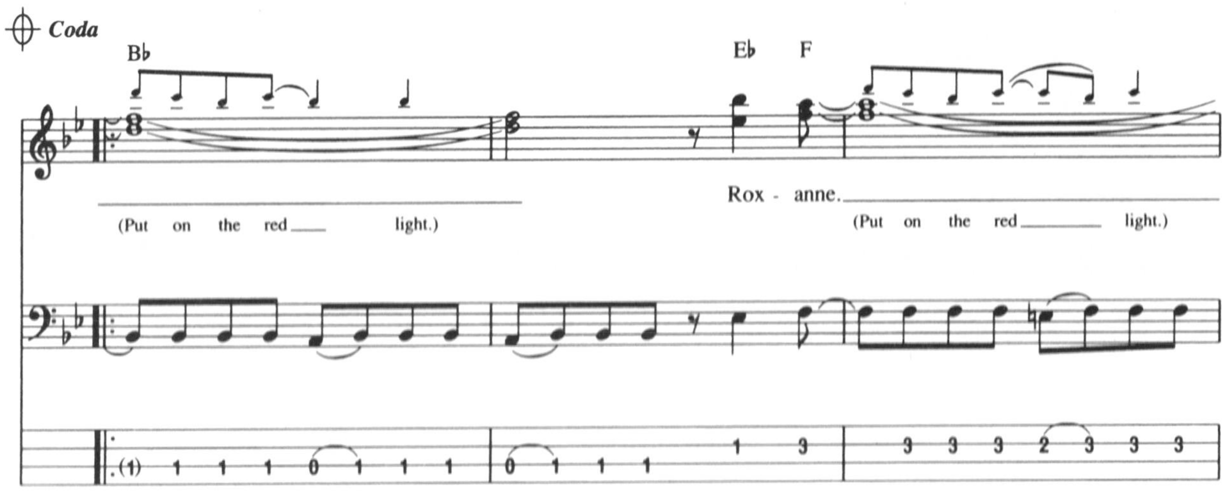
Coda
B♭
E♭
F
Rox - anne.
(Put on the red light.)
(Put on the red light.)
(1) 1 1 1 0 1 1 1
0 1 1 1 1 3
3 3 3 2 3 3 3

Repeat and Fade
F
Gm
Cm
B♭
Rox - anne.
(Put on the red light.)
Rox - anne.
2 3 3 3 1 3
3 3 3 2 3 3 3
2 3 3 3 3 1

Scar Tissue

Words and Music by Anthony Kiedis, Flea, John Frusciante and Chad Smith

Dm C F C5
young Ken-tuck - y girl in a push up bra. Fall- in' all o - ver my - self to lick
Chorus
Bass: w/ Bass Fig. 2, 2 times
D5 C5 F C Dm C
your heart and taste _ your health 'cause with the birds I'll share this lone - ly ___ view, ___
(Share _ this lone - ly…
F C Dm C
with the birds I'll share this lone - ly ___ view, ___
Share ___ this lone - ly…
Interlude
F Csus4 C Dm Dm
with the birds I'll share this lone - ly view. ___
Share ___ this lone - ly…)
Bass
Bass Fill 1
End Bass Fill 1
8va
C
loco
Dm Em
let ring
Verse
Bass: w/ Bass Fig. 1, 1 1/2 times
F C Dm C
3. Blood loss in a bath - room stall, south - ern girl with a scar - let drawl.
Bass: w/ Bass Fill 2
Chorus
Bass: w/ Bass Fig. 2, 2 times
F C5 D5 F C
Wave good-bye ___ to ma and pa 'cause _ with the birds I'll share, _ with the birds I'll share this lone -
(Share _ this lone -
Bass Fill 2

Dm
C
F
C
Dm
C
- ly ___ view, ___
- ly…
with the birds I'll share this lone - ly ___ view. ___
Share ___ this lone - ly…)
Verse
F
C
Dm
C
4. Soft spo-ken with a bro - ken jaw, step out - side, but not to brawl. _
Bass
F
C5
D5
Au-tumn's sweet, we ___ call it fall, I'll make it to the moon if I have to crawl. _
Chorus
Bass: w/ Bass Fig. 2, 2 times
F
C
Dm
C
F
C
With the birds I'll share this lone - ly ___ view, ___ with the birds I'll share this lone -
(I will share ___ this lone - ly… I will share ___ this lone -
Dm
C
Bass: w/ Bass Fill 1
F
Csus4
C
Dm
- ly ___ view, ___ with the birds I'll share this lone - ly view. ___
- ly… I will share ___ this lone - ly…)
Guitar Solo
D5
C5
8va
Bass
loco

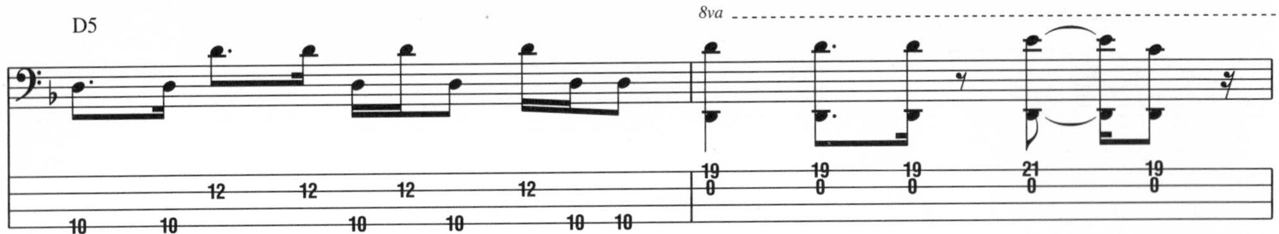
D5
8va

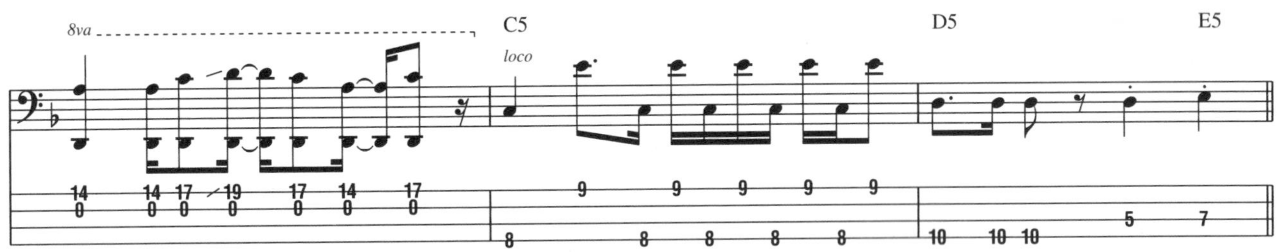
8va
C5
loco
D5
E5

Verse
Bass: w/ Bass Fig. 1, 1 1/2 times
F
C
Dm
C5
5. Scar tis - sue that I wish you saw,
sar - cas - tic mis - ter know it all.

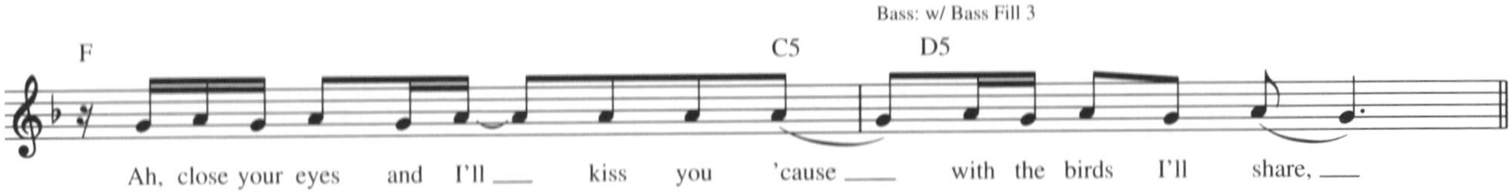
Bass: w/ Bass Fill 3
F
C5
D5
Ah, close your eyes and I'll kiss you 'cause with the birds I'll share,

Chorus
Bass: w/ Bass Fig. 2, 2 times
F
C
Dm
C
F
C
with the birds I'll share this lone - ly view,
(I will share this lone - ly...
with the birds I'll share this lone -
I will share this lone -

Bass: w/ Bass Fill 1
Dm
C
F
Csus4
C
Dm
- ly view,
- ly...
with the birds I'll share this lone - ly view.
I will share this lone - ly...)

Bass Fill 3

Outro-Guitar Solo

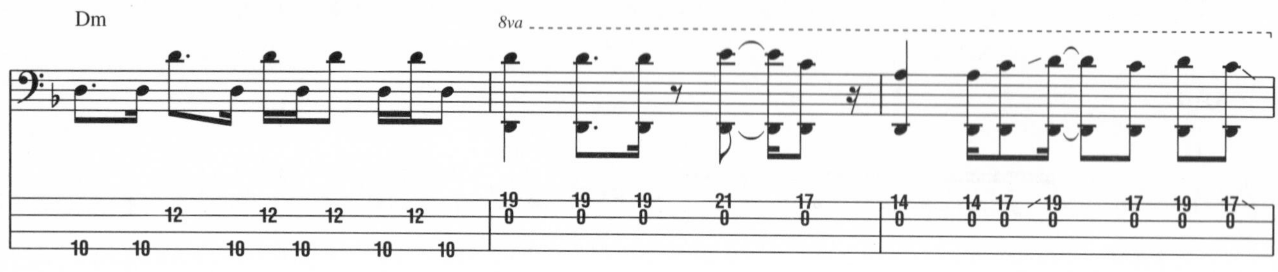

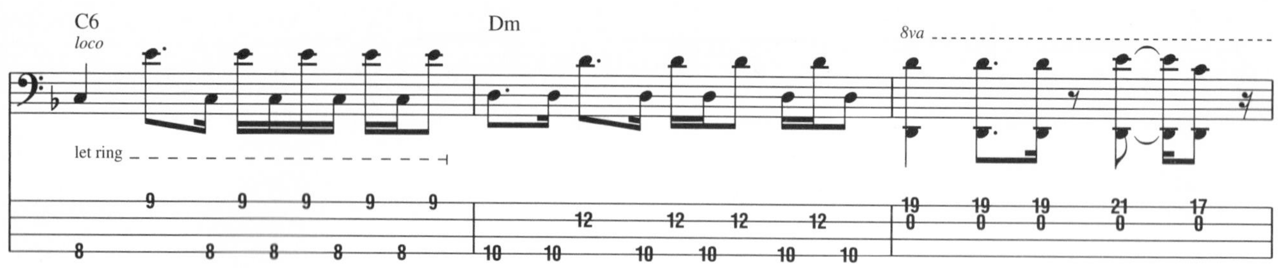

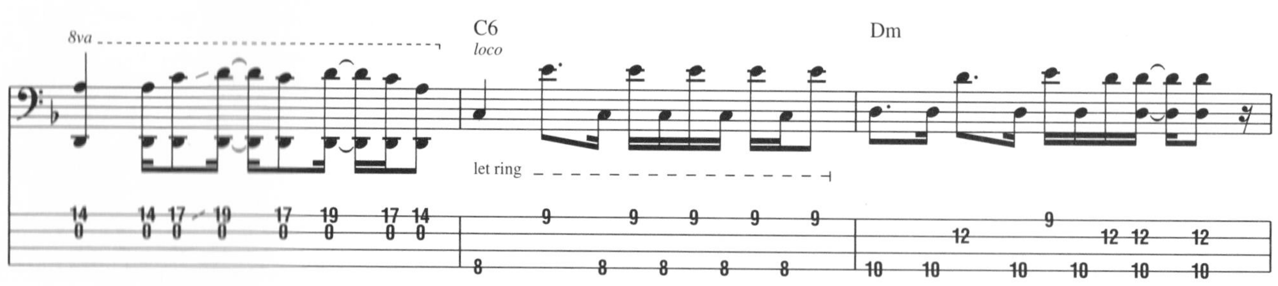

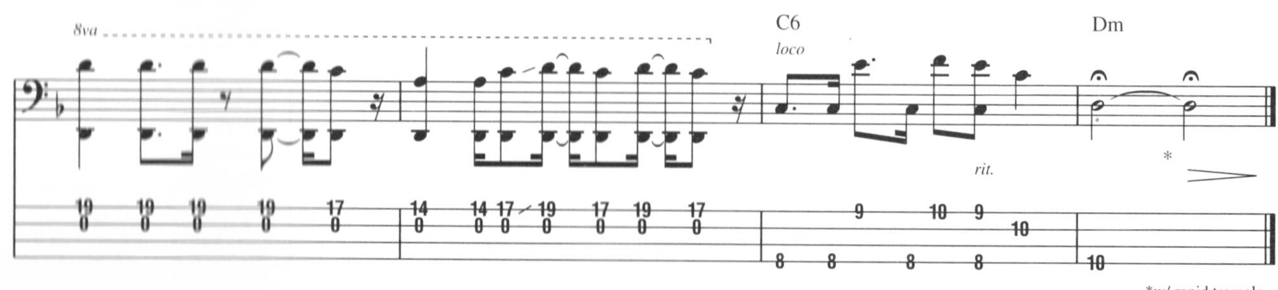

*w/ rapid tremolo using vol. knob.

School's Out

Words and Music by Alice Cooper, Neal Smith, Michael Bruce, Glen Buxton and Dennis Dunaway

E5 A/E Em E5 A/E E5 Em7 E5 A/E Em E5 A/E E5 Em7
mak-in' all their noise, 'cause they found new toys.
E5 A/E Em
Pre-Chorus
C5
D5 E♭5
Well, we can't sa-lute ya, can't find a flag. If that don't suit ya,
3
Chorus
G5 B♭5 C5 F5 G5
that's a drag. School's out for sum-mer!
F5 G5 B♭5 C5 F5 G5 F5 G5
School's out for ev-er
Bass Fig. 1
End Bass Fig. 1

w/ Bass Fig. 1
B♭5
C5
F5
G5
F5
G5
School's been blown to piec - es!
Bridge
C
Csus2♯11
C
Csus2♯11
C
Csus2♯11
C
Csus2♯11
No more pen - cils, no more books,
Dsus4/2
D
D9
D
Dsus4/2
D
no more teach - er's dir - ty looks. Yeah!
(No more teach - er's dir - ty looks.)
Guitar Solo
E5
A/E
N.C.
Em
E5
A/E
Em
Play 3 times
E5
A/E
E5
Em
E5
A/E
Em
2. Well, we got

Verse
E5 A/E E5 Em7 E5 A/E Em E5 A/E E5 Em7 E5 A/E Em
— no class, — and we got — no prin - ci - ples, — and we got —
sim.
E5 A/E E5 Em7 E5 A/E Em E5 A/E E5 Em7 E5 A/E Em
— no in - no - cence. We can't e - ven think of a word that rhymes! —
Chorus
w/ Bass Fig. 1 (2 times)
G5 B♭5 C5 F5 G5 F5 G5 B♭5 C5 F5 G5 F5 G5
School's out for sum - mer! School's out for ev - er! My
G5 F C/G
school's been blown to piec - es!
Bridge
C Csus2♯11 C Csus2♯11
No more pen - cils,
C Csus2♯11 C Csus2♯11 Dsus 2/4 D D9 D Dsus 2/4 D
w/ children's laughter & talking
no more books, — no more teach - er's dir - ty

D9 D C Csus2#11 C Csus2#11 C Csus2#11 C Csus2#11
looks Out for sum - mer, out til fall.
Dsus2/4 D D9 D Dsus2/4 D N.C.
We might not go back at all!
Chorus
w/ Bass Fig. 1 (3 times)
G5 B♭5 C5 F5 G5 F5 G5 G5 B♭5 C5
School's out for ev - er! School's out for
F5 G5 F5 G5 B♭5 C5 F5 G5 F5 G5
sum-mer! School's out with fe - ver!
w/ school bell
w/ children's cheers & tape effects
Gm F C
School's out com - plete - ly!

Selling the Drama

Lyrics by Edward Kowalczyk
Music by Edward Kowalczyk, Chad Taylor, Patrick Dahlheimer and Chad Gracey

3rd time to Coda II
Em
A
Em
A
Em
A
2nd time to Coda I
Em
A
Cadd9
1/2
P
2nd Verse
G
D
Dsus4
D
Dsus4
G
D
Dsus4
sl. D
It's the sun
that burns...
sl.
Em
Bm7
Cadd9
N.C.
1/2
P
G
D
Dsus4
D
Dsus4
G
D
Dsus4
sl. D
sl.
D.S. al Coda I
Em
Bm7
Cadd9
Csus2
I've willed,

Coda I
Cadd9
Dsus2
Esus2
Dsus2
Csus2
N.C.
1/2
P
G
D
G
D Dsus4 D Dsus4
3rd Verse
G
D Dsus4 D Dsus4
G
D
Dsus4
D
sl.
And to love:
a god...
sl.
D.S. al Coda II
Em
Bm7
Cadd9
Csus2
I've willed,
Coda II
Em
A
1/2
Em
A
Em
A
Em
A
Em
2
A
Cadd9

Shake, Rattle and Roll

Words and Music by Charles Calhoun

C7
F
roll my break - fast 'cause I'm a hun - gry man. I said,
shake, rat - tle and roll. I said, shake, rat - tle and roll. I said,
B♭
F
shake, rat - tle and roll. I said, shake, rat - tle and roll. You
C7
1,2
F
nev - er do noth - in' to save your dog - gone soul.

Additional lyrics:

VERSE 2

Wearin' those dresses, your hair done up so nice,
Wearin' those dresses, your hair done up so nice,
You look so warm, but your heart is cold as ice.

VERSE 3

I'm like a one-eyed cat, peepin' in a seafood store,
I'm like a one-eyed cat, peepin' in a seafood store,
I can look at you, tell you don't love me no more.

VERSE 4

I believe you're doin' me wrong and now I know,
I believe you're doin' me wrong and now I know,
The more I work, the faster my money goes.

She

Words and Music by Gene Simmons and Steve Coronel

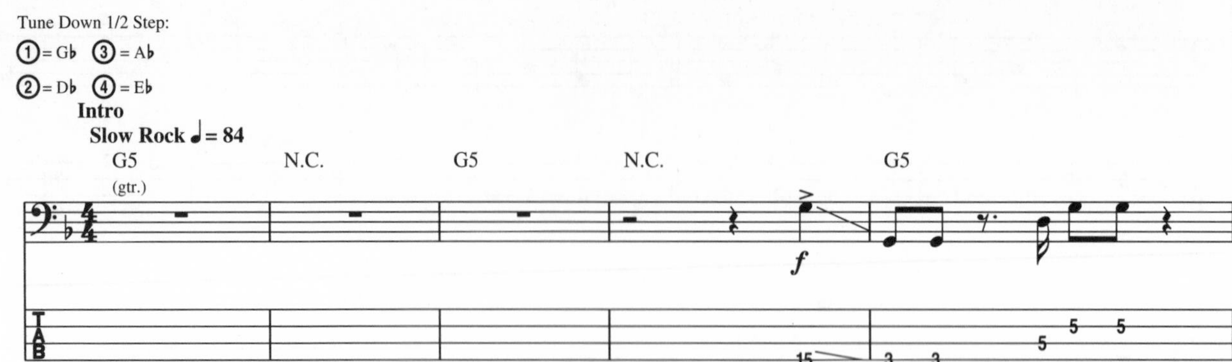

G5
N.C.
G5
N.C.
En-chant-ed star - light.
Nev - er go-ing home.
pow - ers are with - in her
as she takes off her clothes.

To Coda

Chorus
A5
I know she's go - ing down, go-ing.
Ev - 'ry-bod - y knows,
she's so good.

G5
N.C.
G5
N.C.

Interlude
G5
N.C.
N.C.

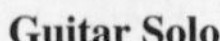
Guitar Solo

Gtrs. tacet, 1st 2 times
N.C.(Gm)
Bb5 C5
play 4 times
N.C.(Gm)
Bb5 C5
play 4 times

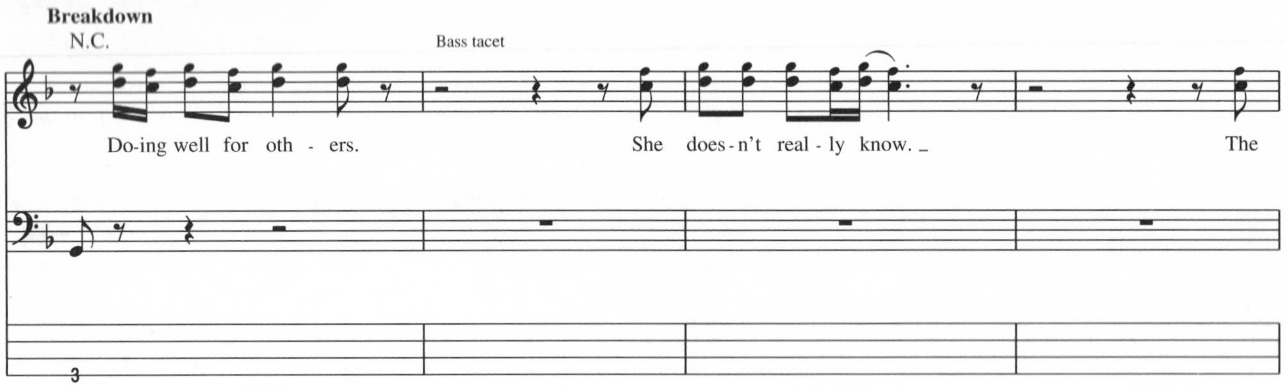
Breakdown
N.C.
Bass tacet
Do-ing well for oth - ers.
She does-n't real - ly know. _
The

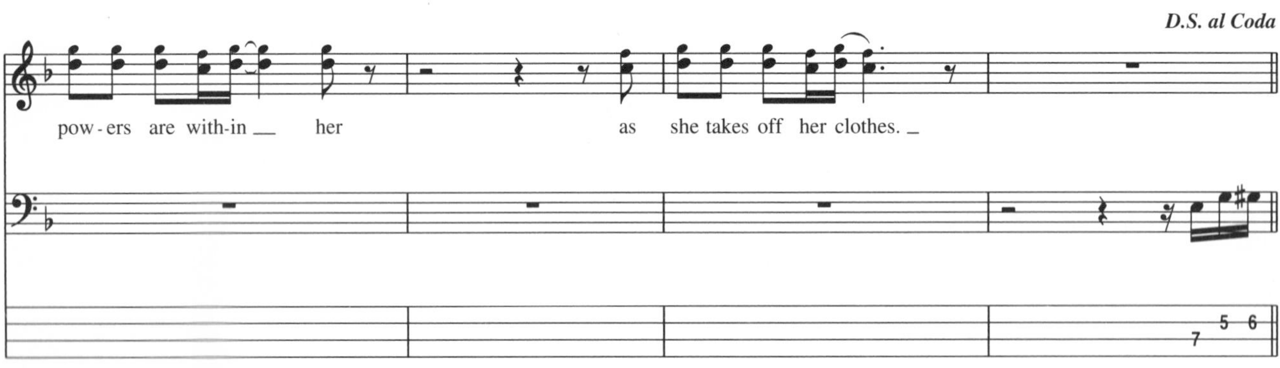
D.S. al Coda
pow - ers are with-in _ her
as she takes off her clothes. _

Coda
Play 4 Times and Fade
Outro
G5
E5
N.C.
E5
N.C.

The Shortest Straw

Words and Music by James Hetfield and Lars Ulrich

N.C.(E)
E5 G5 E5 G5 N.C.(E)
E5 A5 E5 A5 N.C.(E)
G5
F♯5
F5
H P sl.
H P sl.
1st,2nd, 3rd Verses
N.C.(E) F5 N.C.(E) G5 N.C.(E) F5
1. Sus - pi-cion is your_ name. Your hon-es - ty to_ blame. Put dig-ni - ty to_ shame.
2.3. See additional lyrics
N.C.(E) G5 F♯5 F5 N.C.(E) F5 N.C.(E) G5
Dis - hon - or. Witch - hunt mod - ern_ day. De - ter - min - ing de - cay.
N.C.(E) F5 N.C.(E) G5 F♯5 F5 N.C.(F♯) G5
The bla - tant dis - ar - ray. Dis - fig - ure. The pub - lic eye's dis - grace.

N.C.(F♯)
A5
N.C.(F♯)
G5
N.C.(F♯)
A5
A♭5
G5
De - fy - ing com - mon_ place. Un - end - ing pa - per_ chase. Un - end - ing.
N.C.(F♯)
G5
N.C.(F♯)
A5
N.C.(F♯)
G5
Deaf - en - ing. Pains - tak - ing. Reck - on - ing.
N.C.(F♯)
A5
A♭5
G5
N.C.(E)
E5 F5 E5 F5
This ver - ti - go, it doth bring.
N.C.(E)
E5 F5 E5 F5
B5

Tempo I
3rd time substitute Fill 1
E5
F5
B5 C5
N.C.
A5
E5 F5
B5 C5
N.C.
Chorus
E5 F5 E5
F5 E5
G5
B♭5
E5 F5 E5
Short - est straw.
Chal - lenge lib - er - ty.
Downed by law.
F5 E5
B♭5
G5
E5 F5 E5
F5 E5
G5
B♭5
Live in in - fa - my.
Rub you raw.
Witch - hunt rid - ing through.
E5 F5 E5
F5 E5
G5
F♯5
F5
Short - est straw.
This short - est straw has been pulled __ for you. __
Fill 1
D5
E5 F5

To Coda
E5 F5 E5 F5 G5 B♭5 E5 F5 E5
Pulled for you.
(Short - est straw.
F5 E5 B♭5 G5 E5 F5 E5 F5 E5 G5 B♭5 E5 F5 E5
Pulled for you.
Short - est straw.
Pulled for you.
Short-est straw).
Double-time feel
F5 E5 G5 F♯5 F5 N.C.(E) F5
Short - est straw has been pulled for you.
N.C.(E) G5 N.C.(E)
1.
A5 N.C.(E) G5 F♯5 F5
H P sl.

2.
F5
E5
F5
F♯5
G5
F♯5
F5
Guitar solo
N.C.(E)
F5
N.C.(E)
G5
N.C.(E)
F5
1.
N.C.(E)
G5
F♯5
F5
2.
N.C.(E)
G5
F♯5
F5
E5
E5 F5
E5 F5
E5 G5
E5 G5
E5 F5
E5 F5
E5
G5
F♯5
F5
F♯5
G5
G♯5
A5
G♯5
G5
F5

Tempo I
E5 F5 E5
F5 E5 G5 Bb5 E5 F5 E5
(Short - est straw.
Pulled for you.
Short - est straw.
F5 E5 Bb5 G5 E5 F5 E5
F5 E5 G5 Bb5
Pulled for you.
Short - est straw.
Pulled for
E5 F5 E5
F5 E5 G5
Guitar solo II
F♯5 F5 E5 F5 E5
you.
Short - est straw has been pulled for you.
F5 E5 G5 Bb5 E5 F5 E5
F5 E5 Bb5 G5 E5 F5 E5
F5 E5 G5 Bb5 E5 F5 E5
F5 E5 G5 F♯5 F5 E5
D.S. al Coda

Additional Lyrics

2. The accusations fly. Discrimination, why?
Your inner self to die. Intruding.
Doubt sunk itself in you. It's teeth and talons through.
Your living catch two-two. Deluding.
A mass hysteria. A megalomania.
Reveal dementia. Reveal.
Secretly. Silently.
Certainly. In vertigo you will be. *(To Chorus)*

3. Behind you, hands are tied. Your being, ostracized.
Your hell is multiplied. Upending.
The fallout has begun. Oppressive damage done.
Your many turned to none. To nothing.
You're reaching your nadir. Your will has disappeared.
The lie is crystal clear. Defending.
Channels red. One word said.
Blacklisted. With vertigo make you dead. *(To Chorus)*

Shy Boy

Words and Music by Billy Sheehan

D5
Harm.
(15ma)
F5
G5
trem. bar
Harm.
D5
H
Chorus
N.C. (Dm)
Shy
boy,
shy
boy, etc.
B♭5
A5
sl.
P

2nd time to Coda I
3rd time to Coda II
4th time to Coda III
2nd Verse
N.C.
8va
loco
B♭5
A5
G5
F5
D5
sl.
trem. bar
N.C. (G)
Harm.
(8va)
H
P
T
D.S. al Coda I
Coda I
C5
Guitar solo
B5

G5 F5 D5
D.S. al Coda II
Coda II
F5 C5 G5 A5
Interlude
N.C.
8va

8va
loco
Free time
A.H. D.S. al Coda III
(15ma)
A.H.
*Tap & pull off repeatedly
as rapidly as possible.
Coda III Outro
N.C. (E)
(E)
(D)
(A)
(G)
trem. bar
Free time
A.H. Full
(15ma)
Full
A.H.

Sitting on Top of the World

Words and Music by Chester Burnett

C9
B9
C9
C♯9
C9
N.C.
G7
A♭7
G7
N.C.
D7♯9
N.C.
(G7)
(C7)
(G7)
(D7)
N.C.
All the
2nd Verse
G9
F♯9
G9
F♯9
G9
F♯9
G7
F♯9
G9
F♯9
G9
F♯9
G9
sum - mer,
worked on this farm. (etc.)
C9
B9
C9
B9
C9
B9
C9
B9
C9
B9
C9
N.C.
G7
F♯7
G7
N.C.
D7♯9
N.C.

(G7)
(C7)
(G7)
(D7)
N.C.
Guitar solo
G9
sl.
F♯9 G9
F♯9 G9
F♯9 G9
F♯9 G9
F♯9 G9
F♯9 G9
f
sl.
C9
B9 C9
B9 C9
B9 C9
B9 C9
B9. C9
B9 C9 N.C.
G7
F♯7 G7
N.C.
D7(♯9)
sl.
sl.
N.C.
sl.
sl.
(G7)
(C7)
(G7)
(D7)
N.C.
G7♯9
C9
N.C.

G7
F♯7
G7
N.C.
D7♯9
N.C.
(G7)
(C7)
(G7)
(D7)
N.C.
Goin' down to
3rd Verse
G7♯9
the freight - yard, (etc.)
C9
sl.
N.C.
G7
F♯7
G7
N.C.
D7♯9
N.C.
rit.
(G7)
(C7)
(G7)
A♭7♯9
Free time
G7♯9

Space Oddity

Words and Music by David Bowie

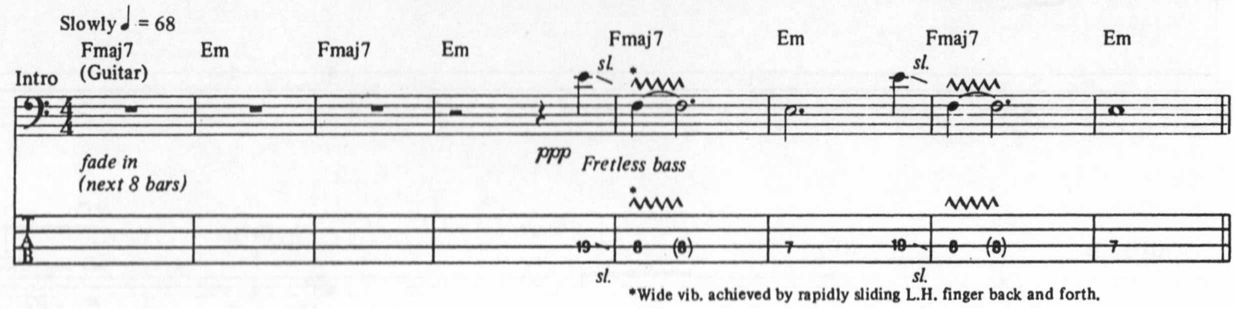

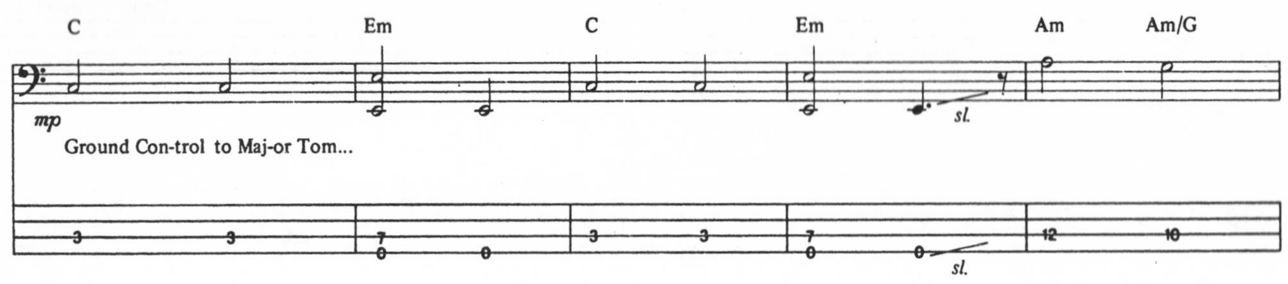

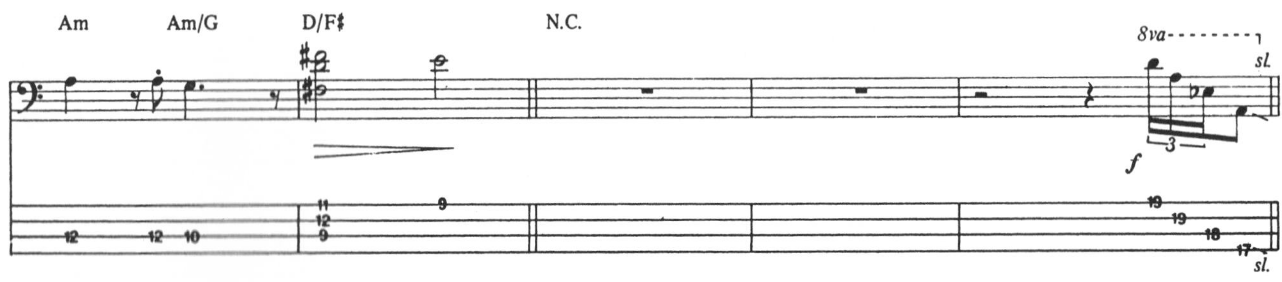

F Fm C F C
E7 F Fm C F
Fm C F Fmaj7 Em7
For here am I sit-ting in a tin can...
Fmaj7 Em7 B♭ Am G
F C F G A C F G A
(Guitar)
Guitar solo I
Fmaj7
Em7 A C/E D/E

E
C
E
E7
F
Though I'm past one hun - dred thou-sand miles...
Fm
C
F
Fm
C
F
G
E7♭9
Am
Am/G
D/F♯
C
G
Fmaj7
Em7
Fmaj7
Here am I float-ing round my tin can.
Em7
B♭
Am
G
F

C F G A C F G A
(Guitar)
Guitar solo II
Fmaj7
Em7
A
C/E
D/E
E
Begin fade
*Bass gradually fades in and out till end.
(Bass out)
Fade out

Spanish Castle Magic

Words and Music by Jimi Hendrix

Chorus
A5
N.C.(F#m)
F#m7sus4
N.C.(A5)
(F#m)
F#m7sus4
N.C.(E5)
(C#7#9)
Hang on my dar - ling.
Hang on if you want to
(E5)
(C#7#9)
(G#m7)
go.
Here, it's a real-ly groov-y place, it's a,
(E)
(E5)
(C#7#9)
(E5)
(C#7#9)
uh, just a lit-tle bit of, said, uh, Span - ish cast - le mag - ic.
Yeah.
Verse
B5/F#
Bb5
D5/A
2. The clouds are real - ly low,
and they o - ver - flow with cot - ton

C#/G#
C#7#9/G#
B5/F#
can - dy, and bat-tle grounds, red and brown. But it's all in your mind,

B♭5
D5/A
C#5/G#
N.C.
don't think your time on bad things, just float your lit-tle mind a - round. Look out! Ooh!

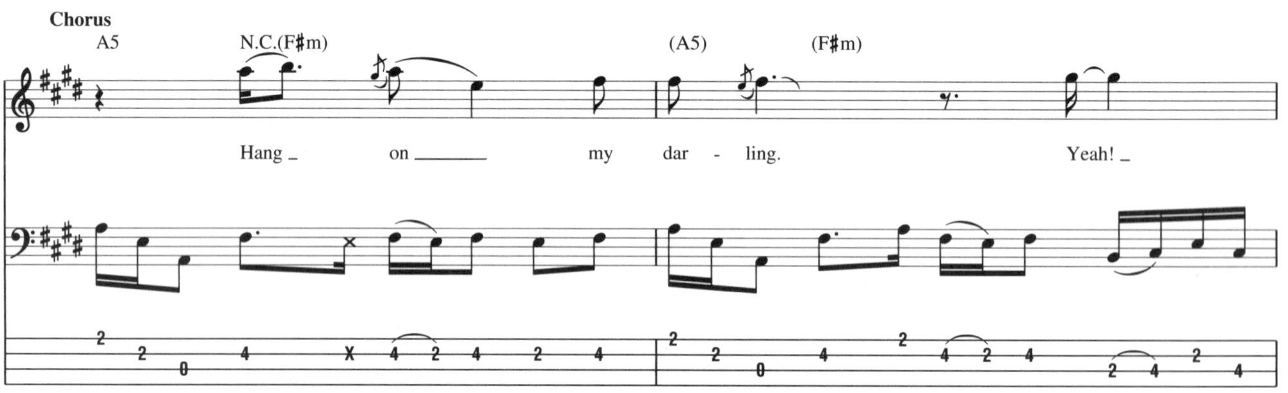
Chorus
A5
N.C.(F#m)
(A5)
(F#m)
Hang on my dar - ling. Yeah!

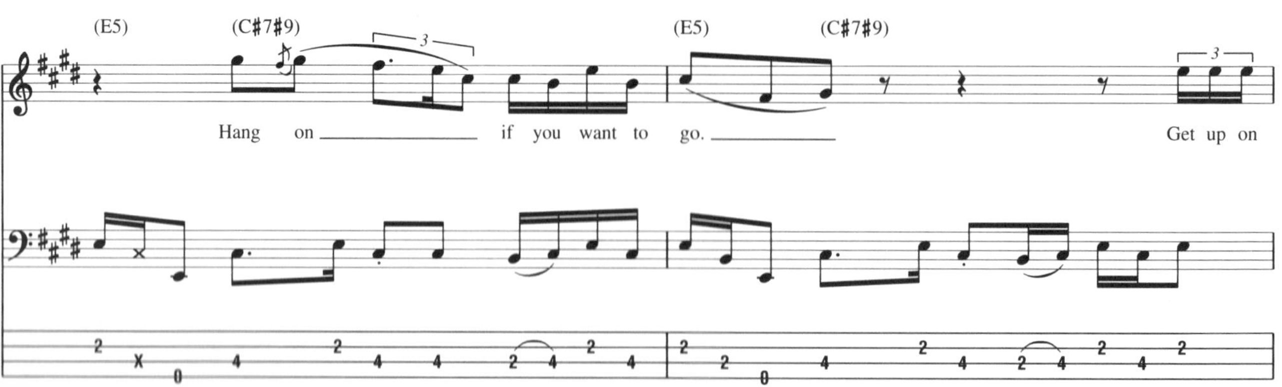
(E5)
(C#7#9)
(E5)
(C#7#9)
Hang on if you want to go. Get up on

(G#m7)
(E)
top, real - ly let me groove you, ba - by, with, uh,
just a lit - tle bit of

(E5)
(C#7#9)
(E5)
(C#7#9)
Span - ish cas - tle mag - ic.
Spoken: Yeah, ba - by, here's some.
Ha!

Guitar Solo

N.C.(C#7#9)
Yeah, O. K. babe, O. K.
It's still all in your mind, babe.

Ow!
Yeah.

Ah!

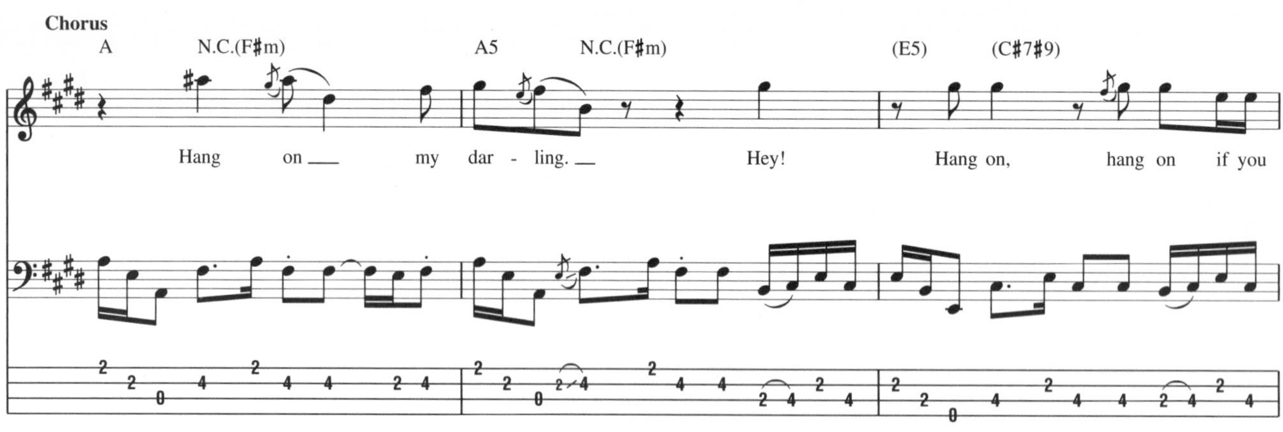
Chorus
A
N.C.(F#m)
A5
N.C.(F#m)
(E5)
(C#7#9)
Hang on my dar - ling. Hey! Hang on, hang on if you

(E5)
(C#7#9)
(G#m)
want to go, and it's hap - pen-ing, oh no, damn, hey! That's right, babe, lis - ten!

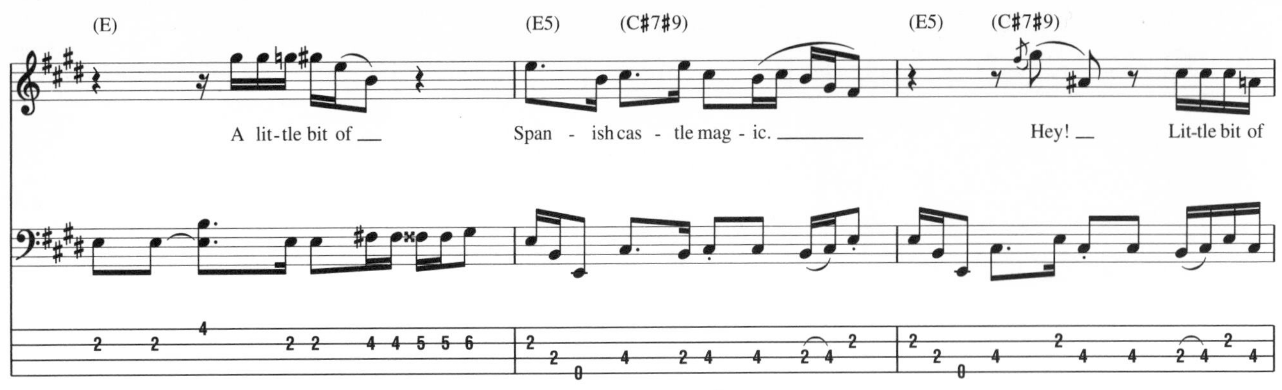
(E)
(E5)
(C#7#9)
(E5)
(C#7#9)
A lit-tle bit of
Span - ish cas - tle mag - ic.
Hey!
Lit-tle bit of

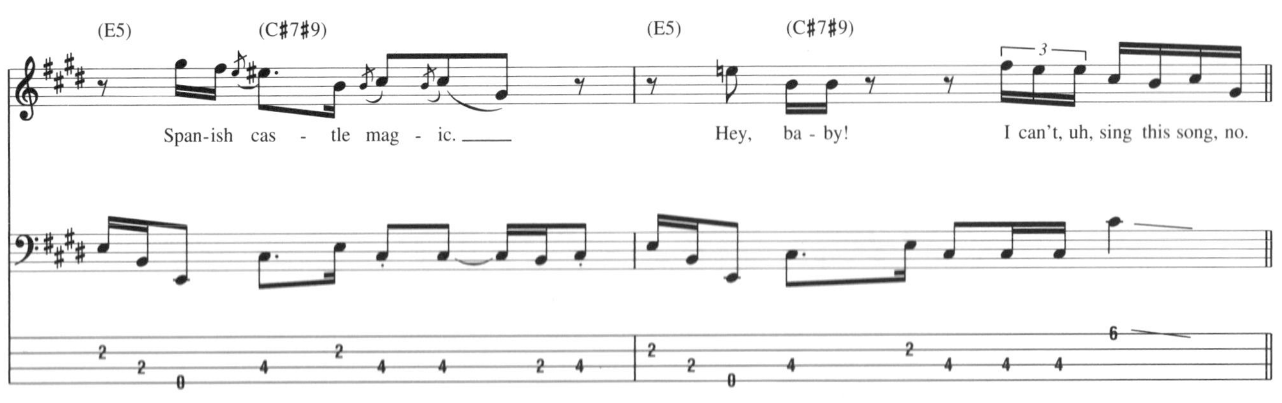
(E5)
(C#7#9)
(E5)
(C#7#9)
Span-ish cas - tle mag - ic.
Hey, ba - by!
I can't, uh, sing this song, no.

Outro
N.C.(E5)
(C#7#9)
(E)
(C#7#9)
Yeah, O. K. ba - by.
Get on ba - by!
Yeah.

(E)
(C#7#9)
(E)
(C#7#9)
It's all in your mind, ba - by!
Spoken: Lit - tle bit of day dream here and there.

(E)
(C#7#9)
Uh!
Yeah!
Ow!

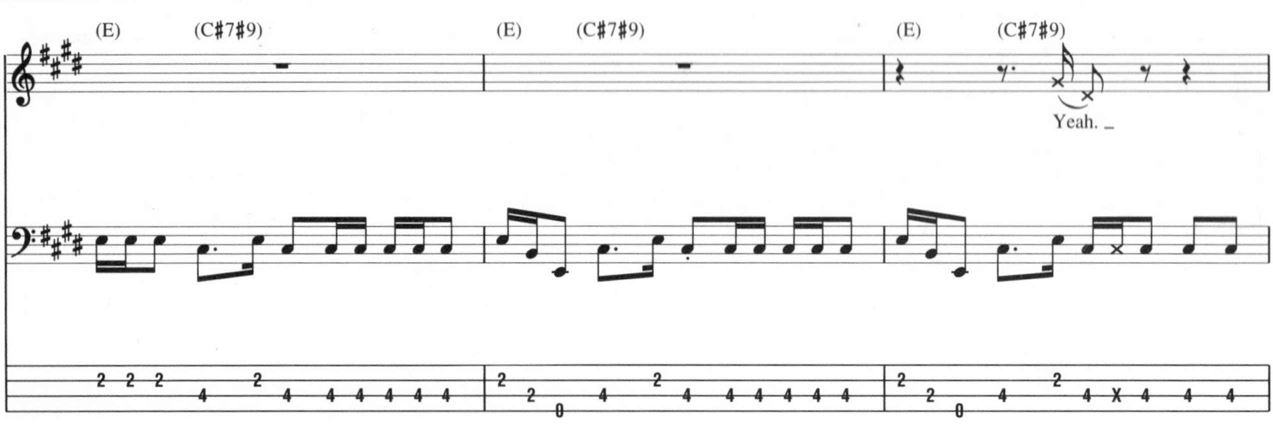
(E)
(C#7#9)
Yeah.

Begin Fade
(E)
(C#7#9)
Ow!

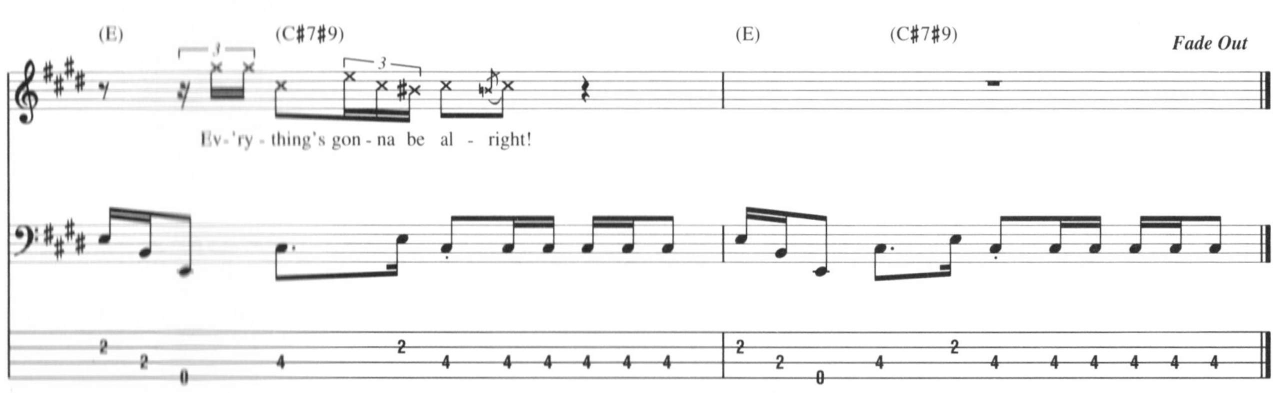
(E)
(C#7#9)
Fade Out
Ev-'ry-thing's gon-na be al-right!

Statesboro Blues

Words and Music by Willy McTell

G7
Wake up, ma - ma, turn your lamp down low.
I woke up this morn - in' an' I had them States - bo - ro blues
D7
A7
Ya got no nerve baby,
Well, I looked o - ver in the cor - ner, ba - by,
G7
1.
D7
ya turn Un - cle John from your door.
your grand - pa seems to have them
A7
2.
D7
A7
too.
Oh!

Guitar Solo
D7
G7
D7
G7
D7
A7
G7
D7
To Coda
A7
D7
G7
D7
G7
D7
A7

G7
D7
A7
3. Well, my
Verse
N.C.(D7)
ma - ma died and left me, my pa - pa died and left me. I
ain't good look - in', ba - by want some - one sweet and kind.
G7
I'm go - in' to the coun - try, ba - by, do you wan - na go?
*even
* Sung as even sixteenth notes.
D7
A7
If you can't make it, ba - by,

G7
even
D7
D.S. al Coda
your sis - ter Lu - cille said she wan-na go.
Spoken: Well, I sho' nuff tell ya...
Coda
D7
G7
D7
G7
D7
A7
G7
D
A
Verse
D7
4. I love that wom - an
G7
bet - ter 'n an - y wom - an I've ev - er

D7
G7
seen.
Well I love that wom - an,
D7
bet - ter 'n an - y wom-an I've ev - er seen.
Well, she
* Sung behind the beat.
A7
G7
treat me like a king, yeah, yeah, yeah, I treat her like a dog -
D7
A7
Verse
D7
gone queen.
5. Well, wake up, ma - ma,

G7
D7
turn your lamp down _ low. ____
G7
D7
Wake _ up, ma - ma, well turn your lamp down low. ___
D7
A7
G7
Ya got no ___ love, __ ba - by, ya turn Un-cle John _ from your
D7
C#6 D6
on cue:
door. ________
yeah. ________

The Story in Your Eyes

Words and Music by Justin Hayward

(Guitar solo 2nd time)
Am C/A D Am C/A D Am C/A
sl.
H
D G C G
3rd time to Coda
Chorus
Em
Lis-ten to the tide
F♯m7add4 G
slow - ly turn - ing...
F♯m7add4 G A Bm
A G D/F♯ E
2nd time D.S. al Coda
2.3. But I'm
Coda
G
Outro
Am Bm/A C/A D/A Am Bm/A C/A Bm/A
Repeat and fade

Strutter

Words and Music by Paul Stanley and Gene Simmons

Bass: w/ Fill 1, 2nd time
B
G
D
She'll let you walk the street be - side __ her. Ooh.
You take her home __ and she says, "May - be, ba - by."
Bass: w/ Fill 3, 3rd time
B
G
D
A
But when she wants, _ she'll pass you by. ____
She takes you down _ and drives you wild. ____
Chorus
To Coda
1.
Bm
G
Bm
G
Ev - 'ry - bod - y says she's look - in' good, _ and the la - dy knows it's un - der - stood. _
N.C.(Bm)
(E)
(D)
(A)
Strut - ter.
Fill 1
Bass
Fill 3
Bass

(Bm)
(E)
(G)
(A)
2.
Guitar Solo
N.C.(Bm)
G
un - der - stood. _
Strut - ter.
(Sing 1st time only)
1., 2.
3.
D.S. al Coda
(E)
(D)
(A)
(E)
(G)
(A)
Coda
Outro
N.C.(Bm)
G
un-der - stood. _
Strut-ter.
1., 2.
(E)
3.
(D)
(A)
(E)
(G)
(A)
B

Sugar

Words and Music by Daron Malakian, Serj Tankian, Shavo Odadjian and John Dolmayan

Drop D tuning down 1 step:
(low to high) C–G–C–F

Chorus

Moderate Rock ♩ = 138

D5 A5 A♭5 G5 D5 A5 A♭5 G5 D5 A5 A♭5 G5 D5 A5 A♭5 G5

The kom - bu - cha mush - room peo - ple,

Bass — Bass Fig. 1 — End Bass Fig. 1

f

TAB: 12 11 10 9 8 | 0 7 6 5 0 7 6 5 | 0 7 6 5 0 7 6 5

Bass: w/ Bass Fig. 1 (3 times)

D5 A5 A♭5 G5 D5 A5 A♭5 G5 D5 A5 A♭5 G5 D5 A5 A♭5 G5 D5 A5 A♭5 G5 D5 A5 A♭5 G5

sit - ting a - round all day. Who can be - lieve you?

D5 A5 A♭5 G5 D5 A5 A♭5 G5 D5 A5 A♭5 G5 D5 A5 A♭5 G5 D5 A5 A♭5 G5 D5 A5 A♭5 G5

Who can be - lieve you? Let your moth - er pray.

Double-time feel

Bass: w/ Bass Fill 1

N.C.

(Su-gar.)

Interlude

Bass: w/ Bass Fill 1 (2 times)

N.C.

Voc. Fig. 1 — End Voc. Fig. 1

(Su-gar.)

Verse

Bass: w/ Bass Fig. 1 (6 times)

N.C.

1. I'm not there all the time, you know. Some peo - ple, some peo - ple, some peo - ple call it in -

2. I got a gun the oth - er day from Sak - o. It's cute, small, fits right in my

Bkgd. Voc.: w/ Voc. Fig. 1
sane. Yeah, they call it in - sane. I play Rus - sian rou-lette ev - 'ry day, a
pock - et, yeah, right in my pock - et. My girl, you know she lash-es out at me some-times
Bkgd. Voc.: w/ Voc. Fig. 1
man's sport, with a bul-let called life, yeah, ma-ma, called life. You know that
and I just fuck-ing kick her and then, oh, ba - by, she's o - kay.
ev - 'ry time I try to go where I real - ly want to be, it's al - read-y where
Peo-ple al-ways chas-ing me down, try - ing to push my face to the ground, where all they do is suck out my moth-er fuck - ing
End double-time feel
Bkgd. Voc.: w/ Voc. Fig. 2, 2nd time
Chorus
Bass: w/ Bass Fig. 1 (4 times)
D5 A5 Ab5 G5 D5 A5 Ab5 G5
I am, 'cause I'm al-read-y there!
brains, my brains!
The kom - bu - cha mush -
D5 A5 Ab5 G5 D5 A5 Ab5 G5 D5 A5 Ab5 G5 D5 A5 Ab5 G5 D5 A5 Ab5 G5 D5 A5 Ab5 G5
- room peo - ple, sit - ting a - round all day.
D5 A5 Ab5 G5 D5 A5 Ab5 G5 D5 A5 Ab5 G5 D5 A5 Ab5 G5
1.
D5 A5 Ab5 G5 D5 A5 Ab5 G5
Who can be - lieve you? Who can be - lieve you? Let your moth - er pray.
Double-time feel
Bass: w/ Bass Fill 1
D5 A5 Ab5 G5 D5 A5 Ab5 G5 N.C.
(bass & drums)
(Su - gar.)
Voc. Fig. 2
(Su - gar!)

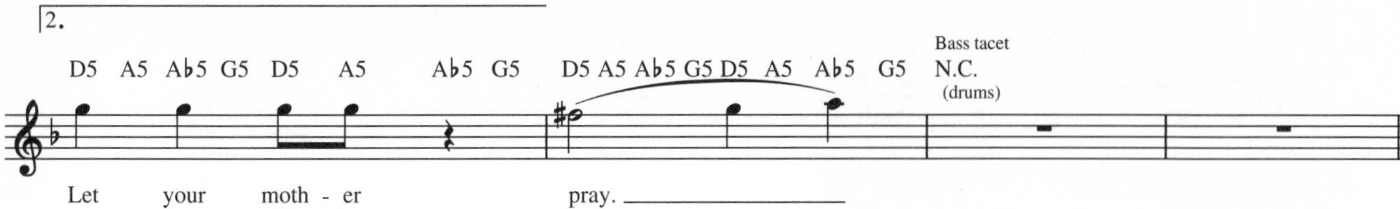
2.
D5 A5 Ab5 G5 D5 A5 Ab5 G5 D5 A5 Ab5 G5 D5 A5 Ab5 G5
Bass tacet
N.C.
(drums)
Let your moth - er pray.

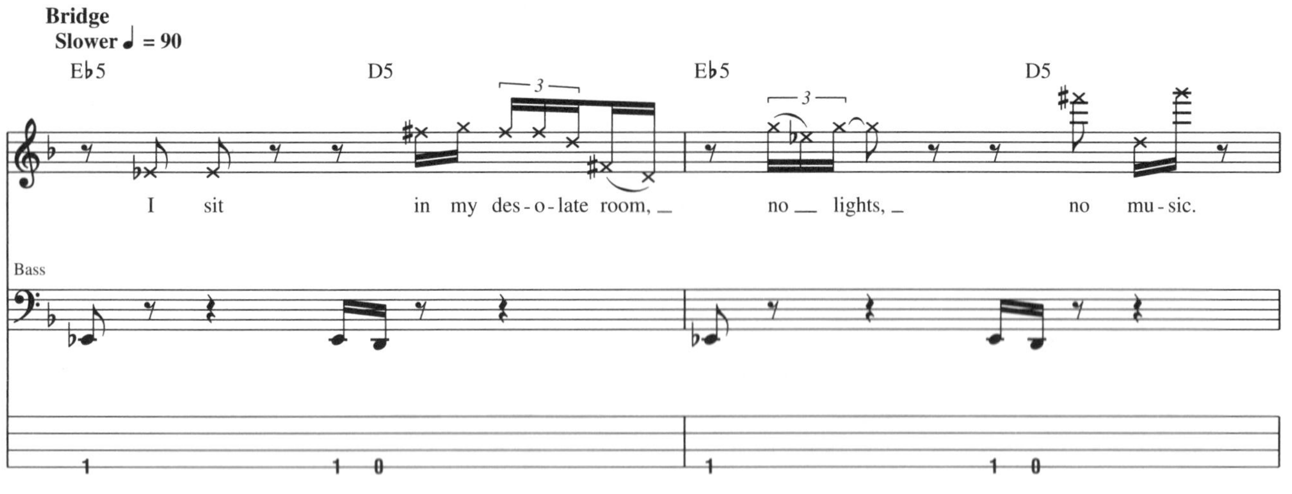
Bridge
Slower ♩ = 90
Eb5 D5 Eb5 D5
I sit in my des-o-late room, no lights, no mu-sic.
Bass

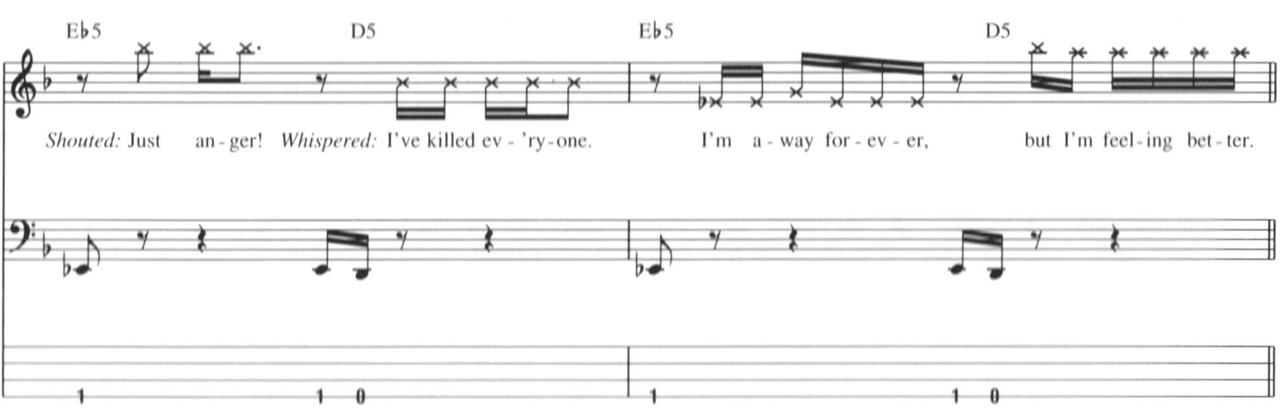
Eb5 D5 Eb5 D5
Shouted: Just an-ger! Whispered: I've killed ev - 'ry-one. I'm a-way for-ev-er, but I'm feel-ing bet-ter.

Outro
Eb5 D5 Eb5 D5 Eb5 D5 Eb5 D5
grad. accel.
How do I feel? What do I say? Fuck you, it all goes a-way.
Bass Fig. 2
End Bass Fig. 2
grad. accel.

Bass: w/ Bass Fig. 2 (5 times)
Eb5 D5 Eb5 D5 Eb5 D5 Eb5 D5
How do I feel? What do I say? Fuck you, it all goes a - way.
Eb5 D5 Eb5 D5 Eb5 D5 Eb5 D5
How do I feel? What do I say? In the end it all goes a - way.
Eb5 D5 Eb5 D5 Eb5 D5 Eb5 D5
How do I feel? What do I say? In the end it all goes a - way.
Eb5 D5 Eb5 D5 Eb5 D5 Eb5 D5
How do I feel? What do I say? In the end it all goes a - way.
Eb5 D5 Eb5 D5 Eb5 D5 Eb5 D5
How do I feel? What do I say? In the end it all goes a - way.
Faster ♩ = 180
Bass: w/ Bass Fig. 1 (4 times)
A5 Ab5 G5 D5 A5 Ab5 G5 D5 A5 Ab5 G5 D5 A5 Ab5 G5
How do I feel? What do I say? In the end it all goes a - way.
D5 A5 Ab5 G5 D5 A5 Ab5 G5 D5 A5 Ab5 G5 D5 A5 Ab5 G5
accel.
How do I feel? What do I say? In the end it all goes a - way.
Faster ♩ = 196
Double-time feel
D5 A5 Ab5 G5 D5 A5 Ab5 G5 D5 A5 Ab5 G5 D5 A5 Ab5 G5
In the end it all goes a - way. In the end it all goes a - way.
D5 A5 Ab5 G5 D5 A5 Ab5 G5 D5 A5 Ab5 G5 D5 A5 Ab5 G5
In the end it all goes a - way. In the end it all goes a - way.

Sultans of Swing

Words and Music by Mark Knopfler

2nd, 4th, 5th, 6th Verses
B♭
C
Dm
C
sl.
2. ... step in - side (etc.)
4. And Har-ry does-n't
5. ...crowd of young boys, (etc.)
6. Then the man he steps (etc.)
B♭
A
mind (etc.)
Dm
C
B♭
A
F
C
B♭
Dm
B♭
H
C
B♭
C
sl.
Chorus
Dm
C
B♭
C
2nd time to Coda I
H

2nd time,
D.S. al Coda I
(5th verse)
3rd time to Coda II
Dm
C
B♭
C
Coda I
Dm
C
B♭
C
H
H
Guitar solo I
Dm
C
B♭
A
Dm
C
B♭
A
F
C
H
H
B♭
H
H
Dm
B♭
C

B♭
C
Dm
C
B♭
H
H
C
Dm
C
B♭
H
H
D.S. al Coda II
C
H
H
Coda II
C
Outro (Guitar solo II)
Dm
B♭
C
P
P
Dm
B♭
C
H
H
Dm
sl.
B♭
C
Play 4 times and fade
H
sl.
H

Sunday Bloody Sunday

Words by Bono
Music by U2

B5
D5
G5
'Cause to - night
we can be as one to -
Ah!
Ah,
Ah,
C Verse
night!
ah.
Bro - ken bot - tles un - der
G
Bm
D
G(6)
chil - dren's feet.
Bod - ies strewn a - cross the dead end street.
But I won't heed the bat - tle call.
It puts my back up, puts my

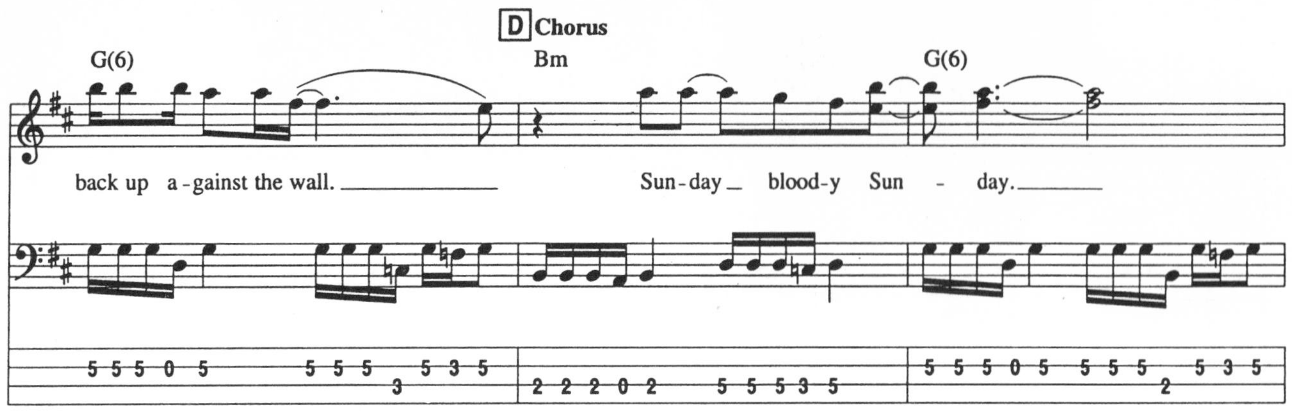
D Chorus
G(6)
Bm
G(6)
back up a-gainst the wall.
Sun-day blood-y Sun - day.

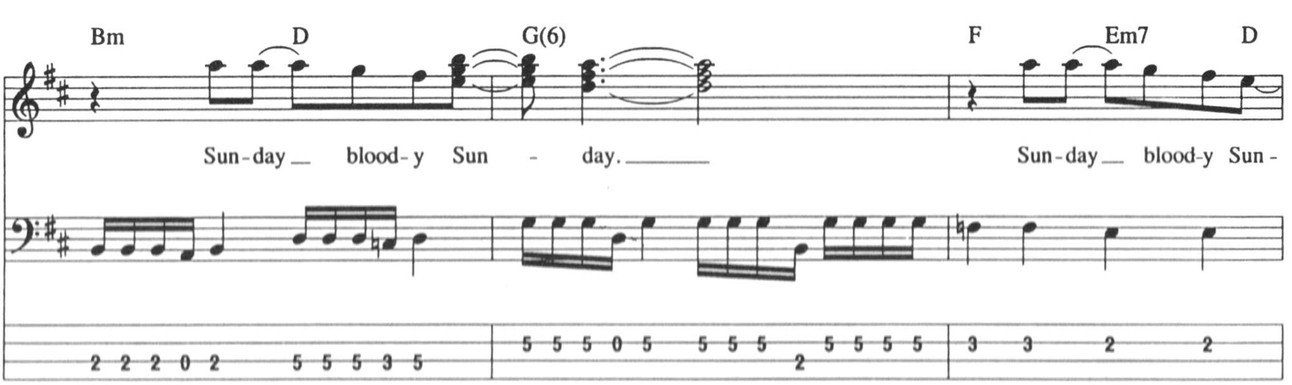
Bm
D
G(6)
F
Em7
D
Sun-day blood-y Sun - day.
Sun-day blood-y Sun -

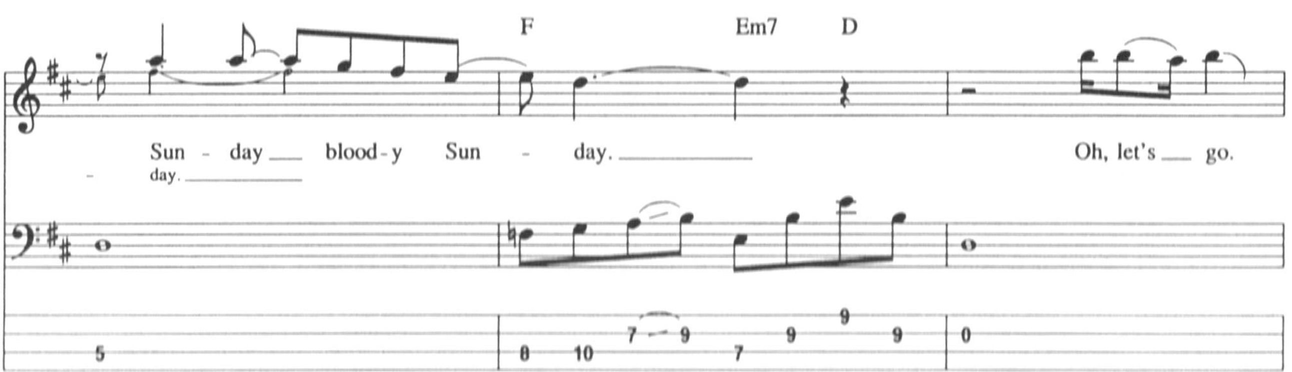
F
Em7
D
Sun - day blood-y Sun - day.
- day.
Oh, let's go.

B5
D5
G
B5
D

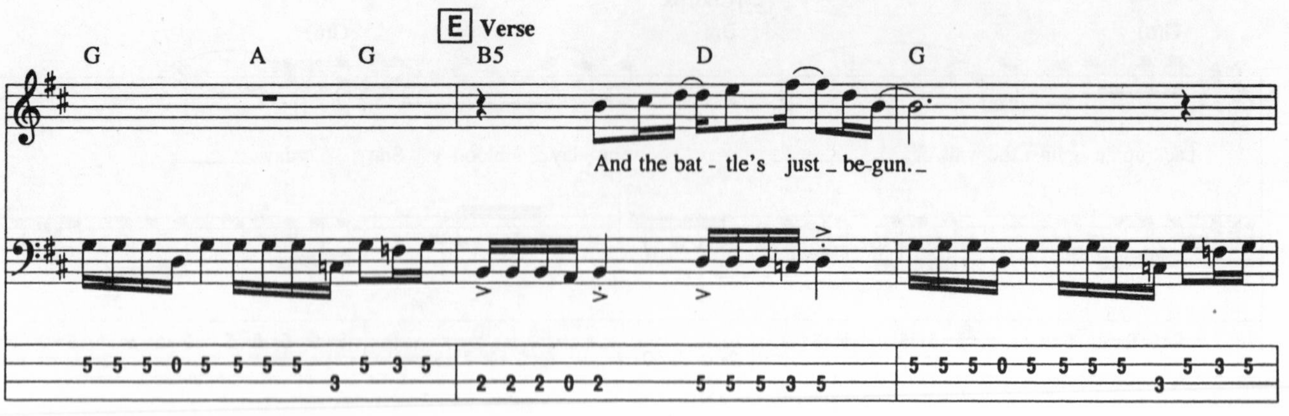
E Verse
G A G B5 D G
And the bat - tle's just _ be-gun. _
5 5 5 0 5 5 5 5 3 5 3 5
2 2 2 0 2 5 5 5 3 5
5 5 5 0 5 5 5 5 3 5 3 5

Bm D G(6) Bm D
There's man-y lost,_ but tell _ me who has won?_
The trench-es dug with-in __ our
3
2 2 2 0 2 5 5 5 3 5
5 5 5 0 5 5 5 5 3 5 3 5
2 2 2 0 2 5 5 5 3 5

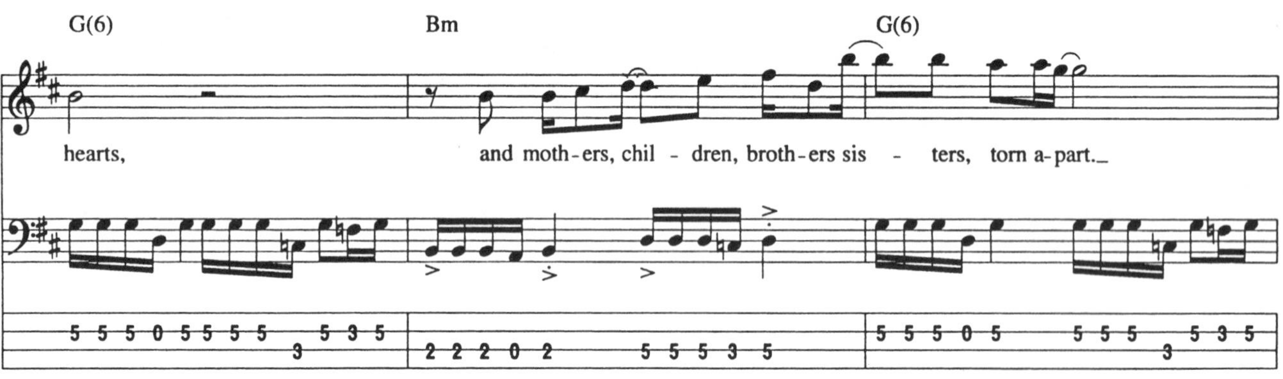
G(6) Bm G(6)
hearts,
and moth-ers, chil - dren, broth-ers sis - ters, torn a-part._
5 5 5 0 5 5 5 5 3 5 3 5
2 2 2 0 2 5 5 5 3 5
5 5 5 0 5 5 5 5 3 5 3 5

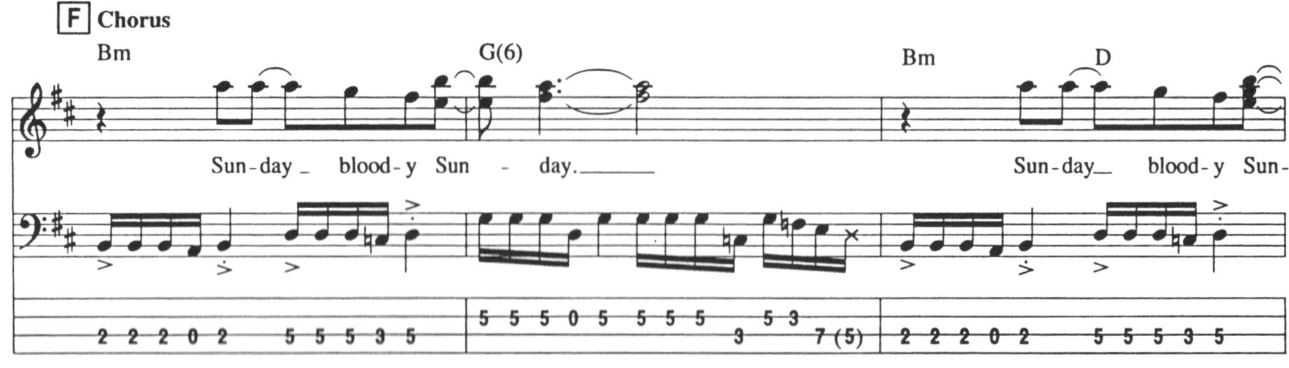
F Chorus
Bm G(6) Bm D
Sun-day _ blood-y Sun - day. ______
Sun-day__ blood-y Sun-
2 2 2 0 2 5 5 5 3 5
5 5 5 0 5 5 5 5 3 5 3 7 (5)
2 2 2 0 2 5 5 5 3 5

G(6)
D
Em
- day.
How long,
how long must we sing this song?
5 5 5 0 5 5 5 5 3 5 3 5
5 5 5 5 5 5
7 9 9 11 9 9 5 2

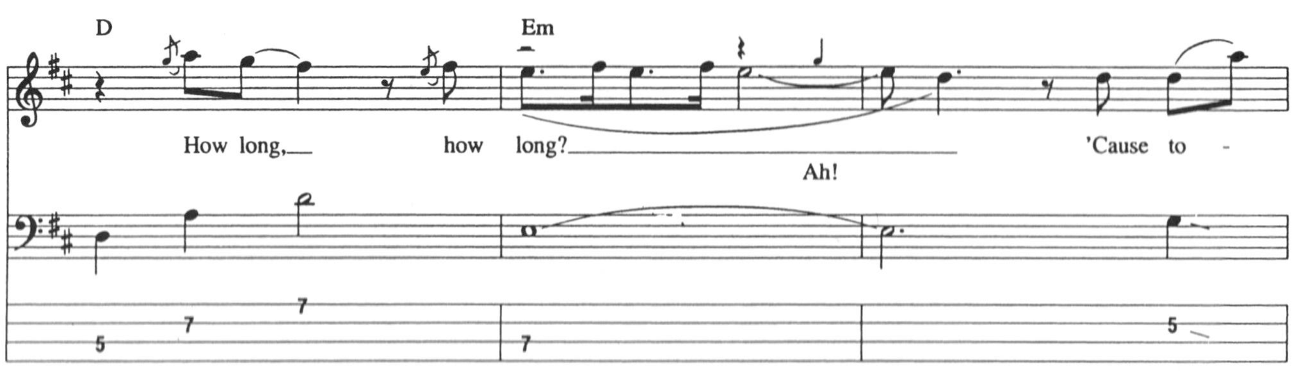
D
Em
How long,
how long?
Ah!
'Cause to -
5 7 7
7
5

B5
D
G
B5
D
night
we can be as one,
to - night!
Ah.
Ah.
2 2 2 2 2 5 5 5 5 5
5 5 5 0 5 5 5 5 3 5 3 5
2 2 2 0 2 5 5 5 3 5

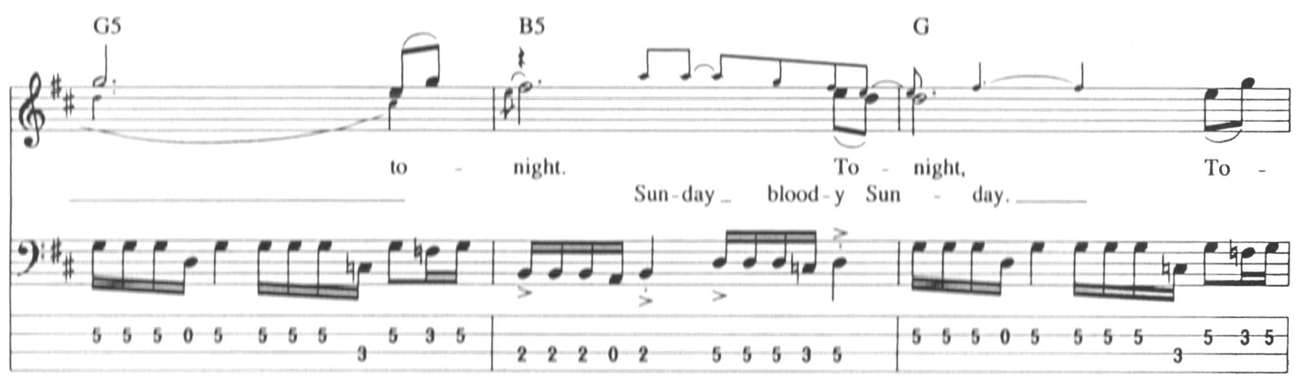
G5
B5
G
to - night.
To - night,
To -
Sun-day blood-y Sun - day.
5 5 5 0 5 5 5 5 3 5 3 5
2 2 2 0 2 5 5 5 3 5
5 5 5 0 5 5 5 5 3 5 3 5

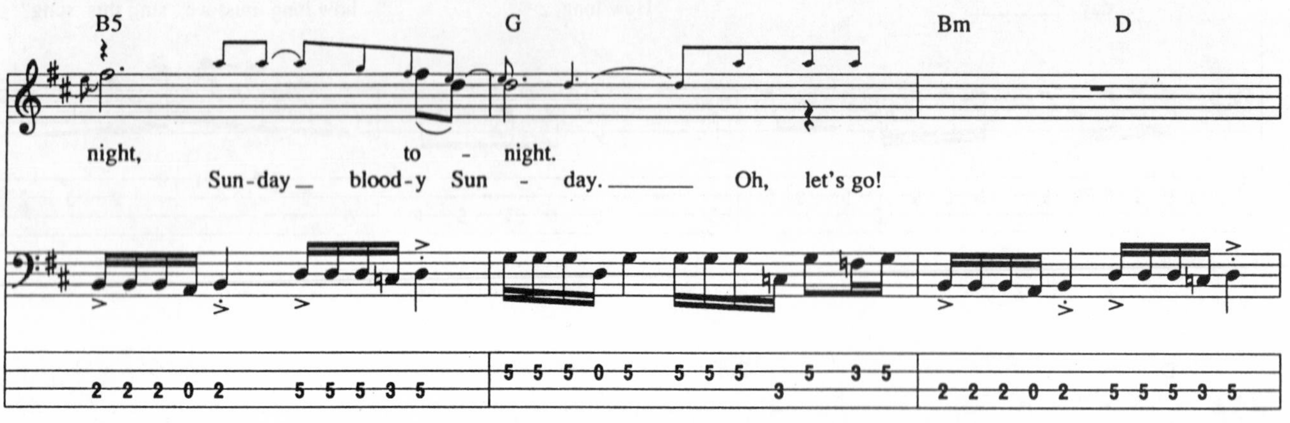
B5
G
Bm
D
night, to - night.
Sun-day blood-y Sun - day. Oh, let's go!

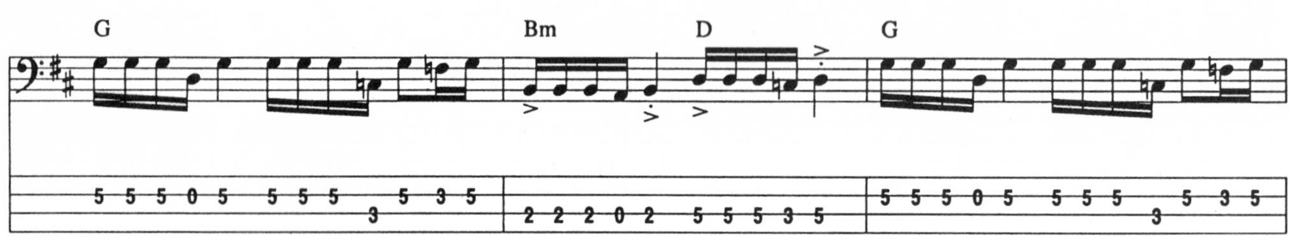
G
Bm
D
G

Bm
D
G
Bm
D

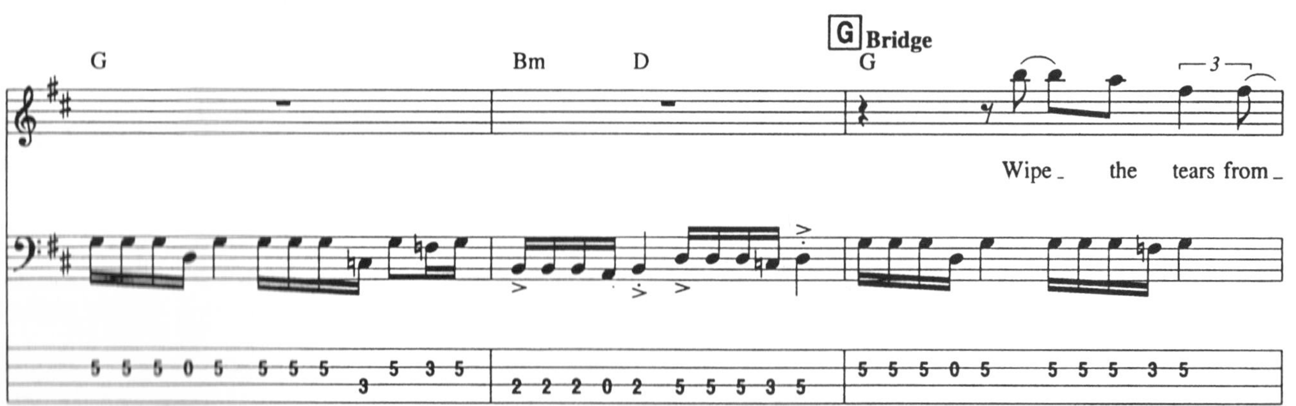
G
Bm
D
G Bridge
G
Wipe the tears from

B5
D
G
B5
D
your eyes.
Wipe the tears a - way.
2 2 2 0 2 5 5 5 3 5
5 5 5 5 5 5 5 5 5 5 5
2 2 2 0 2 5 5 5 3 5

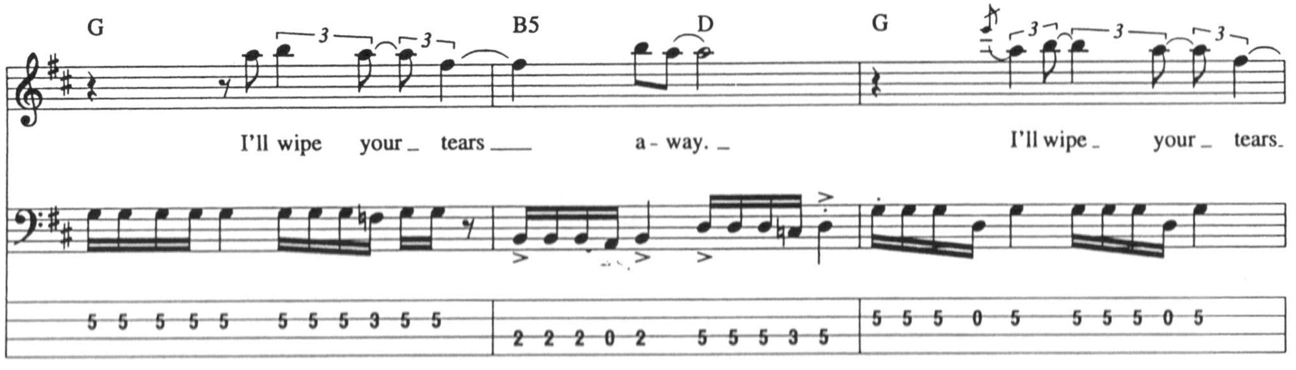
G
B5
D
G
I'll wipe your tears a - way.
I'll wipe your tears
5 5 5 5 5 5 5 5 3 5 5
2 2 2 0 2 5 5 5 3 5
5 5 5 0 5 5 5 5 0 5

B5
D
G
B5
D
a - way. I'll wipe your blood - shot eyes.
Sun-day blood-y Sun - day.
Sun - day blood-y Sun -
2 2 2 0 2 5 5 5 3 5
5 5 5 5 5 5 5 5 5 5 4 5
2 2 2 0 2 5 5 5 3 5

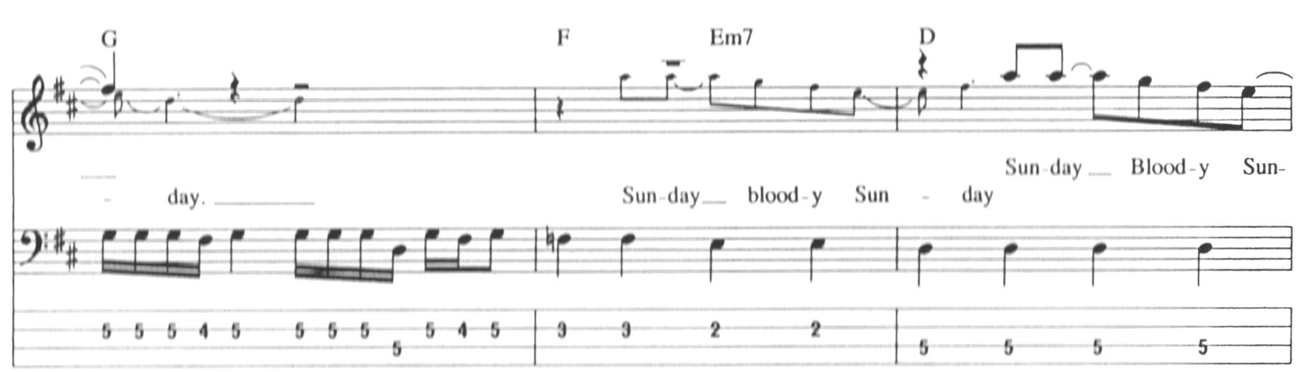
G
F
Em7
D
day.
Sun-day blood-y Sun - day
Sun-day Blood-y Sun-
5 5 5 4 5 5 5 5 5 5 4 5
3 3 2 2
5 5 5 5

F Em7 D F Em7
- day. Ah. Sun-day blood-y Sun-
D F Em7 D
Sun-day blood-y Sun - day. Ah. Yeah, let's go.
- day.
B5 D5 G A G B5 D5
G A G
H Verse
B5 D G
And it's true we are im-mune.
B5 D G B5 D
When fact is fic - tion and T. V. re - al-i-ty.
And to-day the mil-lions
Sun-day blood - y Sun-

G
B5
D
G
— cry, ___
— day, ___
we eat and drink while to - mor-row they_ die._
Sun-day_ blood-y Sun - day. ___
B5
D
G
A
G
B5
D
The real bat - tle just be-gun,_
Sun-day_ blood-y Sun - day. ___
to claim the vic - 'try Je-sus_
Sun - day_ blood-y Sun-
G
G
won on
- day. ___
Sun-day_ blood-y Sun - day! ___
B5
D
G
Bm7
Sun-day_ blood-y Sun - day. ___

Surfin' U.S.A.

Words and Music by Chuck Berry

Eb5
Bb5
Ab5
A bush-y, bush-y blonde hair - do, surf-in' U. S. A.
Tell the teach-er we're surf - in', surf-in' U. S. A.
oo. Oo,
Eb5
Verse
Bb5
2. You'll catch 'em surf-in' at Del Mar, Ven-tu-ra Coun-ty line.
4. And Hag-ger-ties and Swam - ies. Pa-cif-ic Pal-i - sades.
oo.)
(In - side, out - side U. S. A.
Eb5
Bb5
San-ta Cruz and Trest - le, Aus-tra-li-a's Nar-ra - been.
San O-no-fre and Sun - set. Re-don - do Beach L. A.
In - side, out - side U. S. A. In - side, out - side U. S. A.

Eb5
Ab5
Eb5
All o - ver Man - hat - tan __ and down Do-hen - y Way._
All o - ver La Jol - la __ at Wa - i - mi - a Bay._
In - side, out - side U. S. A. __ In - side, out - side U. S. A. __
Bb5
Ab5
Ev - 'ry-bod-y's gone surf - in', __ surf-in' U. S. A. _
In - side, out - side mm. ______ Surf - in'.) __
Eb5
1.
2.
3. We'll all be plan-ning out a
Organ Solo
Bb5
Eb5

Bb5
Eb5
Guitar Solo
Ab5
Eb5
Ev - ry-bod-y's gone
(Mm, _
Outro-Chorus
Bb5
Eb5
surf - in', _ surf-in' U. S. A. ___ Ev - 'ry-bod-y's gone
surf - in'. _ Mm, _
Repeat and fade
Bb5
Ab5
Eb5
2nd time, Bkgd. Voc. w/ Voc. Fill 1
surf - in', _ surf-in' U. S. A. ___ Ev - 'ry-bod-y's gone
surf - in'. Mm.) ___
Voc. Fig. 1
Yeah.

Sweet Emotion

Words and Music by Steven Tyler and Tom Hamilton

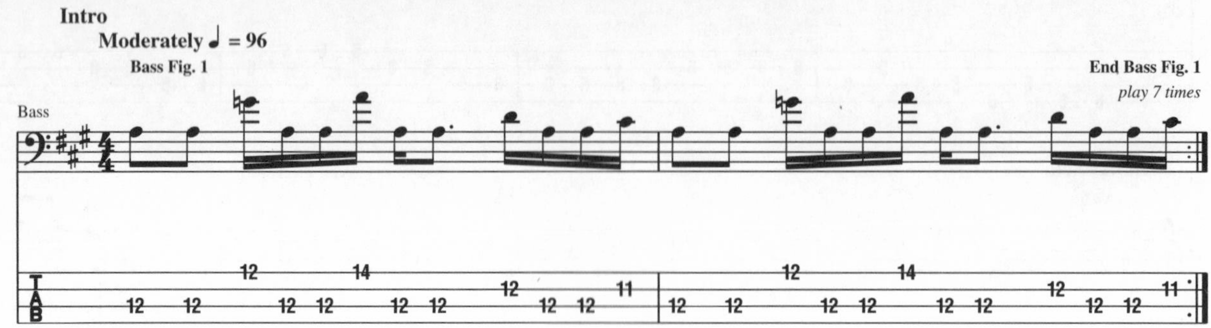

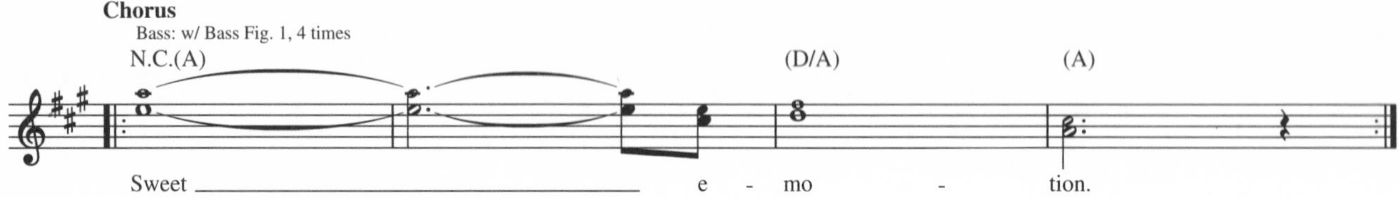

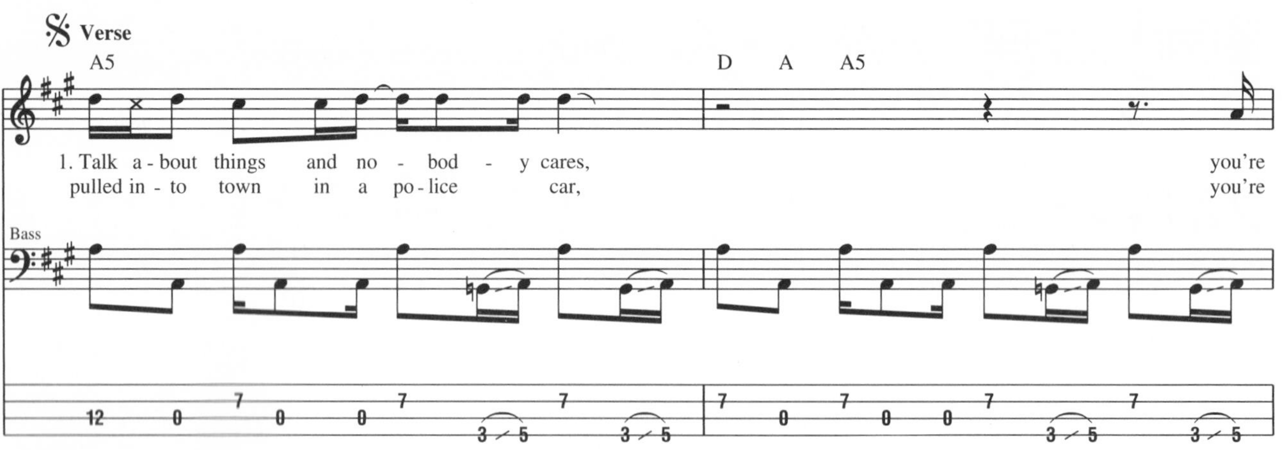

Bass: w/ Bass Fig. 2, 2 times, simile
D A
D A
call - in' my name, but I got - ta make clear,
I
tell - in' her things but your girl - friend lied,
you
D A
D A
can't say, ba - by, where I'll be in a year.
can't catch me 'cause the rab - bit done died.
Yes it did!
Interlude
N.C.
Bass
2. Some
4. You
Verse
Bass: w/ Bass Fig. 2, 4 times, 1st time
Bass: w/ Bass Fig. 3, 4 times, 2nd time
D A
D A
sweet - talk - in' ma - ma with a face like a gent
said my
stand in the front just - a shak - in' yo ass,
I'll
D A
D A
get up and go must - 've got up and went.
Well, I
take you back - stage you can drink from my glass.
I'm
Bass Fig. 3

D A
got good news, she's a real __ good li - ar,
talk-in' bout some - thin' you can sure un - der - stand,
'cause my
'cause a
back - stage boo - gie set yo' pants on fire.
month on the road and I'll be eat - in' from your hand.
Interlude
N.C.
Bass
To Coda
Chorus
Bass: w/ Bass Fig. 1, 4 times, simile
N.C.(A)
(D/A)
(A)
1.
2.
D.S. al Coda
Sweet __ e - mo - tion
tion.
3. I
Coda
Outro
Play 12 Times and Fade

Sweet Little Angel

Words and Music by B.B. King and Jules Bihari

Gb7
Db7
Ab7
G7
Gb7
Db7
Ab7
2nd Verse
Db7
Gb7
Db7
You know, I asked my ba - by for a nick - el, (etc.)
Gb7

Db7
Ab7
Gb7
Gb7
Db7
Ab7
3rd Verse
Db7
Gb7
Db7
Gb7
Db7
Ab7
G7

Seque to "It's My Own Fault" (omitted).

Synchronicity II

Written and Composed by Sting

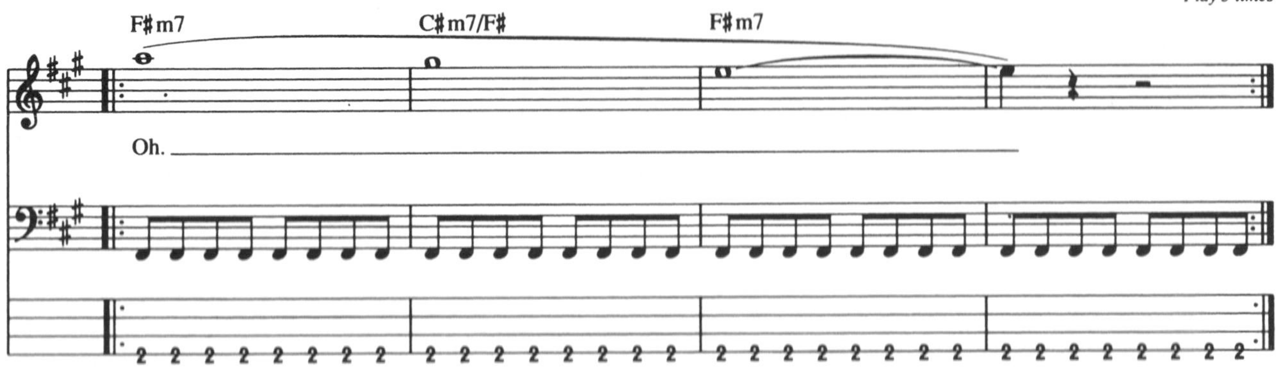

A
C#m
G
Grand - moth-er scream-ing at ___ the ___ wall. _
A
C#m
A/C#
G
We have to shout ___ a - bove _ the din ___ of our ___ Rice _ Krisp-ies. ______
A
C#m
A/C#
G
We can't hear an - y - thing _ at ____ all. __
A
D/A
Adim
D/A
Moth-er chants _ her lit - an - y ___ of bore - dom and ___ frus - tra - tion but
A
D/A
Adim
D/A
we know all ___ her su - i - cides _ are ______ fake. ____________________

Dm7
Dm6
Dm7
Dm6
Dad-dy on - ly stares in - to the dis - tance. There's
Dm7
Dm6
E7sus
on - ly so much more that he can take.
Am(add9)
F/A
G
Dm/F
Man-y miles a - way, some-thing crawls from the slime at the bot-
E
Esus
E
G
D
tom of a dark Scot-tish lake.
A
C#m
A/C#
G
An-oth-er in-dus - trial ug - ly morn - ing. The

A C#m A/C# G
fact-'ry belch - es filth in - to the sky.
A C#m A/C G
He walks un - hind - ered through the pick - et lines to - day.
A C#m A/C# G
He does-n't think to won - der why. The
A D/A Adim D/A
sec- re - tar - ies pout and preen like cheap tarts on a red light street but
A D/A Adim D/A
all he ev - er thinks to do is watch. And

Dm7
Dm6
Dm7
Dm6
ev-'ry sin - gle meet - ing with his __ so called __ su-per-i - or is a hu -
Dm7
Dm6
E7sus
mil - i - at - ing kick in the crotch.
Am(add9)
F/A
G
Dm/F
Man-y miles a - way __ some-thing crawls to the sur-face __ of a dark
E
Esus
E
__ Scot-tish lake.
Guitar Solo - Sound Effects, Feedback, String Scrapes
F#

A
C♯m
A/C♯
G
An-oth-er work - ing day has end - ed,
A
C♯m
A/C♯
G
on - ly the rush hour's hell to face,
A
C♯m
A/C♯
G
packed like lem - mings in - to shi - ny met - al box - es, con -

A C#m A/C# G
tes-tants in a sui - i - ci - dal race.
A D/A Adim D/A
Dad-dy grips the wheel and stares a - lone in - to the dis - tance. He
A D/A Adim D/A
knows that some - thing some - where has to break. He
Dm7 Dm6 Dm7 Dm6
sees the fam - 'ly home now, loom - ing in his head - lights, the
Dm7 Dm6 E7sus
pain up - stairs that makes his eye - balls ache.

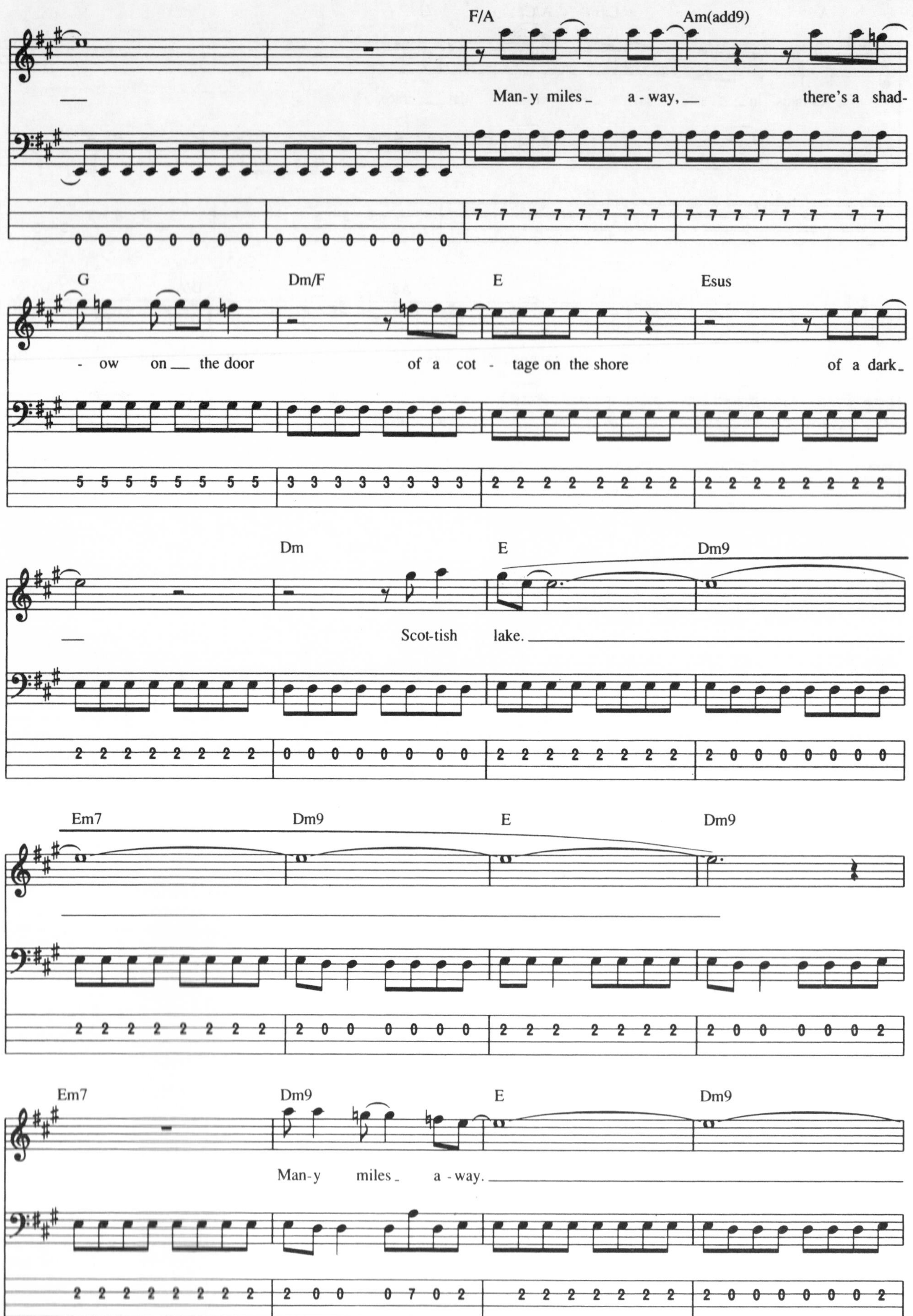
F/A
Am(add9)
Man-y miles _ a - way, _ there's a shad-
G
Dm/F
E
Esus
- ow on _ the door of a cot - tage on the shore of a dark _
Dm
E
Dm9
_ Scot-tish lake. _
Em7
Dm9
E
Dm9
Em7
Dm9
E
Dm9
Man-y miles _ a - way. _

Em7
Dm9
E
Dm9
Man-y miles_ a - way.
Em7
Dm9
E
Dm9
Man-y miles_ a - way.
Em7
Dm9
E
Dm9
Man-y miles_ a - way.
Em7
Dm9
E
Dm9
Man-y miles_ a - way.
Repeat and Fade
Em7
Dm9
E
Dm9
Em7
Man-y miles_ a - way.

Take a Look Around
(Theme from "M: I-2")

from the Paramount Motion Picture M: I-2

Words and Music by Fred Durst and Lalo Schifrin

D6
D/E
good comes the bad, the bad comes the good, but I'm-a live my life like I should.
(Like I should.)
where you gon-na run when you star-in' down the ca-ble of a, a mic point-ed at your grill like a gun?
End Bass Fig. 3

Bass: w/ Bass Fig. 3
F♯m
Am6
Now all the crit-ics wan-na hit it and shit can how we did it just be-cause they don't get it. But
Limp Biz-kit is rock-in' the set. It's like Rus-sian roul-ette when you're plac-in' your bet. So

D6
D/E
I'll stay fit-ted new er-a com-mit-ted. Now this red cap gets a rap from his crit-ics.
don't be up-set when you're broke and you're done, 'cause I'm-a be the one 'til I jet.

1.
Bass: w/ Bass Fig. 1
N.C.(F♯m)
(A)
But do we al-ways got-ta cry? Do we al-ways got-ta live in-side a lie?
(Al-ways got-ta cry? Live in-side a lie?)

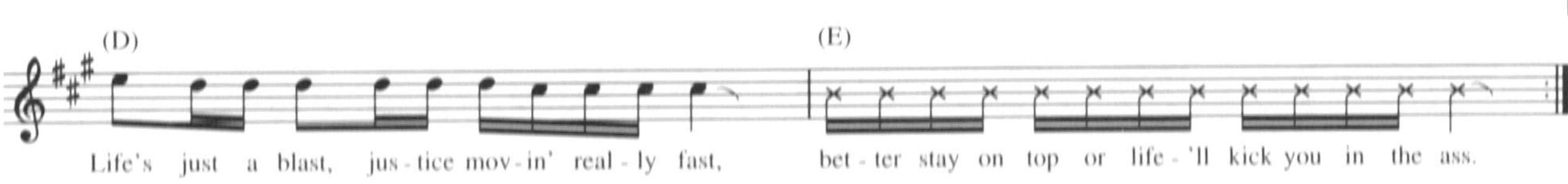
(D)
(E)
Life's just a blast, jus-tice mov-in' real-ly fast, bet-ter stay on top or life-'ll kick you in the ass.

2.
Chorus
N.C.
I know why you wan-na hate me. I know why you wan-na hate me.
Bass

I know why you wan - na hate me. 'Cause hate is all the world has ev - en seen late - ly.
I know why you wan - na hate me. I know why you wan - na hate me.
Now I know why you wan - na hate me. 'Cause hate is all the world's ev - en seen late - ly.
F#5
A5
B5
F#5
E#5
And now you wan - na hate me 'cause hate is all the world has ev - en seen late - ly.

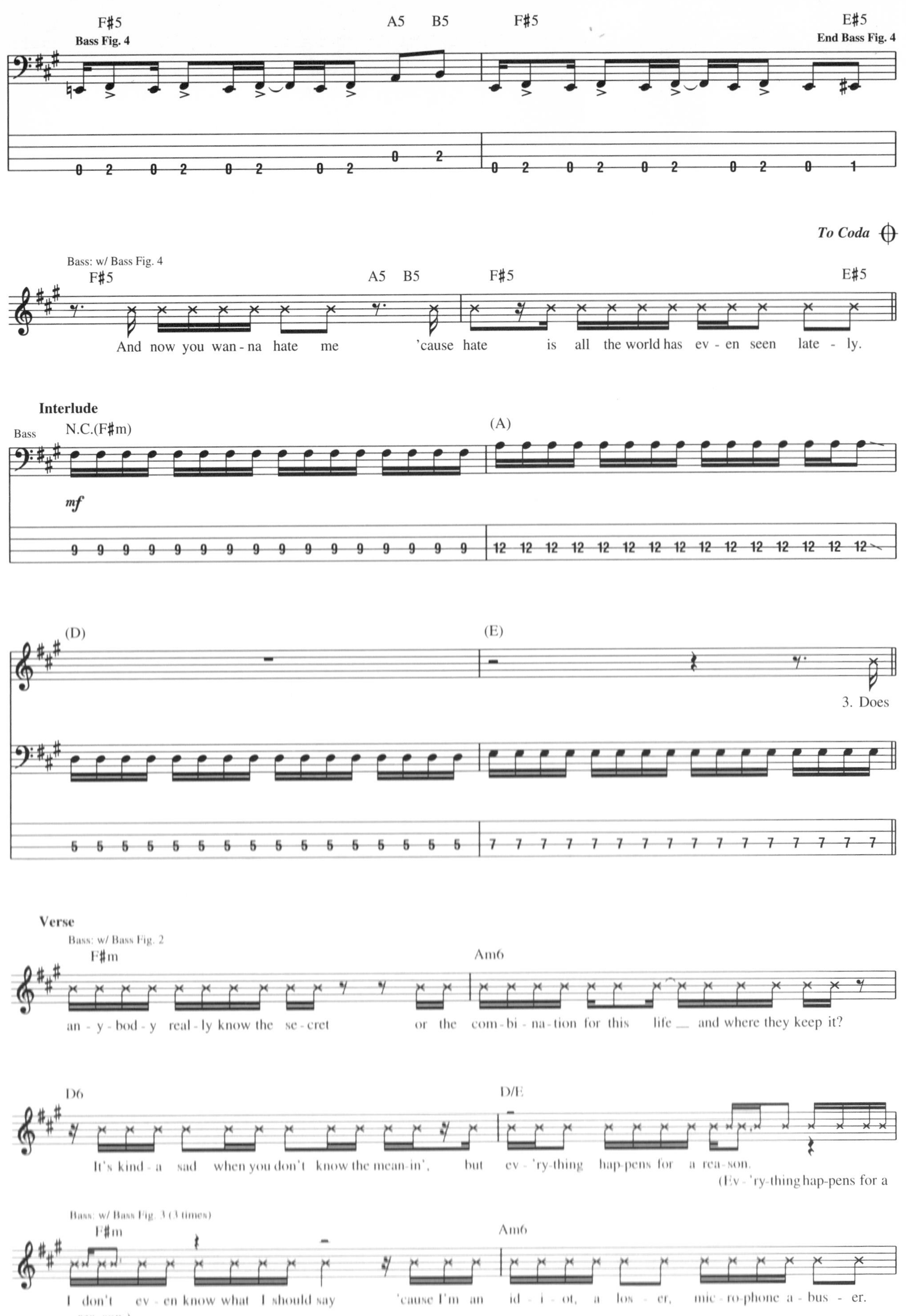

F#5
Bass Fig. 4
A5 B5
F#5
E#5
End Bass Fig. 4
0 2 0 2 0 2 0 2 0 2
0 2 0 2 0 2 0 2 0 1
To Coda
Bass: w/ Bass Fig. 4
F#5
A5 B5
F#5
E#5
And now you wan-na hate me 'cause hate is all the world has ev-en seen late-ly.
Interlude
Bass
N.C.(F#m)
(A)
mf
9 9 9 9 9 9 9 9 9 9 9 9 9 9 9 9
12 12 12 12 12 12 12 12 12 12 12 12 12 12 12
(D)
(E)
3. Does
5 5 5 5 5 5 5 5 5 5 5 5 5 5 5 5
7 7 7 7 7 7 7 7 7 7 7 7 7 7 7 7
Verse
Bass: w/ Bass Fig. 2
F#m
Am6
an-y-bod-y real-ly know the se-cret or the com-bi-na-tion for this life and where they keep it?
D6
D/E
It's kind-a sad when you don't know the mean-in', but ev-'ry-thing hap-pens for a rea-son.
(Ev-'ry-thing hap-pens for a
Bass: w/ Bass Fig. 3 (3 times)
F#m
Am6
I don't ev-en know what I should say 'cause I'm an id-i-ot, a los-er, mic-ro-phone a-bus-er.
rea-son.)

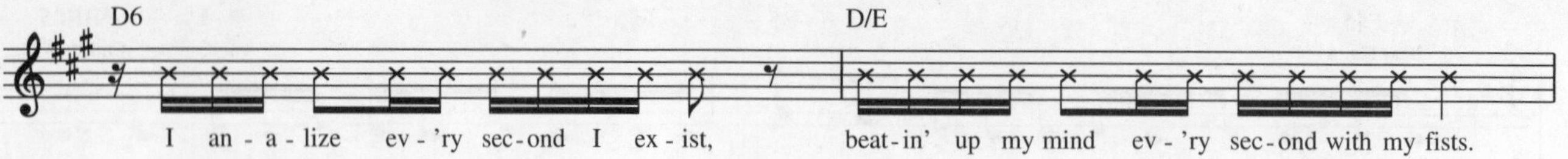
D6
D/E
I an-a-lize ev-'ry sec-ond I ex-ist,
beat-in' up my mind ev-'ry sec-ond with my fists.

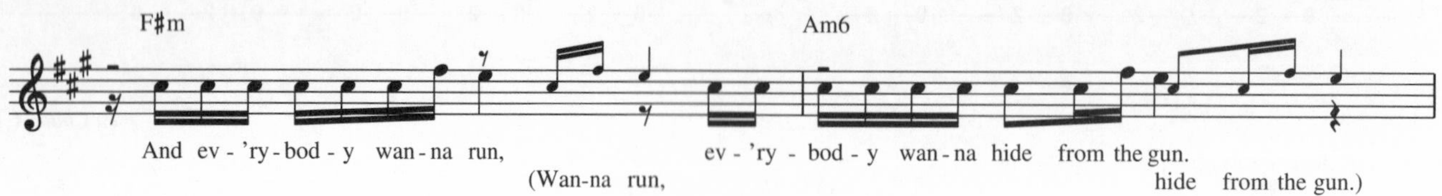
F♯m
Am6
And ev-'ry-bod-y wan-na run,
ev-'ry-bod-y wan-na hide from the gun.
(Wan-na run,
hide from the gun.)

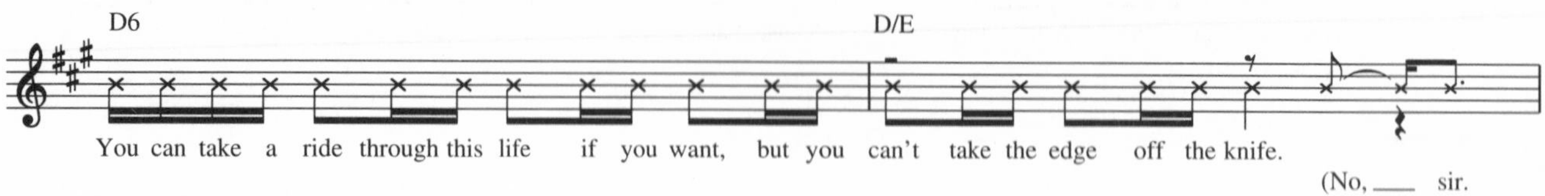
D6
D/E
You can take a ride through this life if you want, but you can't take the edge off the knife.
(No, ___ sir.

F♯m
Am6
And now you want your mon-ey back,
but you're de-nied 'cause your brain's fried from the sack.
Mon-ey back.)

D6
D/E
D.S. al Coda
And there ain't noth-in' I can ___ do 'cause life is a les-son. You'll learn it when you're through.

Coda

Bass
F♯5
A5
B5
E♯5

N.C.
Whispered:
Sh. ___
mf

(F#m)
Now
Bass Fig. 5

(A)
(D)
(E)
I
know
why.
End Bass Fig. 5

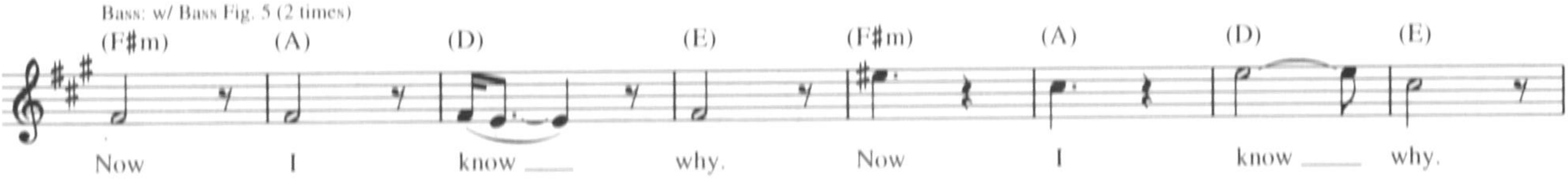
Bass: w/ Bass Fig. 5 (2 times)
(F#m)
(A)
(D)
(E)
(F#m)
(A)
(D)
(E)
Now
I
know
why.
Now
I
know
why.

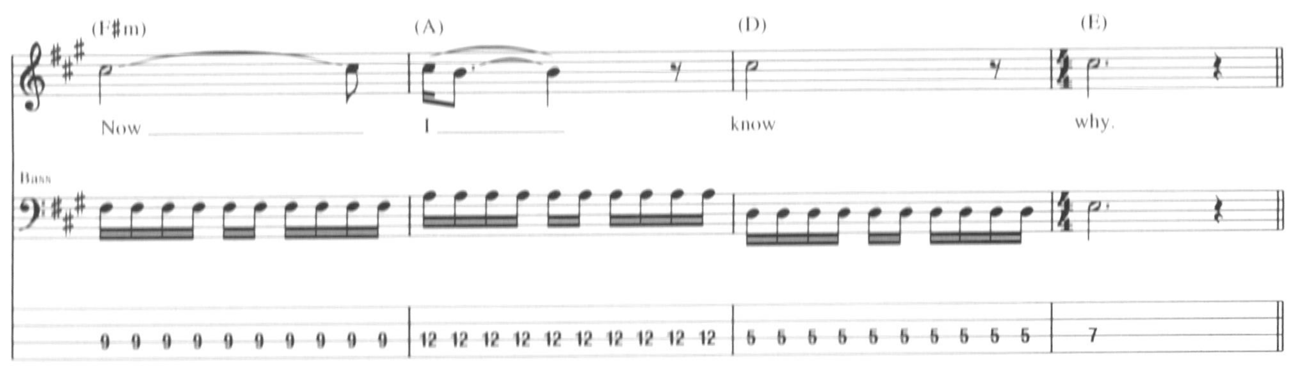
(F#m)
(A)
(D)
(E)
Now
I
know
why.
Bass

F#5
A5
B5
F#5
E#5
Now I know why you wan-na hate me.
Now I know why you wan-na hate me.
f
F#5
A5
B5
F#5
E#5
Now I know why you wan-na hate me, 'cause hate is all the world has ev-en seen late-ly.
F#5
A5
B5
F#5
E#5
'Cause hate is all the world has ev-en seen late-ly.
F#5
A5
B5
F#5
E#5
'Cause hate is all the world has ev-en seen late-ly.
Outro
Bass: w/ Bass Fig. 2 (till fade)
Play 5 times & fade
F#m
Am6
D6
D/E

Takin' Care of Business

Words and Music by Randy Bachman

w/ Bass Fig. 1 (last 3 meas.)
Bb5 F5 C5
get to work by nine and start your slav-ing jobs to get your pay. If you
ly-ing in the sun. Tell them that you like it this way. It's the
w/ Bass Fig. 1
Bb5 F5
ev-er get an-noyed, look at me, I'm self em-ployed. I love to work at noth-ing all day.
work that we a-void and we're all self em-ployed. We love to work at noth-ing all day.
Chorus
w/ Bass Fig. 1 (2 times)
3rd time, w/ Bass Fig. 1 (1st 3 meas.)
C5 C5 Bb5
And I've been tak-ing care of busi-ness ev-'ry day. Tak-
And we've been tak-ing care of busi-ness ev-'ry day. Tak-
3rd time, w/ Bass Fill 1
F5 C5
-ing care of busi-ness ev-'ry way. I've been tak-ing care of busi-ness,
-ing care of busi-ness ev-'ry way. We've been tak-ing care of busi-ness,
3rd time, w/ Bass Fig. 1 (last 3 meas.)
Bb5 F5 C5
To Coda
it's all mine. Tak-ing care of bus-ness and work-ing o-ver-time, work out.
it's all mine. Tak-ing care of busi-ness and work-ing o-ver-time.
1.
Interlude
w/ Bass Fig. 1 (1st 3 meas.)
C5 Bb5 F5
w/ Bass Fill 2
C5
w/ Bass Fig. 1 (last 3 meas.)
Bb5 F5 C5
2. There's work
2.
Guitar solo
w/ Bass Fig. 1 (last 3 meas.)
C5 Bb5
F5
w/ Bass Fill 1
C5
w/ Bass Fig. 1 (last 3 meas.)
Bb5 F5 C5
Bass Fill 2

Interlude
C5
Bass tacet
N.C.
Bridge
C F E♭
Whoa! Al - right. Ow.
Bass Fill 3
End Bass Fill 3
B♭ C F E♭ B♭ C F E♭
Take good care of my busi -
B♭ C F E♭
ness, when I'm a - way, ev - 'ry day. Whoa.
Guitar Solo
w/ Bass Fig. 1
C5 B♭5 F5 C5
D.S. al Coda
B♭5 F5 C5
3. They

Coda
Breakdown
Bass: w/ Bass Fill 3
Bass tacet
N.C.
Tak - ing care of busi - ness.
Whoa. Tak - ing care of busi - ness. Tak -
- ing care of busi - ness. Tak - ing care of busi - ness,
C5 N.C. B♭ N.C. F
Tak - ing care of busi - ness, ev - 'ry day. Tak -
- ing care of busi - ness, it's all mine. Tak -
N.C. C 1. N.C. C 2.
- ing care of busi - ness ev - 'ry way. Tak - work - ing o - ver - time. Whoa!
- ing care of busi - ness
Outro
w/ Bass Fig. 1 (till end)
*C5 B♭5 F5 C5
Tak - ing care of busi - ness. Tak - ing care of busi - ness. We've been tak -
*tie on repeats
Repeat and fade
B♭5 F5 C5
- ing care of busi - ness. We've been tak - ing care of busi - ness. Tak -

That'll Be the Day

Words and Music by Jerry Allison, Norman Petty and Buddy Holly

D
A
D
A
all your hugs and kiss-es and your mon-ey too. W'-ell uh, y' know you love me ba-by, st'-ill you tell me may-be

Chorus
B
E7
D
that some-day, well I'll be blue. Well, that-'ll be the day when you say good-bye. Ye-ea-ah,

A
D
that-'ll be the day when you make me cr-y. You say you're gon-na leave; you know it's a lie, 'cause

Guitar Solo
A
E7
A
A
that-'ll be the day that I die.

D

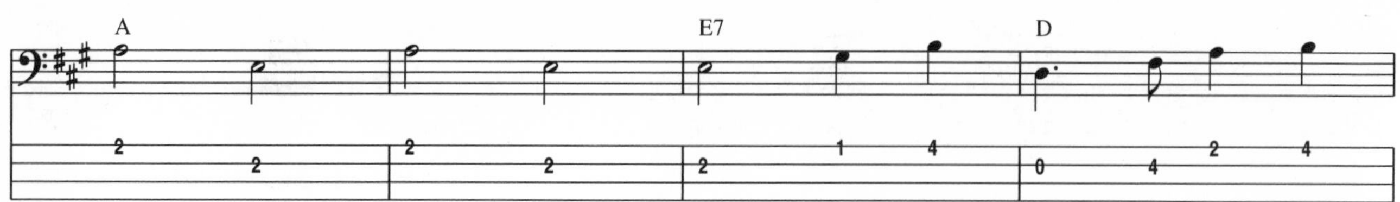
A
E7
D

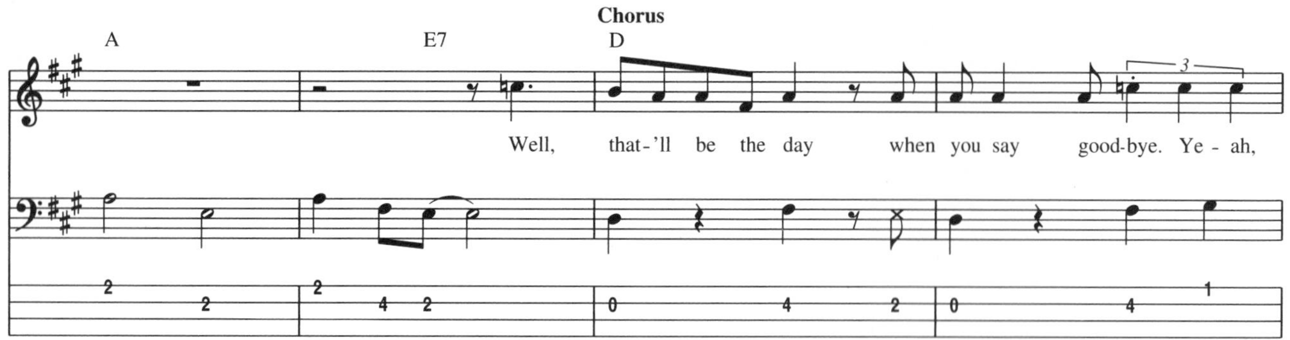
Chorus
A
E7
D
Well, that-'ll be the day when you say good-bye. Ye - ah,

A
D
that - 'll be the day when you make me cr - y. You say you're gon-na leave; you know it's a lie, 'cause

Verse
A
E7 A
D
A
that - 'll be the day that I die. Well uh, when Cu-pid shot his dart, he shot it at your heart.

D
A
D
A
So, if we ev-er part, then I'll leave you. You sit and hold me and you tell me bold-ly

Chorus
B
E7
D
that some - day, well, I'll be blue. Well, that - 'll be the day when
A
D
you say good-bye. Ye-ea - ah, that-'ll be the day when you make me cry - y. You say you're gon-na leave; you
A
E7 A
D
know it's a lie, 'cause that-'ll be the day that I die. Well, that-'ll be the day.
A
Ooh, that - 'll be the day. Ooh,
Fine
D
A
that - 'll be the day. Ooh, that-'ll be the day.

That's All Right

Words and Music by Arthur Crudup

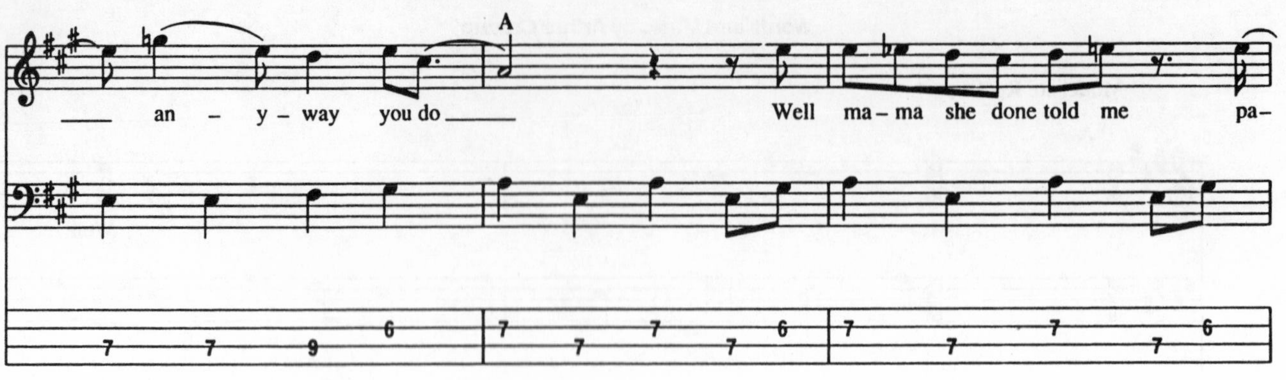
A
an - y - way you do
Well ma - ma she done told me pa-

- pa done told me too
son that gal you fool - in' with she
ain't no good for you that's all

D
E
right
that's all
right
that's all
right
now ma - ma

A
- an - y - way you do

A
D
E
A
I'm leav-in' town to-day I'm
leav-in' town for sure. Well then you won't be both-ered with me hang-in' 'round your door but that's all
D
E
right that's all right that's all right now ma-ma

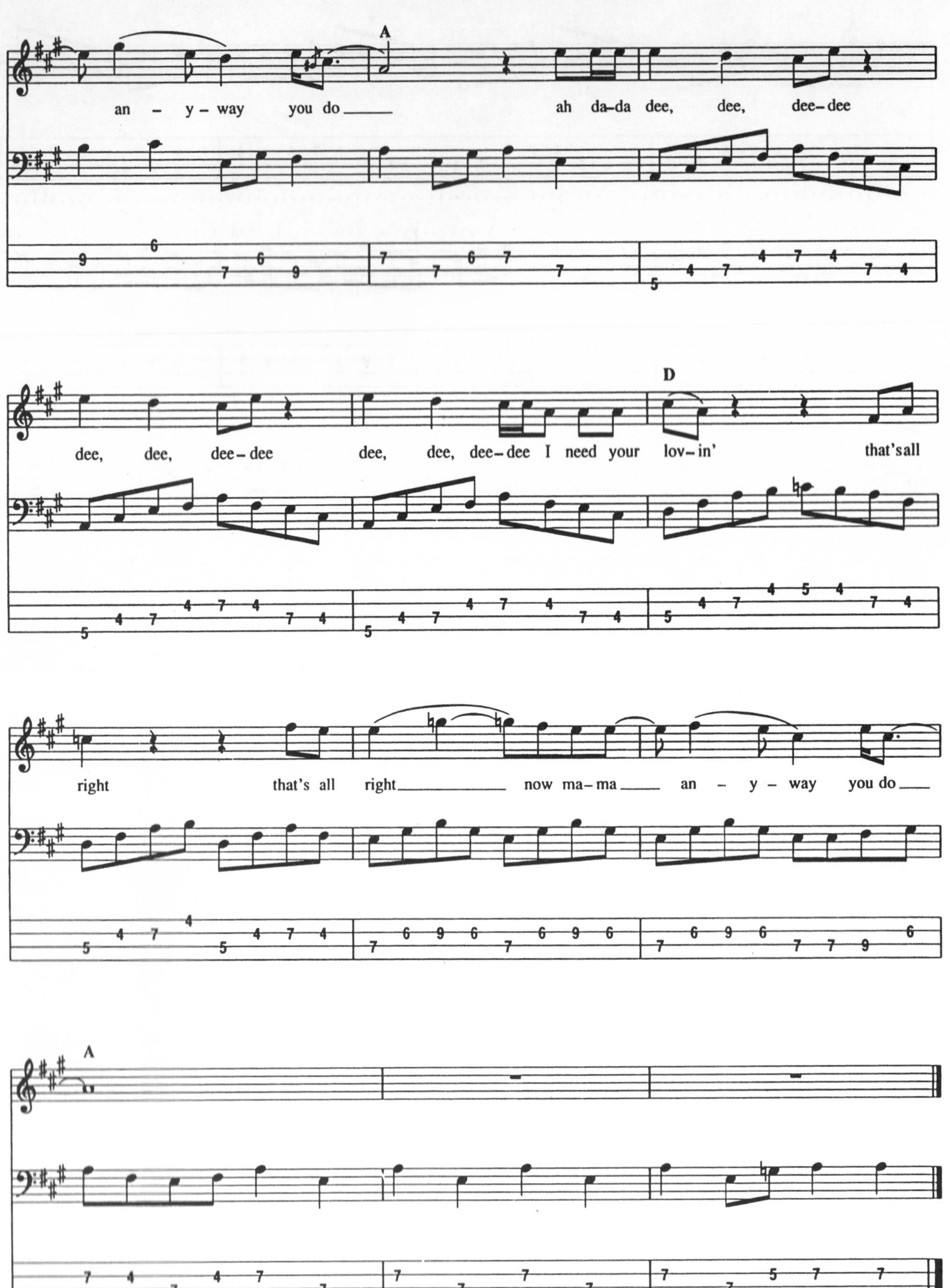
A
an – y – way you do ah da-da dee, dee, dee-dee
D
dee, dee, dee-dee dee, dee, dee-dee I need your lov-in' that'sall
right that's all right now ma-ma an – y – way you do
A

The Things That I Used to Do

Words and Music by Eddie "Guitar Slim" Jones

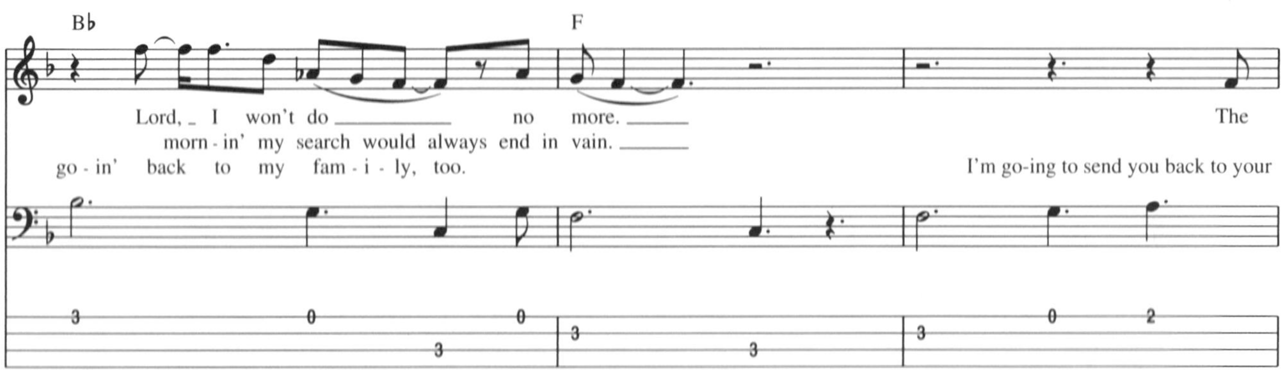

F
C7/G
more.
vain.
I used to sit and hold your hand, ba - by,
But I knew all a - long, dar - lin',
'Cause noth - ing I do that please you ba - by,
To Coda
B♭
F
cry - in', beg-gin' you not to go.
that you was head out with your oth - er man.
Lord, I just can't get a - long with you.
Guitar Solo
D.S. al Coda
Coda
F N.C.
G♭9 F9
3. I'm go-ing to send you back to your
rit.

Thunderbird

By Walter Jacobs

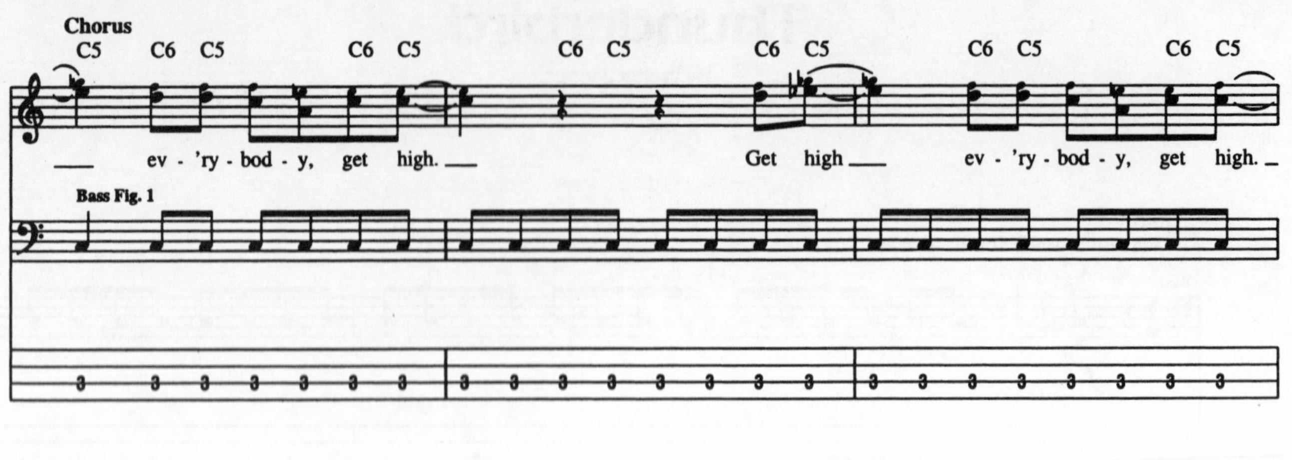
Chorus
C5 C6 C5 C6 C5 C6 C5 C6 C5 C6 C5 C6 C5
ev - 'ry - bod - y, get high.
Get high
ev - 'ry - bod - y, get high.
Bass Fig. 1

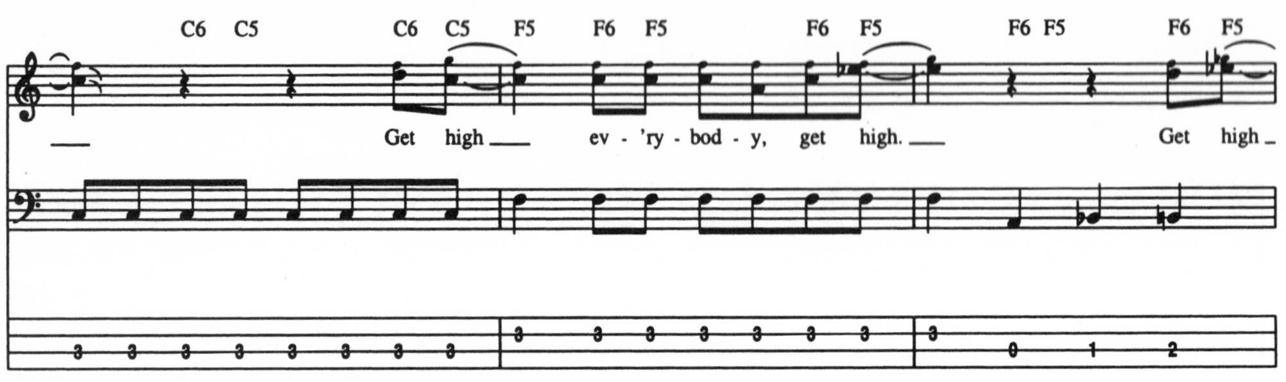
C6 C5 C6 C5 F5 F6 F5 F6 F5 F6 F5 F6 F5
Get high
ev - 'ry - bod - y, get high.
Get high

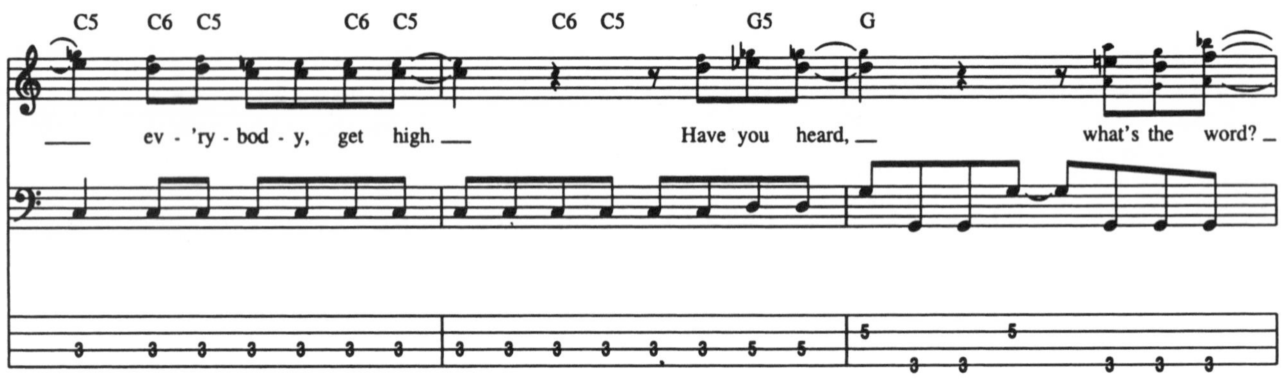
C5 C6 C5 C6 C5 C6 C5 G5 G
ev - 'ry - bod - y, get high.
Have you heard,
what's the word?

F C7 G7
Thun - der - bird.
1. Well, all
End Bass Fig. 1

Verse
C5 C6 C5 C6 C5 C6 C5 C6 C5 C6 C5 C6 C5
you kids from Tex - as, huh, grow so big an' tall.

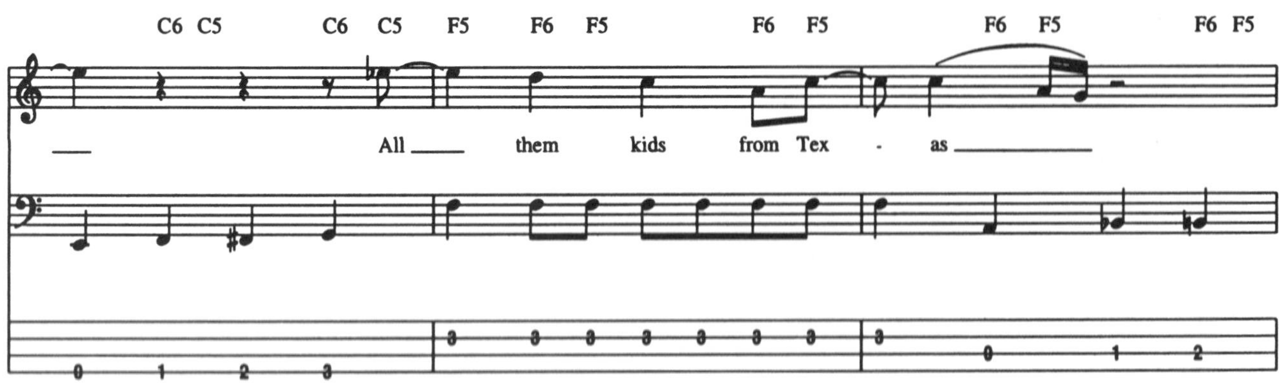
C6 C5 C6 C5 F5 F6 F5 F6 F5 F6 F5 F6 F5
All them kids from Tex - as

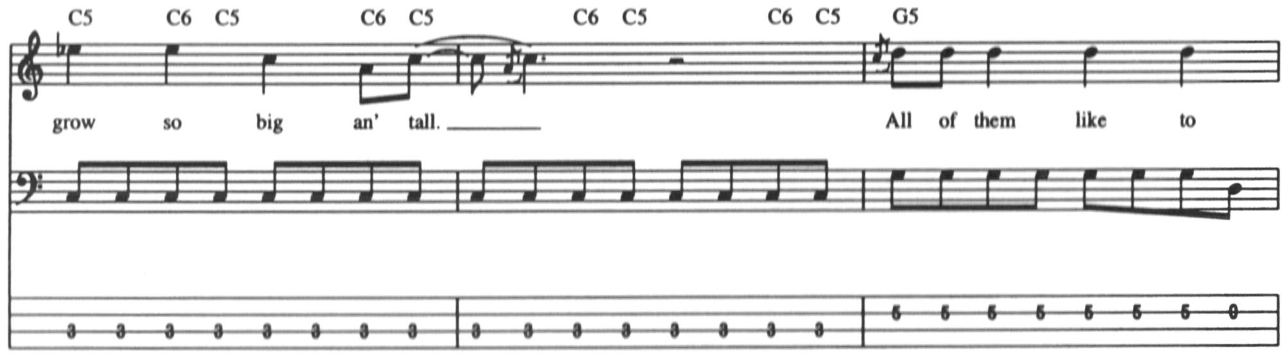
C5 C6 C5 C6 C5 C6 C5 C6 C5 G5
grow so big an' tall.
All of them like to

F5 C5 C6 C5 C6 C5 C6 C5 C6 C5
roam in that T - Bird, oh.
Get

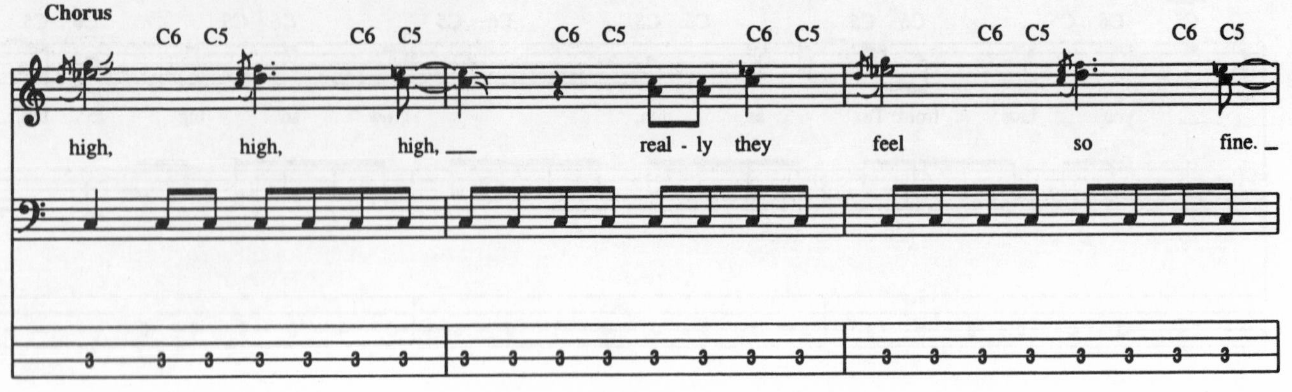
Chorus
C6 C5 C6 C5 C6 C5 C6 C5 C6 C5 C6 C5
high, high, high, real - ly they feel so fine.
3 3 3 3 3 3 3 3 3 3 3 3 3 3 3 3 3 3 3 3 3 3 3

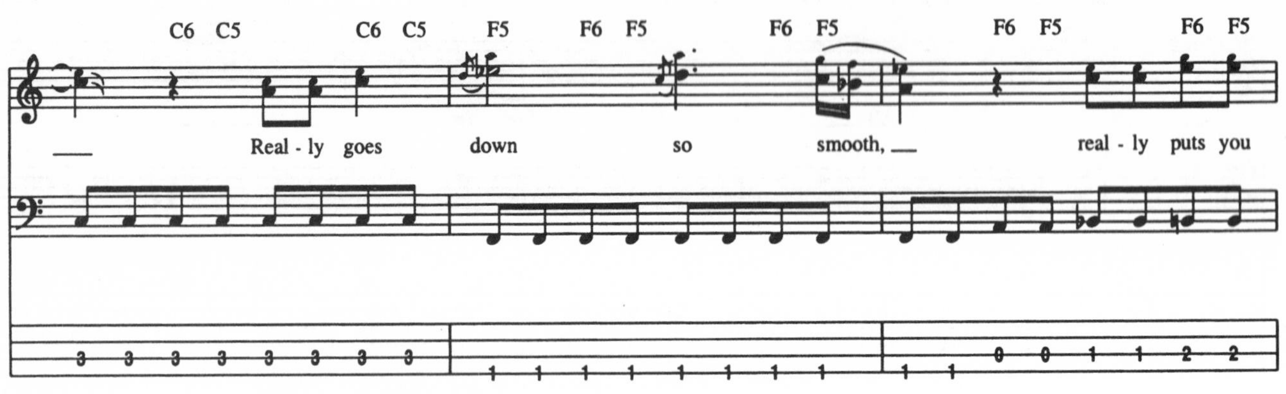
C6 C5 C6 C5 F5 F6 F5 F6 F5 F6 F5 F6 F5
Real - ly goes down so smooth, real - ly puts you
3 3 3 3 3 3 3 3 1 1 1 1 1 1 1 1 1 1 0 0 1 1 2 2

C5 C6 C5 C6 C5 C6 C5 C6 C5 G
in the groove. Have you heard, what's the word?
3 3 3 3 3 3 3 3 3 3 3 3 3 3 5 5 5 3 3 5 3 3 3

F9 C7 G7
It's Thun - der - bird.
1 1 1 3 0 1 3 0 1 2 3 0 1 2

Guitar Solo

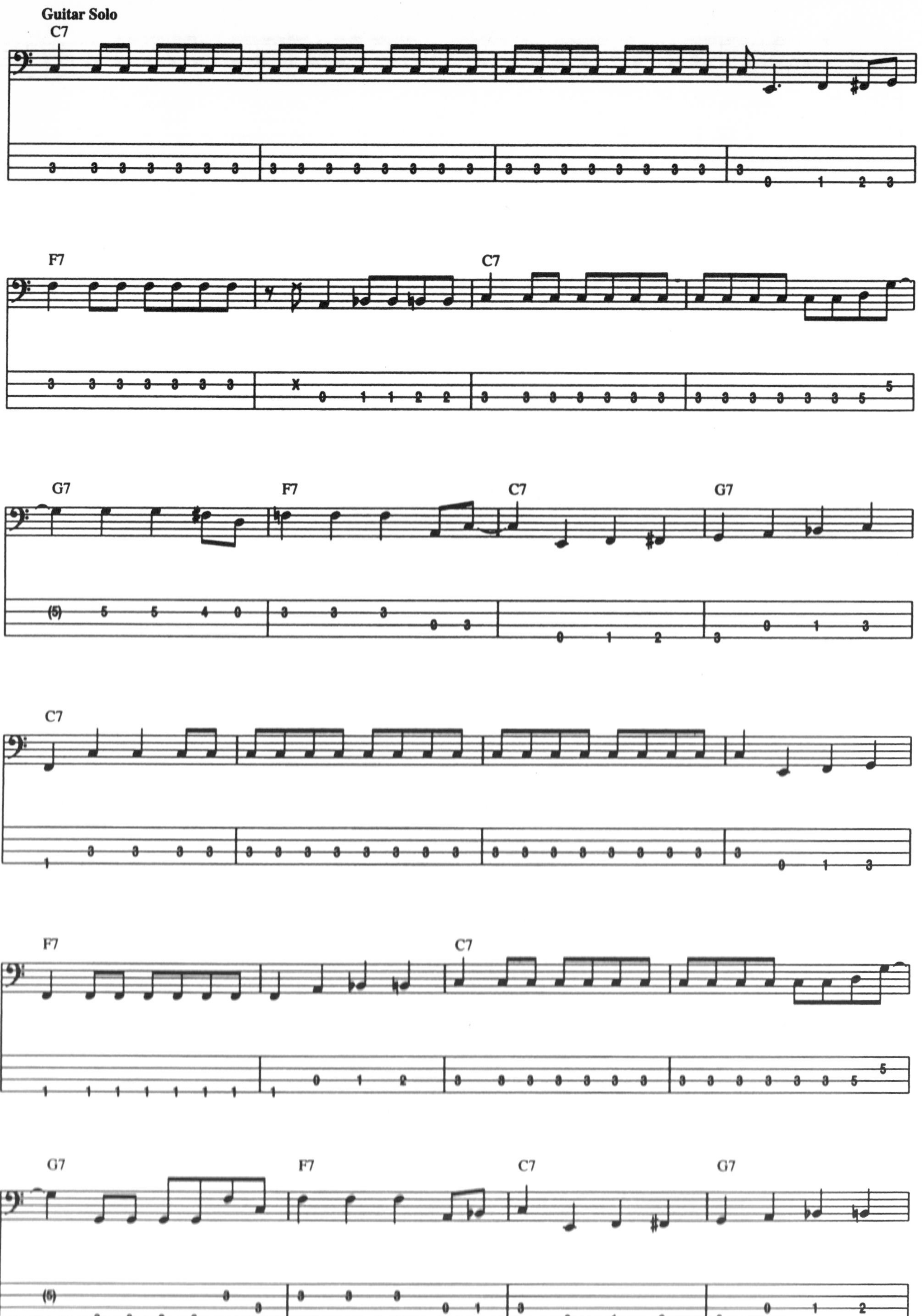

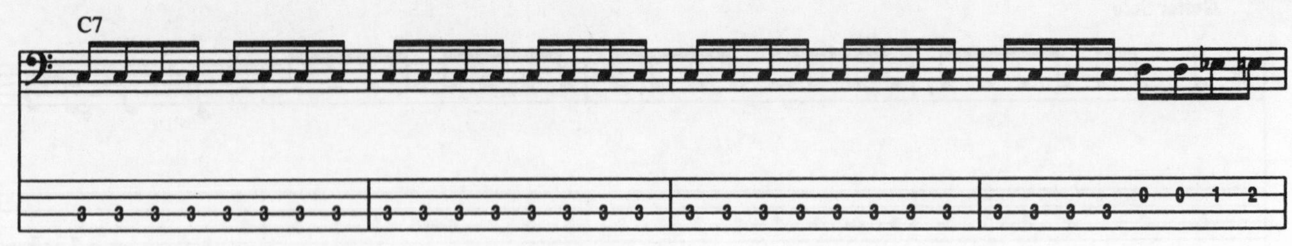
C7

F7
C7

G7
F7
C7
G7

Verse

C7
2. Juice, juice, juice, real - ly make you loose, loose, loose.
mp

F7
F
Real - ly goes down so smooth, real - ly puts you

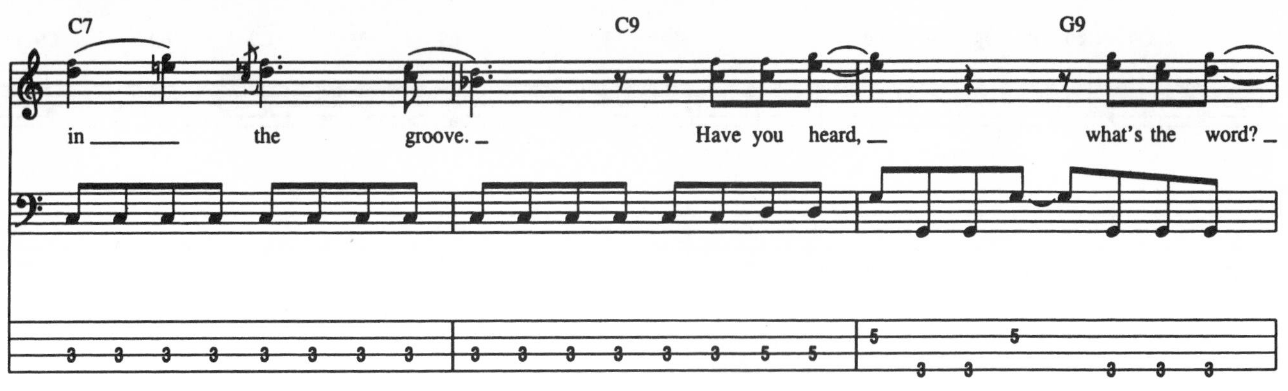
C7
C9
G9
in the groove.
Have you heard,
what's the word?
3 3 3 3 3 3 3 3
3 3 3 3 3 3 5 5
5 3 3 5 3 3 3

F9
N.C.(C7)
G7
It's Thun - der - bird.
Get
cresc.
1 1 1 3 0 1
3 0 1 2
3 0 1 2

Chorus
Bass: w/ Bass Fig. 1
C5 C6 C5 C6 C5 C6 C5 C6 C5 C6 C5 C6 C5 C6 C5 C6
high, high, high, way up in the sky. I'm gon - na get

F5 F6 F5 F6 F5 F6 F5 F6 C5 C6 C5 C6
yes sir - ree, when you come and rock with me.

C5 C6 C5 C6 G5 G6 G9 F9 C7
Have you heard, what's the word? It's Thun-der - bird.

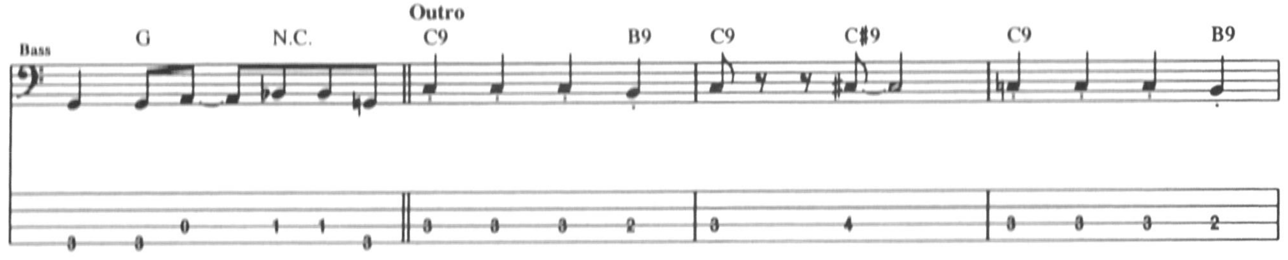
Outro
Bass
G N.C.
C9 B9 C9 C#9 C9 B9
3 3 0 1 1 3
3 3 3 2
3 4
3 3 3 2

C9 C#9 D9 D#9 E9
F9
E9
F9
E9
F9
C9
B9
C9

A7#5b9
D9
C#9 D9
C#9
C9 C#9
C9 D#9 D9 C#9
D9 G7#5b9

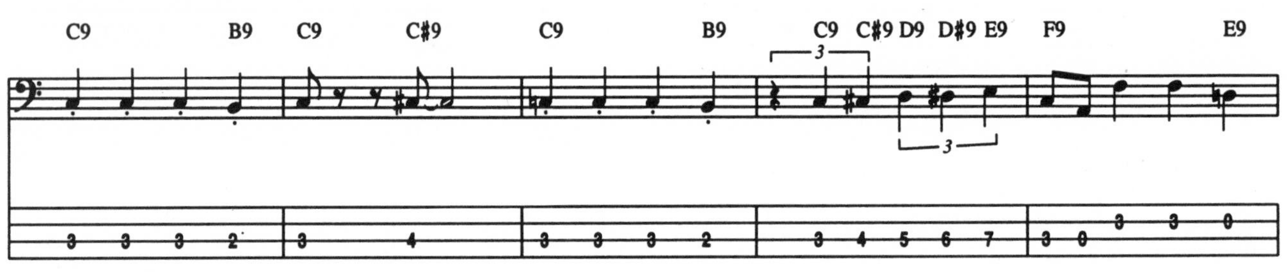
C9
B9
C9
C#9
C9
B9
C9 C#9 D9 D#9 E9
F9
E9

F9
E9 F9
C9
B9 C9
A7#5b9
D9
C#9 D9
C#9
C9 N.C.

Free Time
C7#9
N.C.
On Cue:

Today
Words and Music by Billy Corgan
Tune down 1/2 step:
④= Eb ②= Db
③= Ab ①= Gb
Slowly ♩ = 88
N.C.(E)
Gtr. I
4
E5
B5
A5
f
T
A
B
sl.
C♯5
Esus2
B
A
To - day is the great - est...
F♯5
I want - ed more...

C♯5 F♯5 A5 G♯5 D♯5 E5 D♯5 E5 D♯5 E5 D♯5 E5
Esus2 B A B Esus2 B A B
To - day is the great - est...
Esus2 B A B Esus2 B
C♯5 F♯5 A5 E5 B5
Pink rib - bon scars...
F♯5 A5 E5 B5 F♯5 A5
E5 B5 F♯5 A5 G♯5 D♯5 E5 D♯5 E5 D♯5 E5 D♯5 E5
E5 B5 E5 B5 A5 E5 B5
To - day is...

E5
B5 A5
E5
B5
C♯5
A5
sl.
sl.
E5
B5
C♯5
F♯5
A5
C♯5
I want to turn you on.
F♯5
A5
2
C♯5
F♯5
A5
C♯5
F♯5
A5
E5
B5
C♯5
A5
B5
E5
B5
To - day is the great - est.
C♯5
A5
B5
E5
B5
C♯5
A5
B5
E5
B5
C♯5
A5
B5 E5

Tragic Comic

Words and Music by Nuno Bettencourt and Gary Cherone

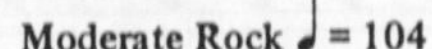

Moderate Rock ♩ = 104

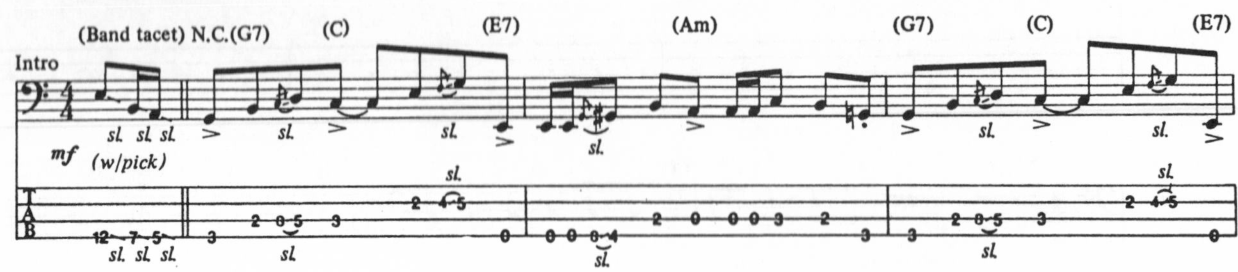

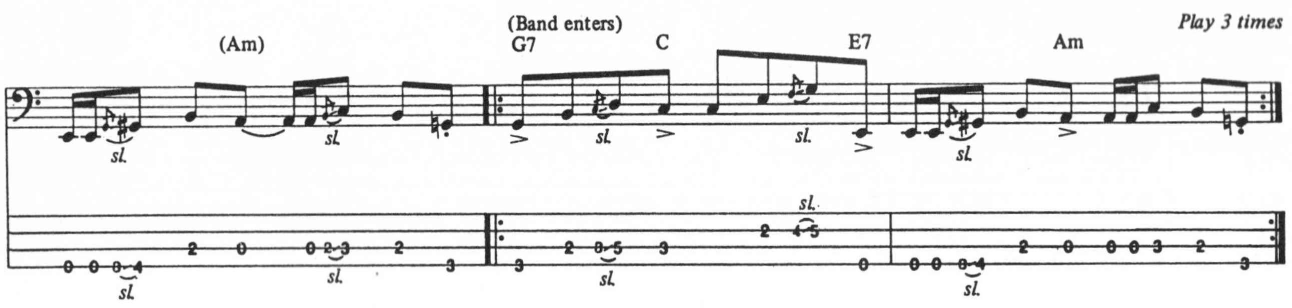

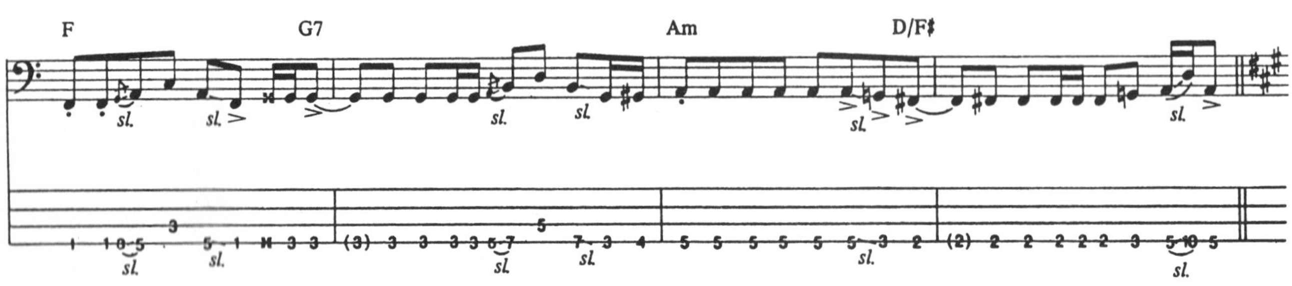

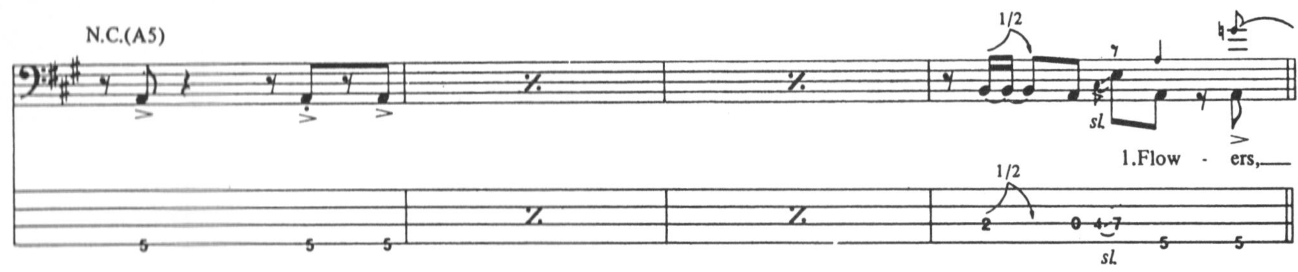

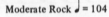

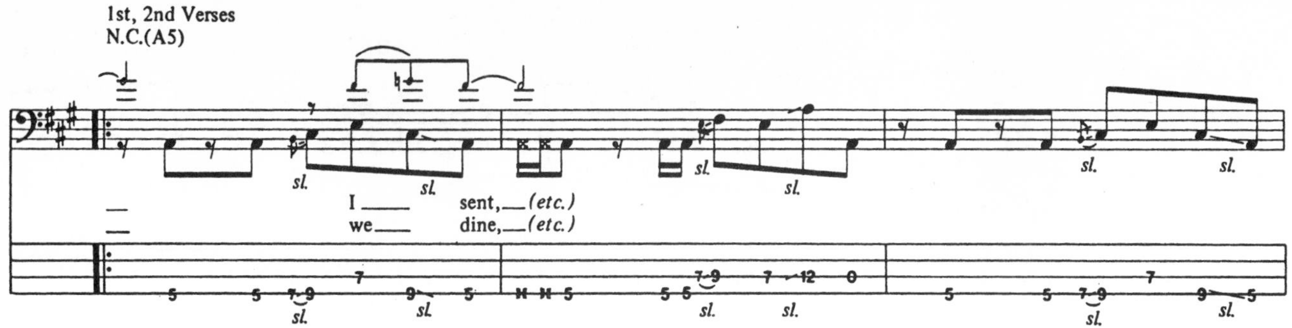
1st, 2nd Verses
N.C.(A5)
I ___ sent, __(etc.)
we ___ dine, __(etc.)

A7
D/A

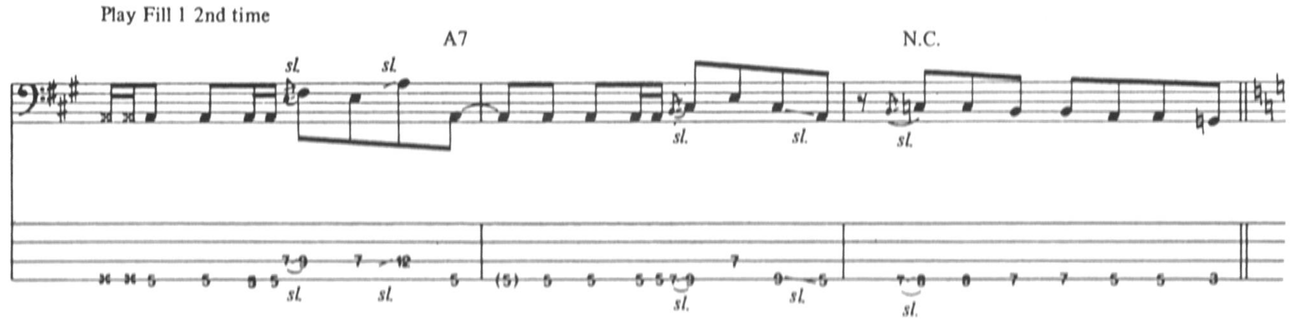
Play Fill 1 2nd time
A7
N.C.

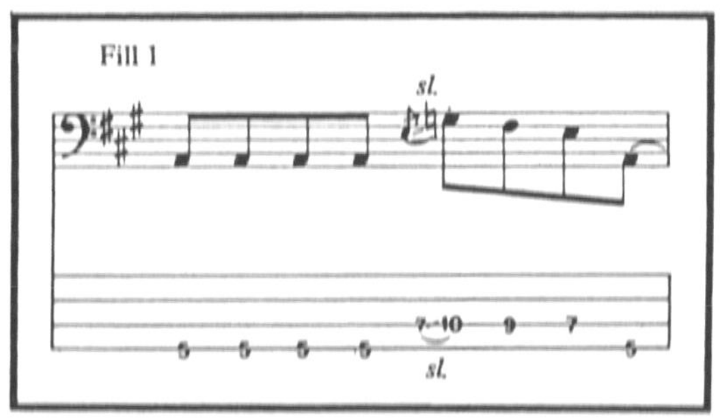
Fill 1

Chorus
G7
C
E7
Am
G7
C
E7
I'm a hap - less ro - man - tic. (etc.)
Am
G7
C
E7
Am
F
G7
3rd time to Coda
Am
D/F♯
Am
D/F♯
1.
N.C.(A5)
2. And when
2.
C
D
E♭°
E
Bridge
E
C♯m
D
A
N.C.

E C♯m C♯ D E
F♯m E D C B7sus4 E7
A5 N.C.(A5)
D.S. al Coda
Coda Am G7 C E7 Am
Play 3 times
F G Am D/F♯
Am D/F♯ C D E♭° E7
poco rit.
sl.
P

Turn! Turn! Turn!
(To Everything There Is a Season)

Words from the Book of Ecclesiastes
Adaptation and Music by Pete Seeger

A
Asus4
D
Dsus4
A
Asus4
D
Dsus4
G
Dadd9/F♯
Em
Asus4
D
Dsus4
D
2.
A
Asus4
D
Dsus4
A
Asus4
D
Dsus4
...up, a time to break down. (etc.)
A
Asus4
D
Dsus4
G
Dadd9/F♯
Em
Asus4
D
Dsus4
D
3rd Verse
Dadd9
G6
Dadd9/F♯
A
Asus4
D
G6
Dadd9/F♯
Aadd9
Asus4

G6
Dadd9/F♯
Em
Asus4
D
Dsus4
D
Dsus4
Aadd9
Asus4
D
Dsus4
A
Asus4
D
Dsus4
...love, a time_ of hate. (etc.)
A
Asus4
D
Dsus4
G
Dadd9/F♯
Em
Asus4
D
Dsus4
D
Guitar solo
Dadd9
G6
Dadd9/F♯
Asus4
Dadd9
G6
Dadd9/F♯
Asus4
G6
Dadd9/F♯
Em7
N.C.(D)
D
G6
G
A
A7sus4
Dadd9
Dsus4
A
A7sus4
Dadd9
Dsus4

A A7sus4 Dadd9 Dsus2 G6 Dadd9/F♯ Em7
4th Verse
D Dsus4 D Dadd9 G6 Dadd9/F♯ A
Asus4 D G6 Dadd9/F♯ A Asus4 G6 Dadd9/F♯
Em Asus4 D Dsus4 D Dsus4 A Asus4
D Dsus4 A Asus4 D Dsus4 A Asus4
D Dsus4 G6 Dadd9/F♯ Em Asus4 D Dsus4
Repeat and fade
D N.C.(D) (G) (Dadd9/F♯) (Em) D6 A N.C.(D) (G) (Dadd9/F♯) (Em) D6 A

Two Princes

Words and Music by Spin Doctors

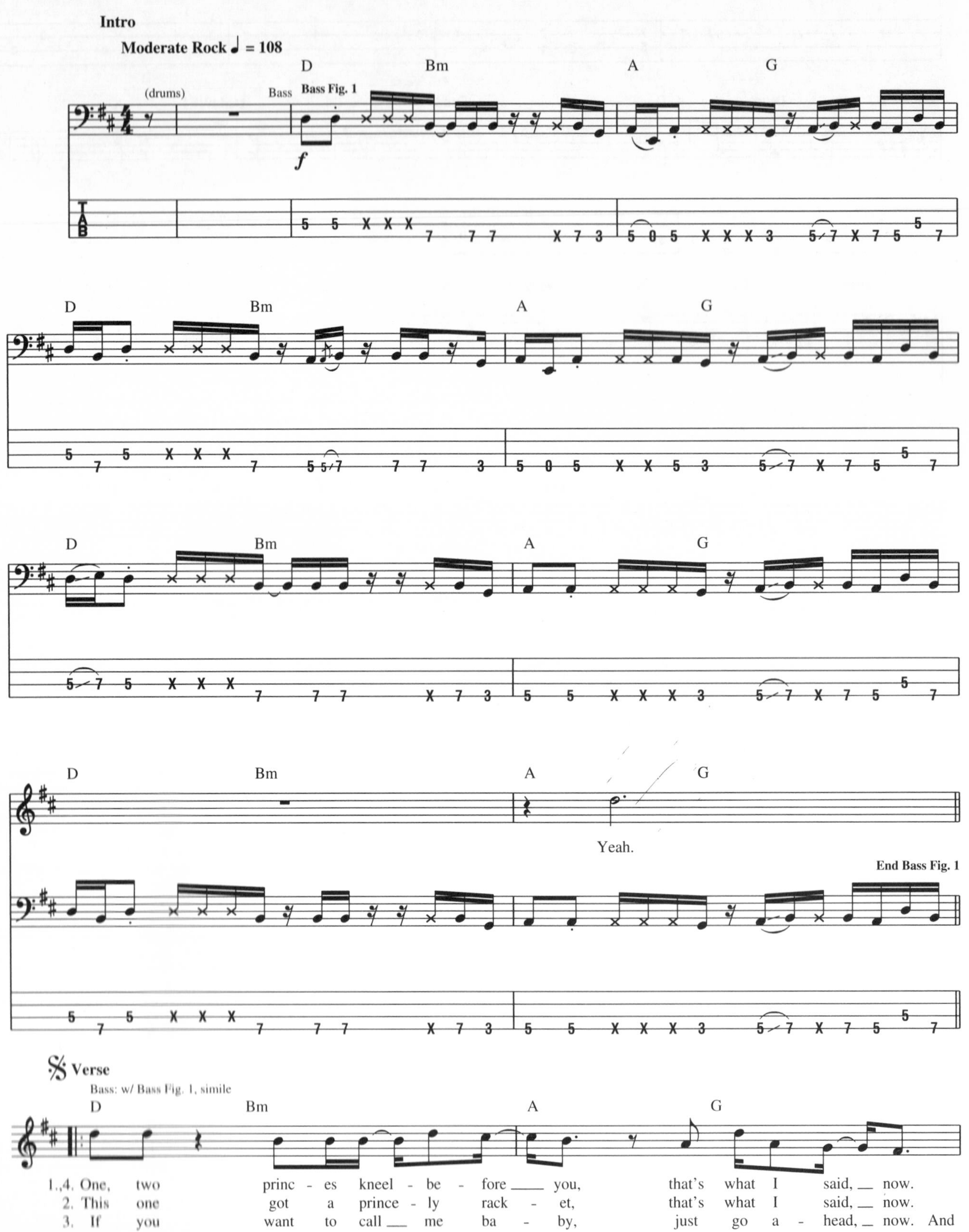

D Bm A G
Princ - es, princ - es who a - dore you. Just go a - head, now.
Got some big seal up - on his jack - et, ain't in his head, now. You
if you like to tell me may - be, just go a - head, now. And
D Bm A G
One has dia-monds in his pock - ets, and that's some bread, now.
mar - ry him your fa - ther will con - done you, how 'bout that now? You
if you wan - na buy me flow - ers, just go a - head, now. And
To Coda 1
D Bm A G
This one, said he wants to buy you rock - ets, ain't in his head, now.
mar-ry me, your fa - ther will dis - own you, he'll eat his hat, now.
if you like to talk for hours, just go a - head, now.
1.
Bass: w/ Bass Fig. 1, 1st 3 meas., simile
D Bm7 A G D Bm7
Yeah, yeah, yeah. De de de dit. D-be, be be de. Be-dee-dl-y
2.
A G G D
de - bu du - bu du - bu du - bu du - bu du - bu du - bu du - bu. Mar-ry him or ma - ry me. I'm
Bass
simile on repeat
G
the one that loves you ba - by, can't you see? I ain't got no fu - ture or fam - 'ly tree, but

To Coda 2
D.S. al Coda 1
A
I know what a prince and lov - er ought to be.
I know what a prince and lov - er ought to be. Said...
Coda 1
Guitar Solo
D
Bm
A
G

D.S. al Coda 2
(take 2nd ending)

Chorus
Bass: w/ Bass Fig. 1, till end, simile
D Bm7 A G D Bm7
if you want to call me ba - by, just go a - head, now. And if you like to tell me may -
A G D Bm7 A G
- by, just go a - head, now. And if you like to buy me flow - ers, just go a - head, now. And
Outro
D Bm7 A G D Bm
if you like to talk for hours, just go a - head, now. If you want to call me ba - by,
A G D Bm A G
just go a - head, now. And if you'd like to tell me may - be, just go a - head, now.
D Bm A G D Bm
If you want to buy me flow - ers, just go a - head, now. And if you like to talk for hours,
A G D Bm7 A G
just go a - head, now. Oh, ba - by. Oh,
A (Just go a - head, now.)
D Bm7 A G
oh, just, just go a - head, now.
(Just go a - head, now.)
D Bm7 A G D Bm7
Oh, your maj - es - ty, come on for - get the king and
(Just go a - head now.)
w/ Lead Voc. ad lib.
A G D Bm7 A G
Play 4 Times & Fade
mar - ry me.
(Just go a - head, now.) (Just go a - head, now.)

Walk of Life

Words and Music by Mark Knopfler

Verse
A
B7
E
1., 3. Here comes John - ny sing-ing old - ies, gold - ies.
2. Here comes John - ny gon - na tell you the sto - ry.
End Bass Fig. 1

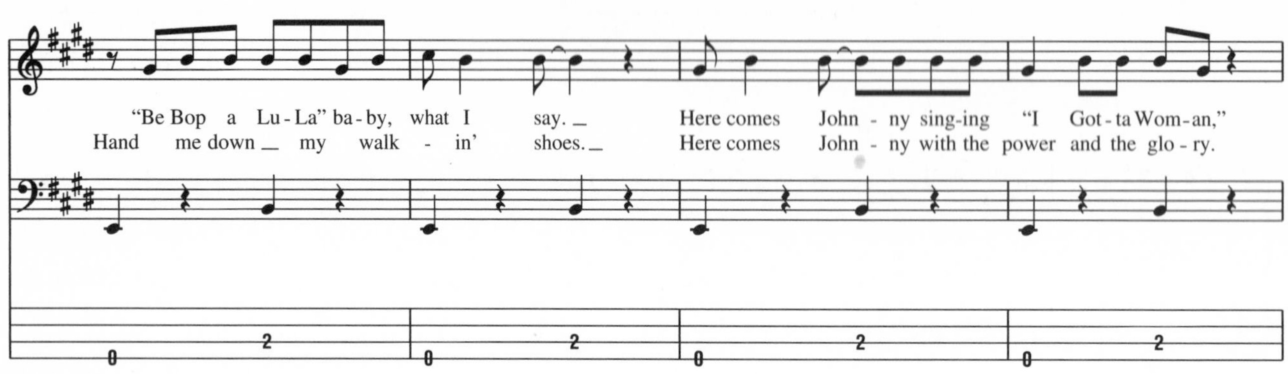
"Be Bop a Lu - La" ba - by, what I say. Here comes John - ny sing-ing "I Got - ta Wom - an,"
Hand me down my walk - in' shoes. Here comes John - ny with the power and the glo - ry.

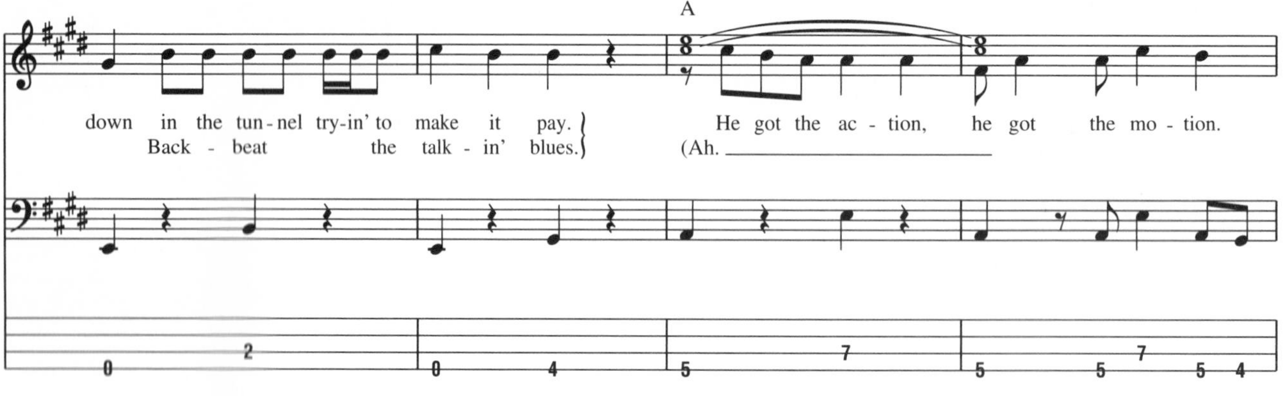
A
down in the tun - nel try-in' to make it pay. He got the ac - tion, he got the mo - tion.
Back - beat the talk - in' blues. (Ah.

To Coda
E
A
Oh, yeah, the boy can play. De - di - ca - tion, de - vo - tion;
Yeah, the boy can play. Ah.

E
Voc. Fig. 1
B
turn-ing all the night time in - to the day. He do the song a - bout the sweet lov - in' wom-an, he do the
Turn-ing all the night time in - to the day.
E
A
E
B
song a - bout the knife.
Well, he do the walk, do the walk of life.
He do the walk, do the walk of
Interlude
A
B7
End Voc. Fig. 1
E
Voc. Fig. 2
End Voc. Fig. 2
A
Yeah! He do the walk of life.
life.)
(Ah.)
B
A
B7
Ooh.
D.S. al Coda
w/ Bass Fig. 1
E
A
B
A
B7
Ooh.

Coda
Bkgd. Voc.: w/ Voc. Fig. 1
E
turn - ing all the night time in - to the day, and af - ter all that vio - lence and
B
E
A
dou-ble talk, there's just a song in all the trou - ble and the strife. You do the
E
B
A
B7
walk, yeah! You do the walk of life, mm you do the walk of life.
1st time, Bkgd. Voc.: w/ Voc. Fig. 2
w/ Lead Voc. ad lib on repeats
E
A
Ooh.
Repeat and fade
B
A
B7

Walk This Way

Words and Music by Steven Tyler and Joe Perry

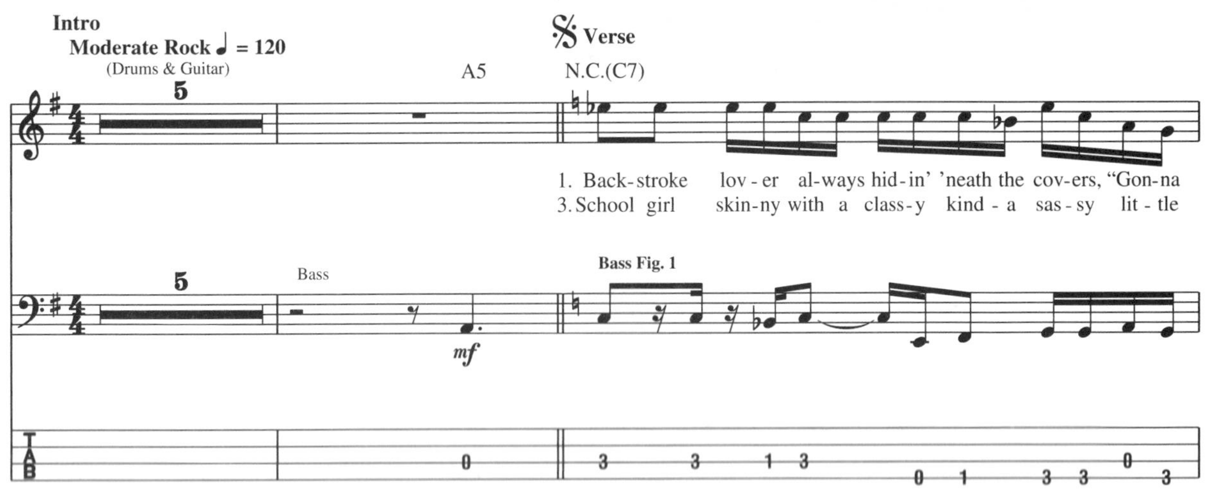

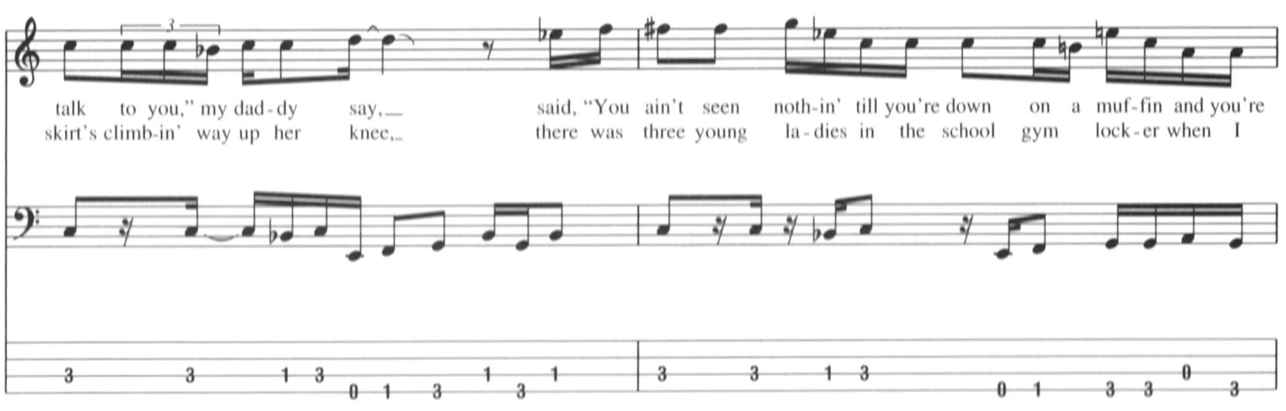

times I could rem - i - nisce, 'cause the best things in lov - in' with a sis - ter and a cou - sin on - ly
boys told me some-thin' I missed, then my next door neigh-bor with a daugh-ter had a fav - or so I
End Bass Fig. 1
Interlude
2nd time, Bass: w/ Bass Fill 2
A5
E5
start - ed with a lit - tle kiss, a - like this!
gave her just a lit - tle kiss a - like this!
Bass Fig. 2
A5
End Bass Fig. 2
Verse
Bass: w/ Bass Fig. 1
N.C.(C7)
2., 4. See - saw swing-in' with the boys in the school and your feet fly - in' up in the air, I sing,
Bass Fill 2

"Hey did - dle did-dle" with your kit - ty in the mid - dle of the swing like you did - n't care. _ So I

took a big chance at the high school dance with a miss - y who was read - y to play, _ was a
* Sing harmony 1st time only.

Bass: w/ Bass Fill 1
To Coda
me she was fool-in' 'cause she knew what she was do-in'
and I know'd love was here to stay _ when she told me to...
when she told me how to walk this way. _ She told _ me to...

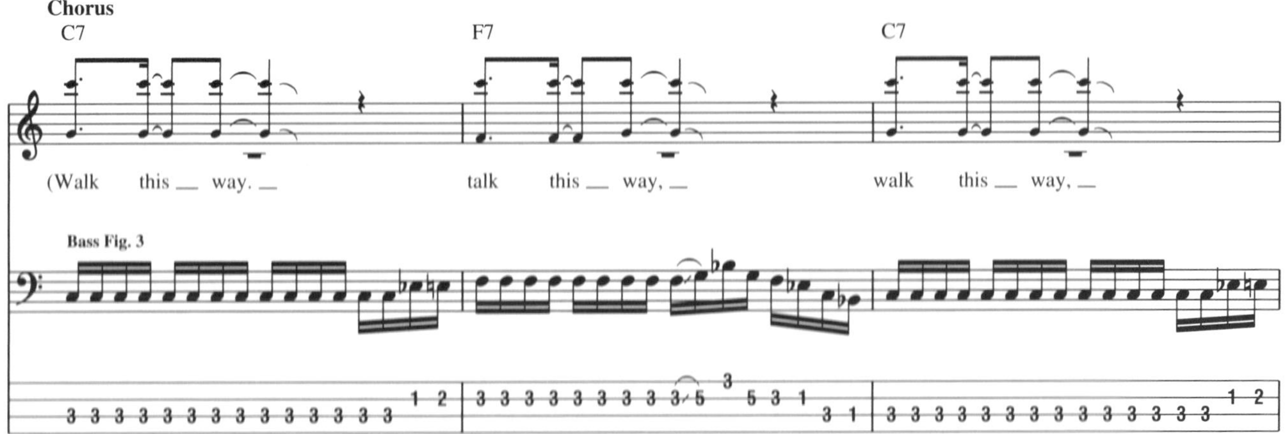
Chorus
C7
F7
C7
(Walk this _ way. _
talk this _ way, _
walk this _ way, _
Bass Fig. 3

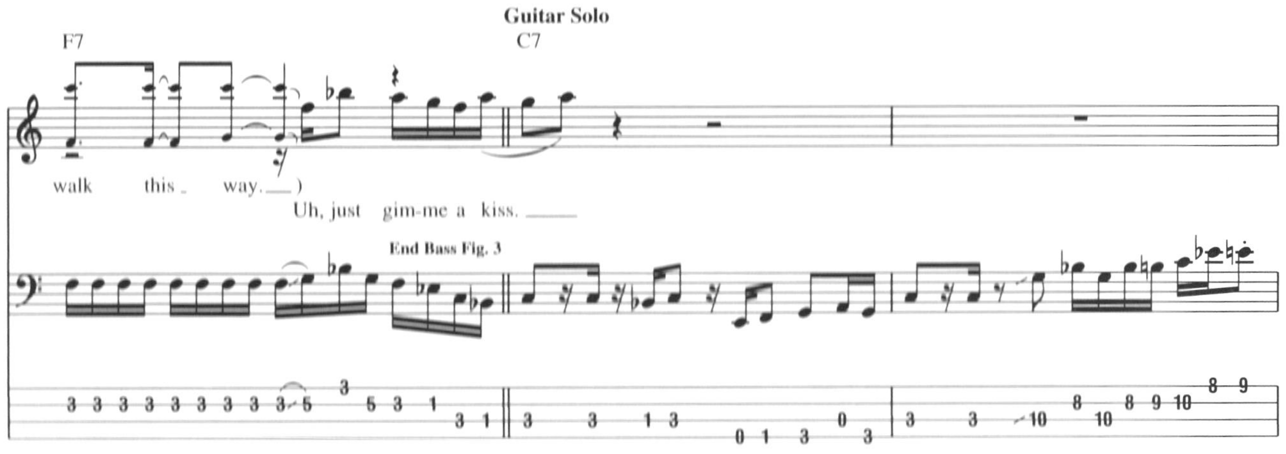
Guitar Solo
F7
C7
walk this _ way. _)
Uh, just gim-me a kiss. _
End Bass Fig. 3

Bass Fill 1

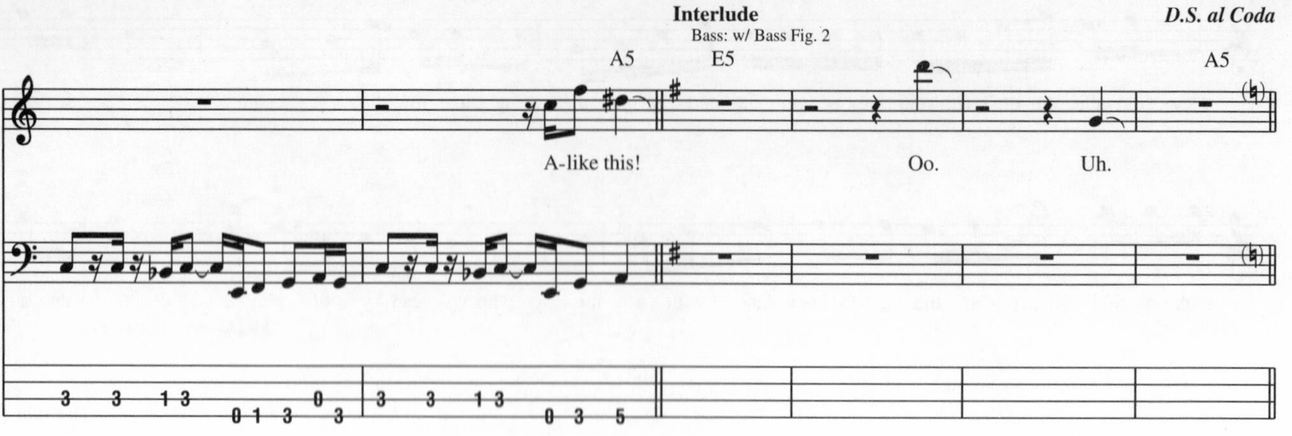
Interlude
D.S. al Coda
Bass: w/ Bass Fig. 2
A5
E5
A5
A-like this!
Oo.
Uh.

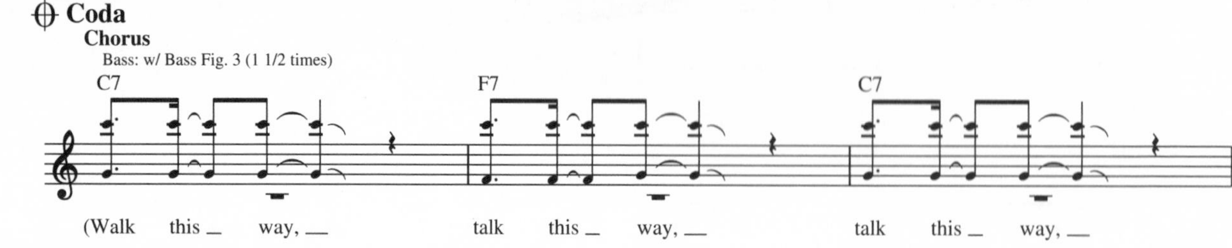
Coda
Chorus
Bass: w/ Bass Fig. 3 (1 1/2 times)
C7
F7
C7
(Walk this way,
talk this way,
talk this way,

F7
C7
F7
walk this way,
talk this way,
talk this way,

Guitar Solo
C7
F7
N.C.(C7)
walk this way,
talk this way.)
Uh, just gim-me a kiss.

A5
Like this.
E5
A5
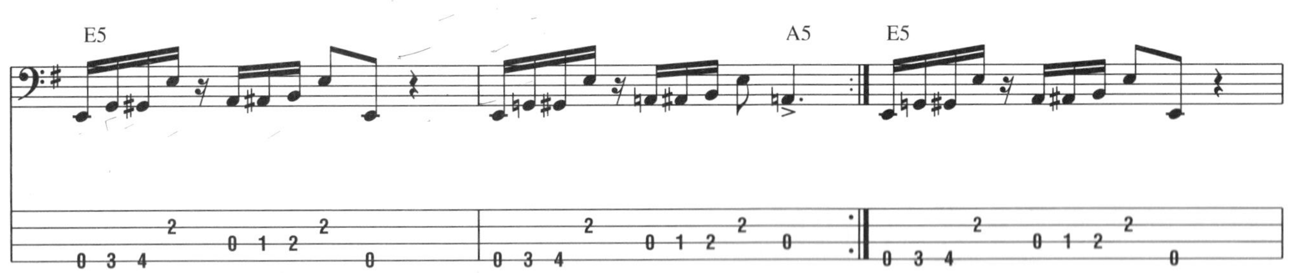
E5
A5
E5

A5
E5
A5

E5
A5
E5

A5
E5
Repeat and fade
A5

War Pigs

Words and Music by Frank Iommi, John Osbourne, William Ward and Terence Butler

1st,4th Verses
D5 E5
Play 4 times
1. Gen-'rals gath-ered in their mass - es, (etc.)
4. Now in dark-ness, world stops turn - ing, (etc.)
Chorus
D5 E5
G5 F♯5
F5
E5
1.
2.
2nd time to Coda
N.C.
sim.
2nd Verse
N.C.
Pol - i - ti - cians hide them-selves a - way. (etc.)

3rd Verse
N.C.
Time will tell_ on their_ pow - er_ minds,_(etc.)
1.
2.
N.C.
Chorus
D5 F5
G5 F#5 F5
E5
D5 E5
G5 F#5
1.
F5
E5
2.
F5
E5
Guitar solo
N.C.(E)

H
1/2
sl.
Full
P
1/4
E5
D5
E5
H
D5
D.S. (w/repeats) al Coda

Coda
N.C.(E7(no3rd))
E5 B5 D5
N.C.

E5 G5 E5
1/2
1/2
N.C.
E5 B5 D5
N.C.

E5 G5 E5
1/2
1/2
N.C.(E7(no3rd))

(D7(no3rd))
H

(C7(no3rd))
H
H
B5 C5

B5
E5
N.C.(D)

E5
N.C.(D)
E5

N.C.(D)
E5
N.C.(D)

(E5)
(D)
(E5)

(D)
(E5)
(D)

*Tape speeds up; last note sounds 10½ whole steps higher.

When Worlds Collide

Lyrics by Spider
Music by Powerman 5000

Tune down 1/2 step:
(low to high) Eb–Ab–Db–Gb

Intro
Moderately fast Rock ♩ = 148

Verse

* Synth. arr. for bass

Db(b5)
N.C.
in your head?
What lit - tle life that you had just died.
Db(b5)
N.C.
I'm gon - na be the one that's tak - in' o - ver.
Db(b5)
N.C.
Now this is what it's like when
Chorus
G5 F5 G5 F5 G5
G5
F5 G5 F5 G5
F5 G5 F5 G5
worlds col - lide!
Are you read - y to go?
'Cause I'm read - y to go.
End Bass Fig. 1
Bass Fig. 2
F5 G5 F5 G5
F5 G5 Bb5
G5
F5 G5 F5 G5
What you gon - na do, ba - by, ba - by?
Are you go - ing with me?

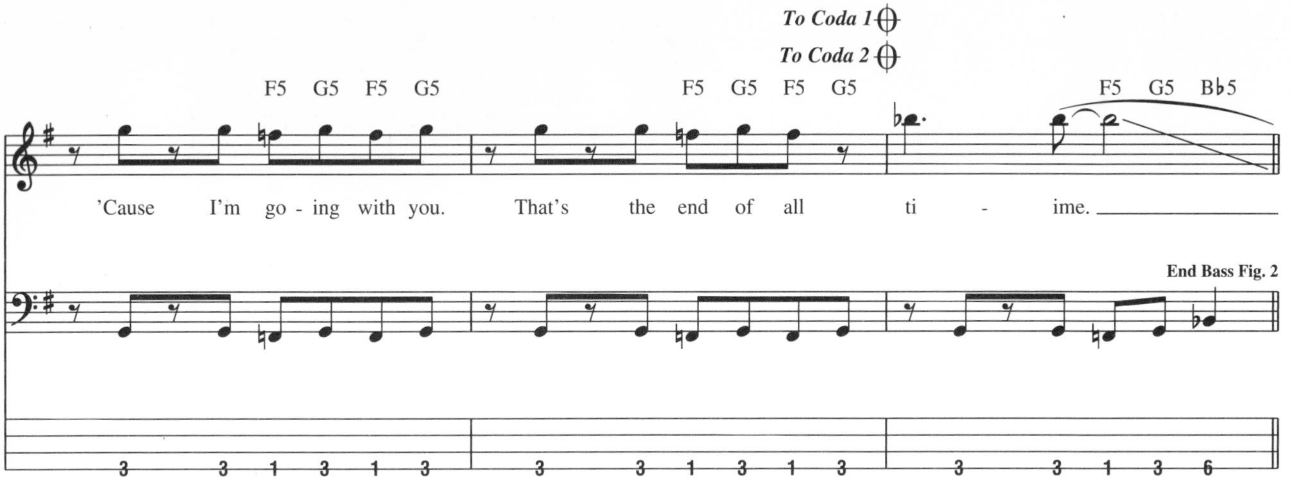
To Coda 1
To Coda 2
F5 G5 F5 G5
F5 G5 F5 G5
F5 G5 Bb5
'Cause I'm go - ing with you. That's the end of all ti - ime.
End Bass Fig. 2
3 3 1 3 1 3
3 3 1 3 1 3
3 3 1 3 6

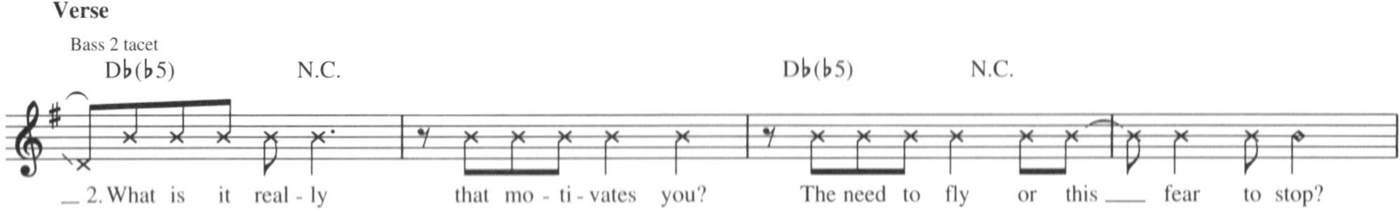
Verse
Bass 2 tacet
Db(b5) N.C. Db(b5) N.C.
2. What is it real - ly that mo - ti - vates you? The need to fly or this fear to stop?

Bass 1: w/ Riff A (3 times)
Db(b5) N.C. Db(b5) N.C.
I'll go a - long, then you real - ize. When we get there I say

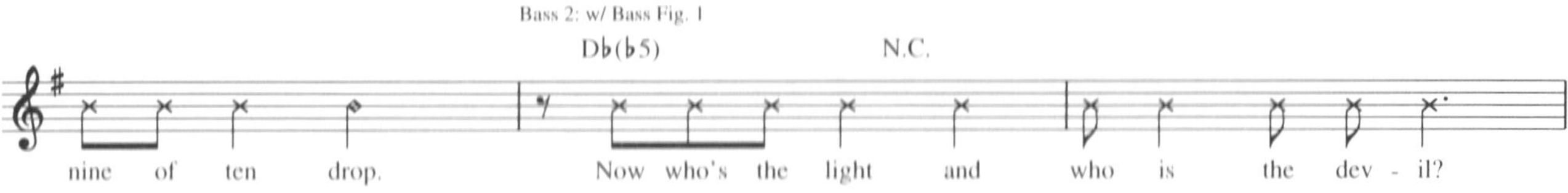
Bass 2: w/ Bass Fig. 1
Db(b5) N.C.
nine of ten drop. Now who's the light and who is the dev - il?

Db(b5) N.C. Db(b5) N.C.
You can't de - cide so I'll be your guide. And one by one they will

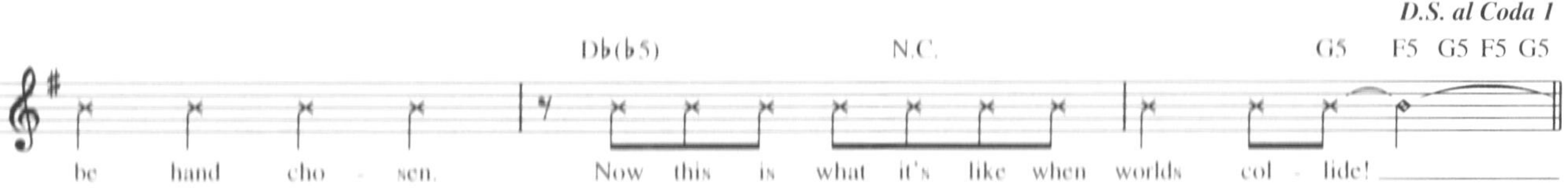
D.S. al Coda 1
Db(b5) N.C. G5 F5 G5 F5 G5
be hand cho - sen. Now this is what it's like when worlds col - lide!

Coda 1
Interlude
Bass 2 tacet
F5 G5 N.C.
Em
Dm
C#m
Play 3 times
ti - ime.
Spoken: You are a robot.
Bass 2
*Sing 1st time only
Cm
Interlude
N.C.
Now this is what it's like when
Bass 2
worlds col - lide.
Now this is what it's like.
Now this is what it's like when worlds col - lide.
Now this is what it's like.
Harm.
Verse
Bass 1: w/ Riff A (2 times)
Bass 2: w/ Rhy. Fig. 1
Db(b5) N.C. Db(b5) N.C.
3.What is it real - ly when they're fall - ing o - ver? Ev - 'ry-thing you thought was de - nied.

D.S. al Coda 2
Db(b5) N.C. Db(b5) N.C. G5 F5 G5 F5 G5
I'm gon - na be the one that's tak - in' o - ver. Now this is what it's like when worlds col - lide!
Coda 2
Bass 2: w/ Bass Fig. 2 (last meas.)
Bass 2: w/ Bass Fig. 2
F5 G5 Bb5 G5 F5 G5 F5 G5 F5 G5 F5 G5
ti - ime. Are you read - y to go? 'Cause I'm read - y to go.
F5 G5 F5 G5 F5 G5 Bb5 G5 F5 G5 F5 G5
What you gon - na do, ba - by, ba - by? Are you go - ing with me?
F5 G5 F5 G5 F5 G5 F5 G5 F5 G5 Bb5
'Cause I'm go - ing with you. That's the end of all ti - ime.
Outro
2nd time, Bass 2: w/ Bass Fill 1
Db5 C5 G5 F5 G5 F5 G5
Are you read - y? Keep 'em read - y. That's the end of all
Are you go - ing? Keep 'em go - ing. That's the end of all
Bass 2
1. 2.
Freely
F5 G5 Bb5 F5 G5 Bb5
ti - ime. ti - ime.
Bass Fill 1

Wild World

Words and Music by Cat Stevens

F
G
F
C
Dmadd2
E
2nd Verse
Am
D
G
C
F
Dm
mp
2. You know I've seen a lot of what the world can do...
E
Am
D
G
C
F
Dm
E
G
G7
G6
G
Chorus
C
G
mf
Ooh, ba - by, ba - by, it's a
F
G
F
C
N.C.
wild world...
C
G
F
N.C.
G
F
C
Dmadd2
E
To Coda

3rd Verse
Am
D
G
C
mp
3. La la la la la la la la la la...
F
Dm
E
Am
D
D.S. al Coda
G
C
F
Dm
E
G
G7
G6
G
Coda
Outro
C
G
F
Ooh, ba - by, ba - by, it's a wild world...
G
F
C
N.C.
C
G
F
N.C.
G
F
C

Woke Up This Morning

Words and Music by B.B. King and Jules Bihari

Intro

Moderately Fast ♩ = 153

Bass

N.C. C

f

F7 C

G7 F7 C

Verse

Bass: w/ Bass Fill 1, 3rd time

C

1. I woke up this morn - in', my ___ ba - by was gone.
bo - dy to stay home with me.
4. Oo. ___ I'm all ___ a - lone.
6. *See Additional Lyrics*

F7 C

Woke up this morn - in', my ba - by was gone.
I ain't got no - bo - dy stay-in' home with __ me.
Oh, ________ babe, ________ I'm all ______ a - lone.

To Coda 1 ⊕
To Coda 2 ⊕

G7 F7 C

I was feel-ing so __ bad, __ I'm all __ a - lone.
My ba - by she's gone. I'm in mis - er - y. __ 3. Whoa, ________
I ain't had no lov - ing since my ba - by's been gone. 5. Whoa, ______

1. 2.

Verse

C

2. I ain't got no- ____________ ba - by, I'm all __ a - lone.

G9
C
I ain't had no lov - in' since my ba - by's been gone. Well, al -
Saxophone Solo
G9
C6
F9
- right!
C6
G9
w/ Lead Voc. ad lib.
C
C6
F9
C6
D.S. al Coda 1
G9
C

Additional Lyrics

6. Whoa, baby, take a swing with me.
   Whoa, baby, take a swing with me.
   My baby, she's gone. My baby, she's gone.

Wonderwall

Words and Music by Noel Gallagher

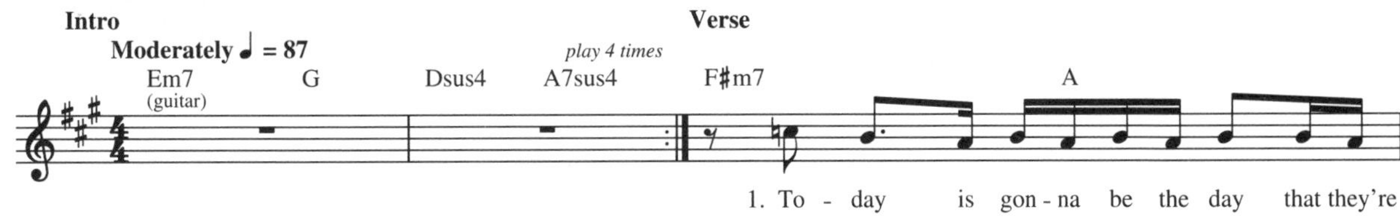

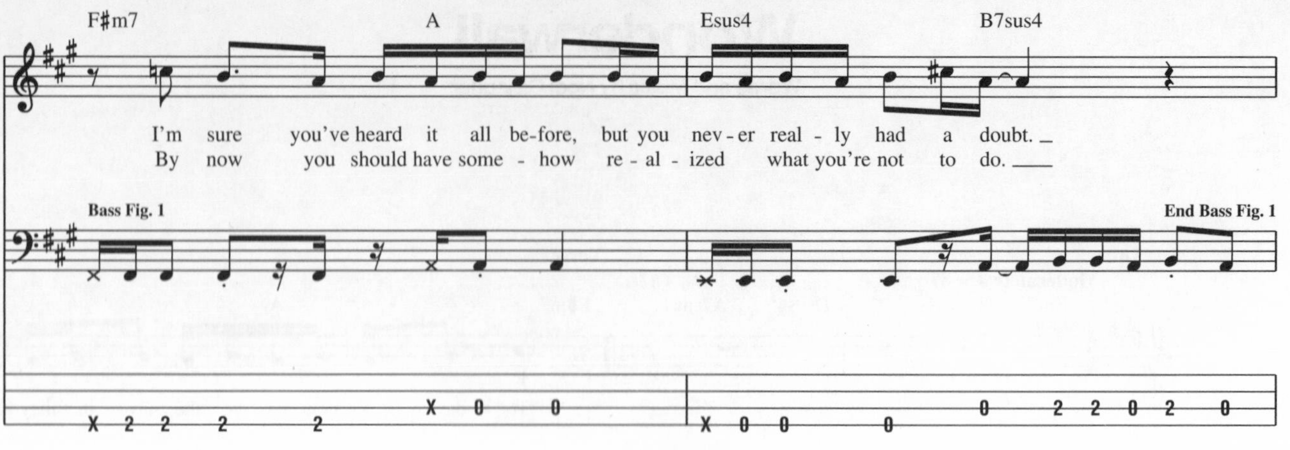
F#m7
A
Esus4
B7sus4
I'm sure you've heard it all be-fore, but you nev-er real-ly had a doubt.
By now you should have some-how re-al-ized what you're not to do.
Bass Fig. 1
End Bass Fig. 1

Bass: w/ Bass Fig. 1, 2 times
F#m7
A
Esus4
B7sus4
F#m7
A
Esus4 B7sus4
I don't be-lieve that an-y-bod-y feels the way I do a-bout you now.
And all
And all

Pre-Chorus
D
E
F#m7
the roads we have to walk are wind-ing, and all
the roads that lead you there were wind-ing, and all
Bass

D
E
F#m7
the lights that lead us there are blind-ing.
the lights that light the way are blind-ing.

D
E
A
E/G#
F#m7
A
There are man - y things that I would like to say to you, but I don't know how.
5 5 5 5 7 7 7
5 4 2 5

B7sus4
Be-cause
I said
7 7 7 7 5 7 5 7 7
5 7 5 7 5 7 7 5 7 7

Chorus
Dadd9
F#m7
A
F#m7
may - be
you're gon - na be the one that
Bass Fig. 2
End Bass Fig. 2
5 5 5 5 7 9 7 9 9
5 5 5 7 9 7 9 9

Bass: w/ Bass Fig. 2, 2 1/2 times
Dadd9
F#m7
A
F#m7
Dadd9 F#m7
A
F#m7
Dadd9
F#m7
saves me.
And af - ter all
you're my won-der - wall.

Chorus

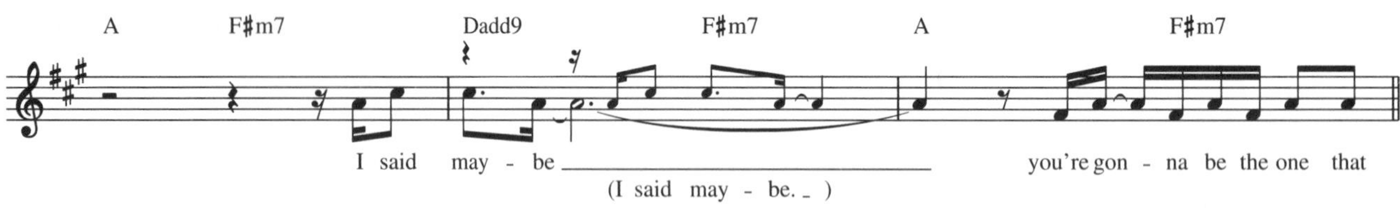

Outro

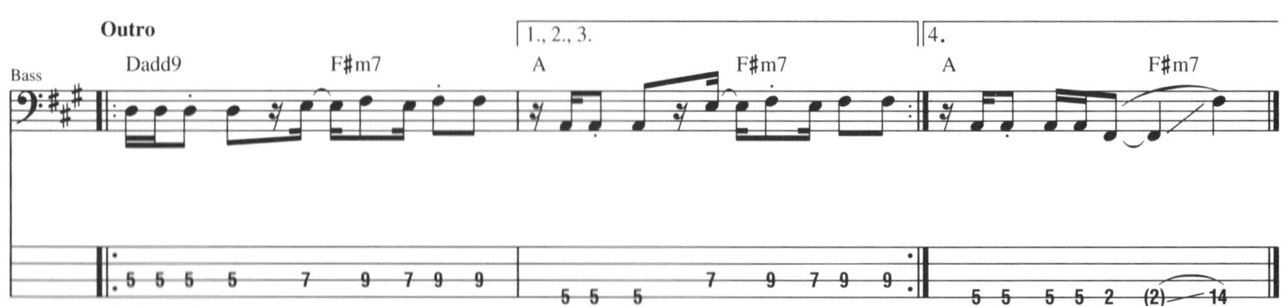

Would?

Written by Jerry Cantrell

Tune Down 1/2 Step:
① = G♭ ③ = A♭
② = D♭ ④ = E♭

Intro

Moderate Rock ♩ = 100

N.C.(F♯m)

Bass

mf

T
A
B

*F♯5 G

1., 2., 3.

Woo.

*Sing 1st time only.

4.

Verse

F♯5 G

1. Know me, broken by
2. Drifting body, it's

F♯5 G F♯5 G

my master. Teach thee
soul deser - tion. Flying,

F#5
G
on child of love here - af - ter.
not yet quite the no - tion.

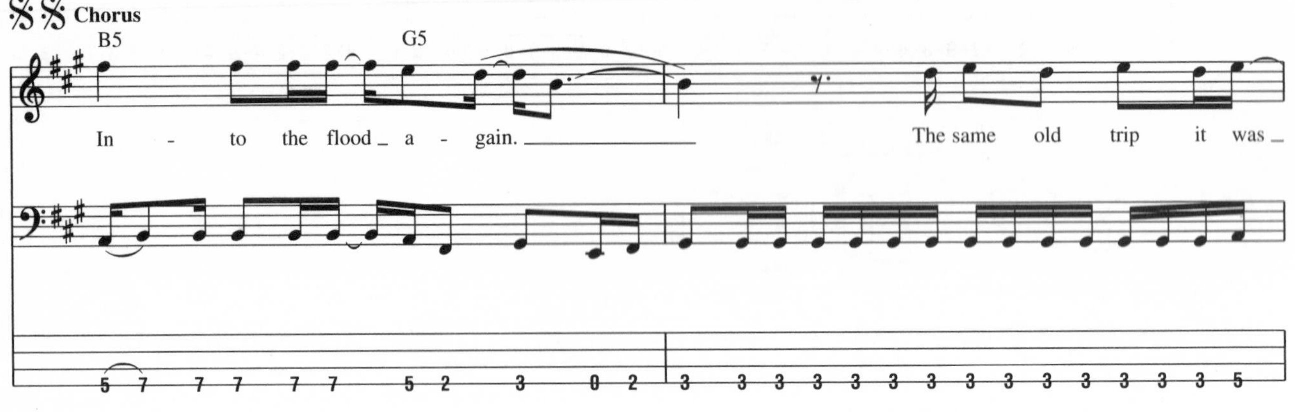
Chorus
B5
G5
In - to the flood a - gain.
The same old trip it was

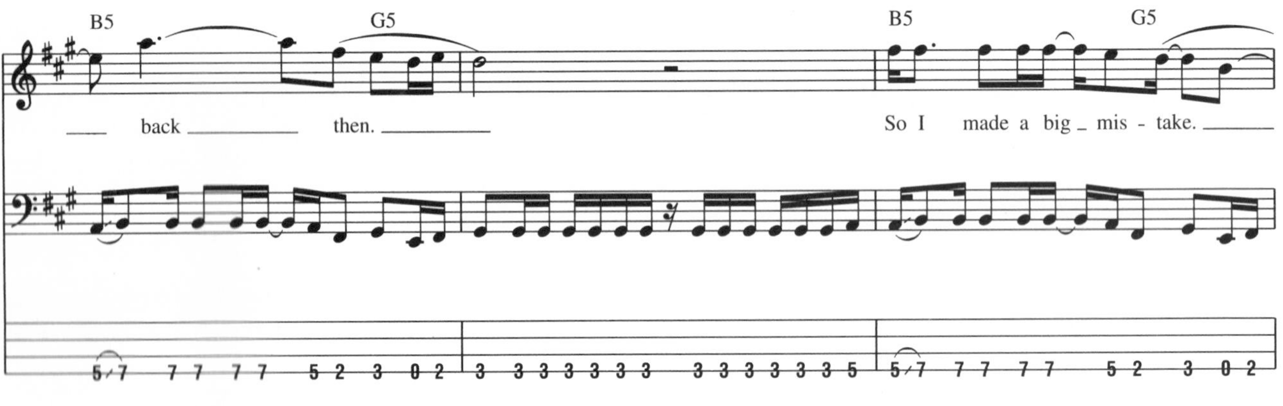
B5
G5
back then.
B5
G5
So I made a big mis - take.

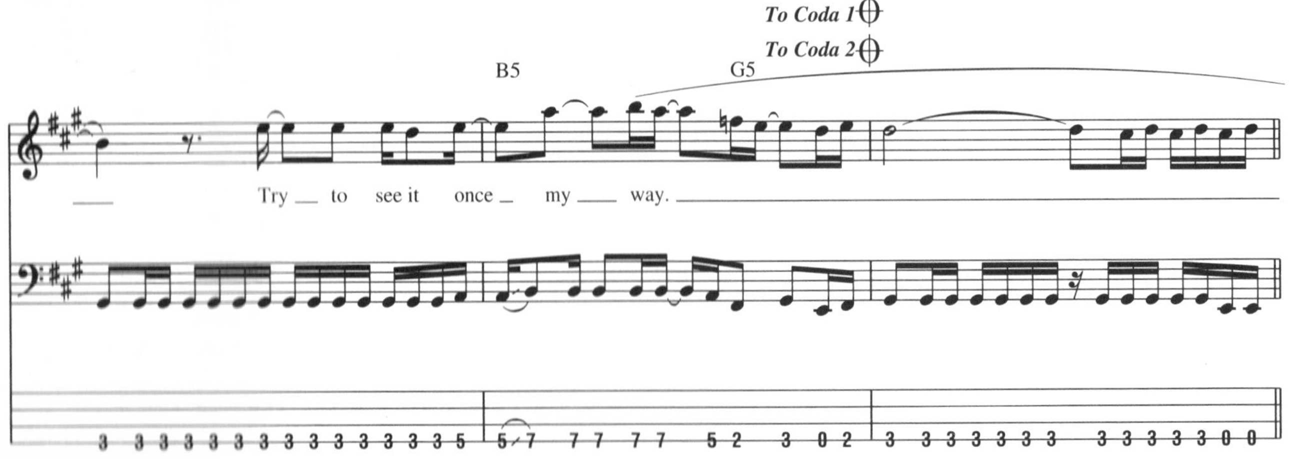
To Coda 1
To Coda 2
B5
G5
Try to see it once my way.

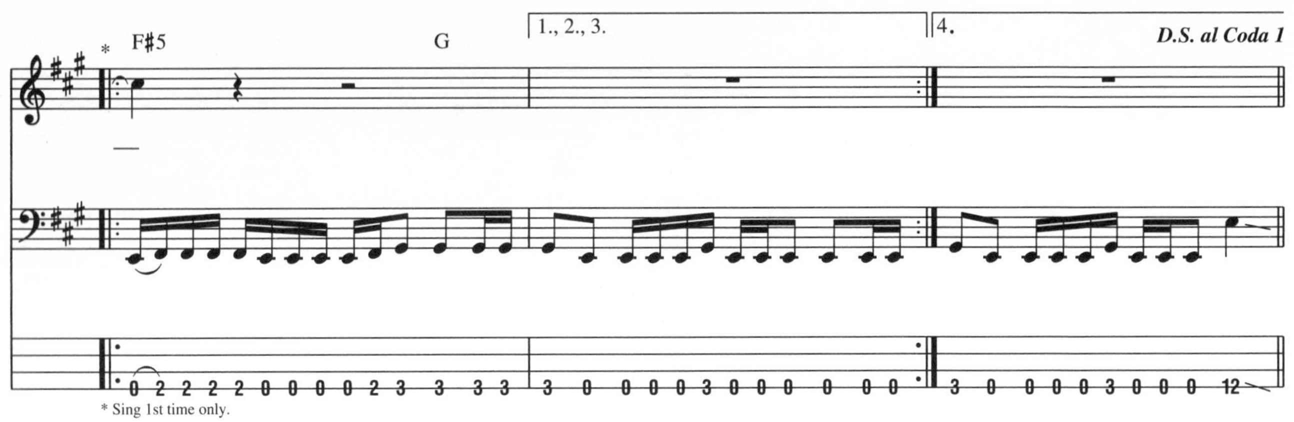

* Sing 1st time only.

Coda 2
Outro
D5
D7(no 3rd)
Yeah.
Am I wrong?
Bass Fig. 1
G#5
G5
E5
N.C.
Have I run too far to get home?
End Bass Fig. 1
Bass: w/ Bass Fig. 1, 3 times
Have I gone, left you here a - lone?
Am I wrong? Have I run too far to get home? Yeah.
D
Freely
D7#9
If I would, could you?
Bass
rit.

Yellow

Words and Music by Guy Berryman, Jon Buckland, Will Champion and Chris Martin

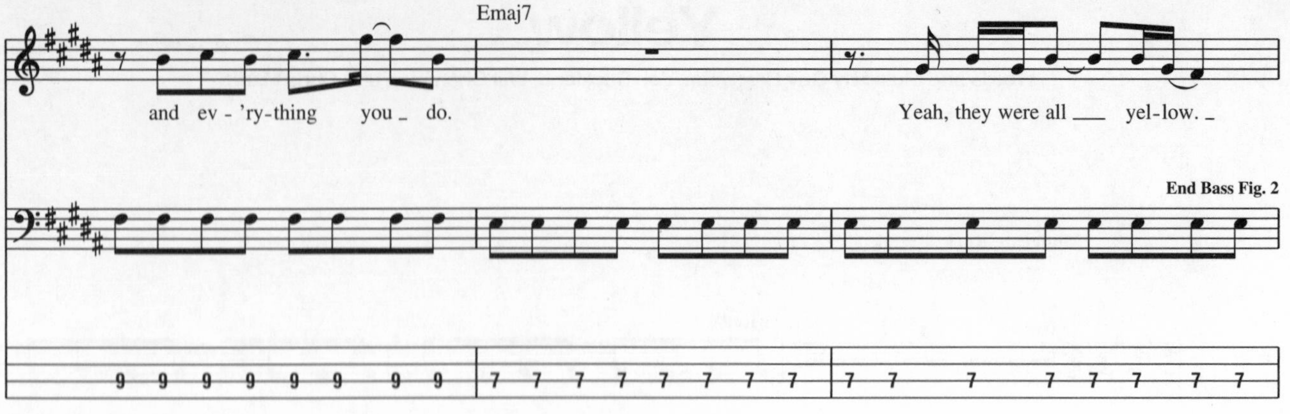
Emaj7
and ev - 'ry-thing you do.
Yeah, they were all yel-low.
End Bass Fig. 2
9 9 9 9 9 9 9 9
7 7 7 7 7 7 7 7 7
7 7 7 7 7 7 7 7

Bass: w/ Bass Fig. 2 (2 times)
B
F#6add11
I came a-long.
I wrote a song for you
and all the things you do,

Emaj7
B
and it was called "Yel-low."
So then I took my

F#6add11
Emaj7
turn.
Oh, what a thing to have done,
and it was all yel-low.

Chorus
B
Bsus4
B
Emaj7
G#m
F#6add11
Your skin. Oh, yeah, your skin and bones
7 7 7 7 7 7 7 7
7 7 7 7 7 7 7 7
7 7 7 9 9 9
6 9 9 9 9

Emaj7
G#m
F#6add11
Emaj7
turn in - to something beau - ti - ful.
Do you know,

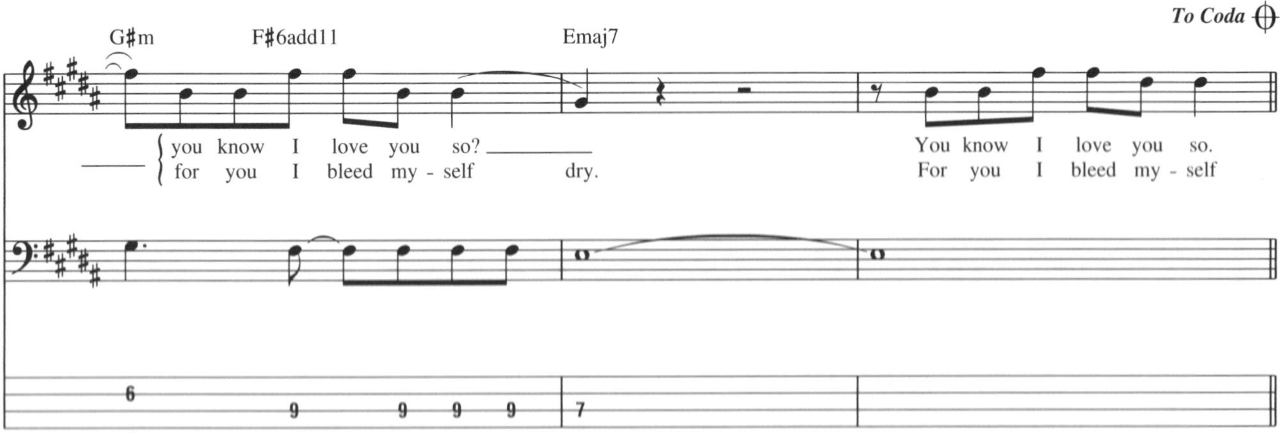
To Coda
G#m
F#6add11
Emaj7
you know I love you so?
for you I bleed my - self dry.
You know I love you so.
For you I bleed my - self

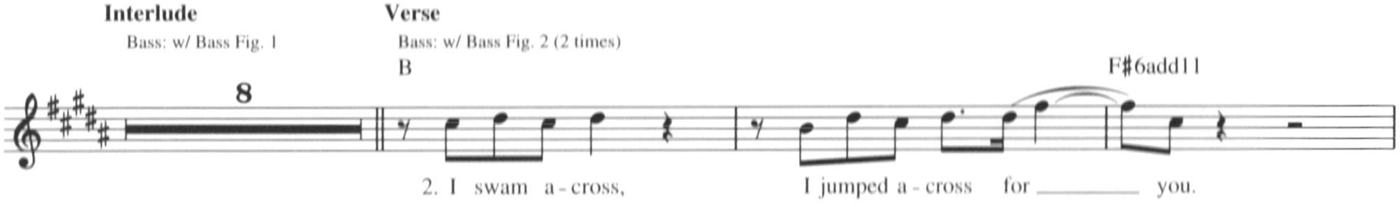
Interlude
Bass: w/ Bass Fig. 1
Verse
Bass: w/ Bass Fig. 2 (2 times)
B
F#6add11
8
2. I swam a - cross,
I jumped a - cross for you.

Emaj7
Oh, what a thing to do,
'cause you were all yel - low.

B
F#6add11
I drew a line,
I drew a line for you.

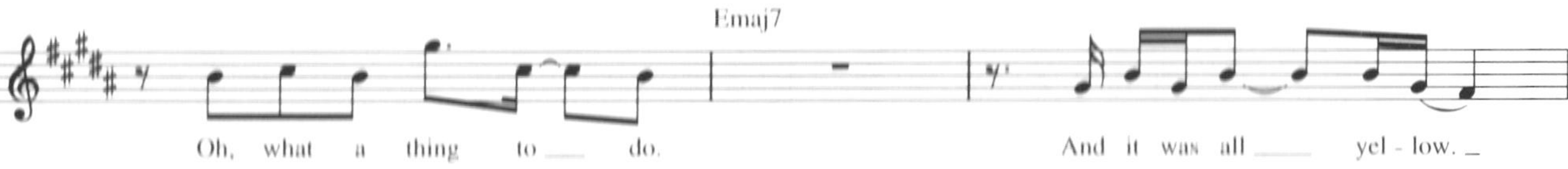
Emaj7
Oh, what a thing to do.
And it was all yel - low.

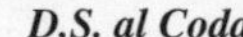
D.S. al Coda

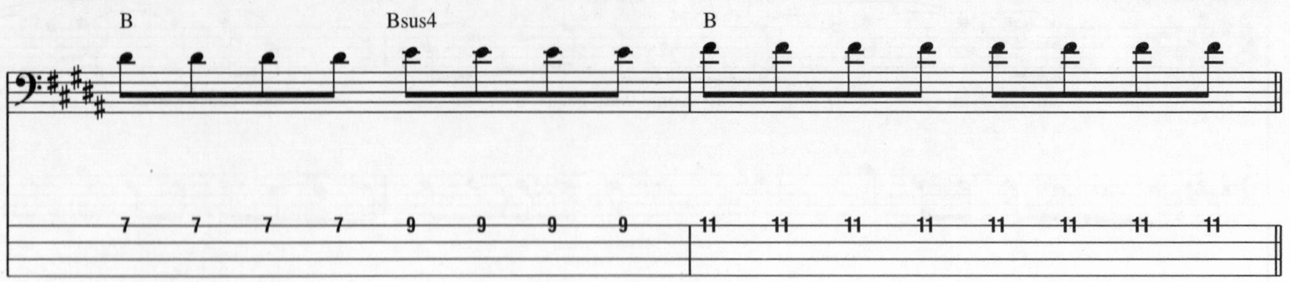
B
Bsus4
B
7 7 7 7 9 9 9 9 11 11 11 11 11 11 11 11

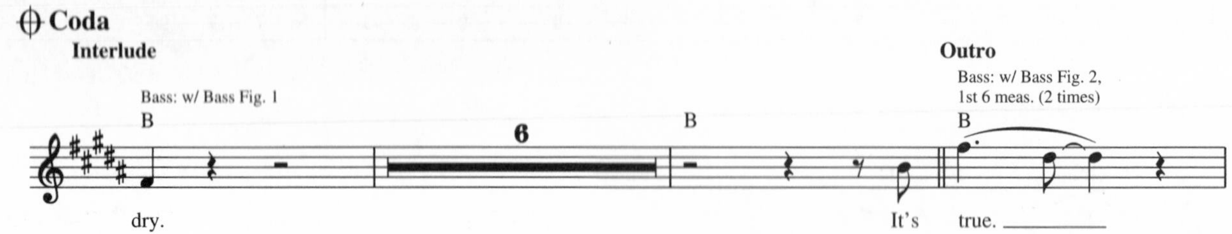
Coda
Interlude
Bass: w/ Bass Fig. 1
B
6
B
Outro
Bass: w/ Bass Fig. 2,
1st 6 meas. (2 times)
B
dry.
It's
true.

F♯6add11
Emaj7
Look how they shine for you.
Look how they shine for you.

B
F♯6add11
Look how they shine for...
Look how they shine for you.

Emaj7
Look how they shine for you.
Look how they shine.

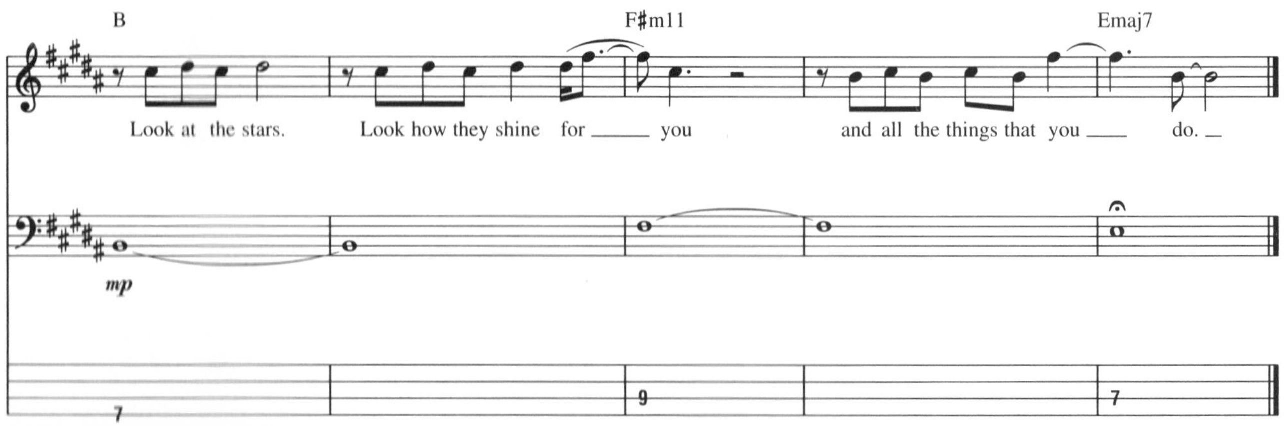
B
F♯m11
Emaj7
Look at the stars.
Look how they shine for you
and all the things that you do.
mp
7
9
7

You Oughta Know

Lyrics by Alanis Morissette
Music by Alanis Morissette and Glen Ballard

C/G
have your ba - by? I'm sure she'd make a real - ly ex - cel - lent moth - er. 'Cause the
Pre-Chorus
Gm7
love that you gave, that we made was - n't a - ble to make it e - nough for you to be o -
C/G
pen wide, no. And ev -
Gm7
'ry time you speak her name does she know how you told me you'd hold me un - til

C/G
you died, 'til you died? But you're still a - live. And I'm here
Chorus
G
F
B♭
to re - mind you of the mess you left when you went
Bass Fig. 1
f
C
G
F
a - way. It's not fair to de - ny me of the cross
End Bass Fig. 1
B♭
C
I bear that you gave to me. You, you, you ought - a know.

Verse
Gm7
C/G
2. You seem ver - y well, things look peace -
Gm7
- ful. I'm not quite as well, I thought
C/G
Gm7
you should know. Did you for - get a - bout me, Mis - ter Du -
C/G
plic - i - ty? I hate to bug you in the mid - dle of din - ner. It was a

Gm7
C/G
slap in the face, how quick-ly I was re-placed and are you think-ing of me when you
8va
loco
P
Harm.
Pre-Chorus
Gm7
fuck her? 'Cause the love that you gave, that we made was-n't a-ble to
C/G
make it e-nough for you to be o-pen wide, no. And ev-
Gm7
-'ry time you speak her name does she know how you told me you'd hold me un-til

C/G
you died, 'til you died? But you're still a - live. And I'm here
Chorus
Bass: w/ Bass Fig. 1
G
F
Bb
to re - mind you of the mess you left when you went
C
G
F
a - way. It's not fair to de - ny me of the cross
Bb
C
I bear that you gave to me. You, you, you ought - a know.
1/4
1/4
Interlude
Bass tacet
C7sus4
C7
Ah.
Gm/C
C
Ah.
C7
Gm/C
Ah. Ah. Ah. Ah. Ah. 'Cause the

Pre-Chorus
Gm7
joke that you laid in the bed, that was me and I'm not gon-na fade as soon as you close
mf
C/G
your eyes, and you __ know it. And ev -
1/2
Gm7
- 'ry time __ I scratch __ my nails __ down some - one else - 's back, __ I hope __ you feel __
C/G
__ it. Well, __ can you feel __ it? Well, I'm here __

Chorus
Bass: w/ Bass Fig. 1, 1st 3 meas.
G
F
Bb
to re - mind you of the mess you left when you went
Bass: w/ Fill 1
C
Bass: w/ Bass Fig. 1, 1st 3 meas., simile
G
F
a - way. It's not fair to de - ny me of the cross
Bb
Bass: w/ Fill 2
C
I bear that you gave to me. You, you, you, ought - a know. I'm here
Bass: w/ Bass Fig. 1, 1st 3 meas.
G
F
Bb
to re - mind you of the mess you left when you went
C
G
F
a - way. It's not fair to de - ny me of the cross
1/2
Bb
C
I bear that you gave to me. You, you, you ought - a know.
Fill 1
Fill 2

You Really Got Me

Words and Music by Ray Davies

real - ly got me. . .
2nd Verse
Please. don't ev - er let me be.
I al - ways wan - na be by your side. . .
You real - ly got me. . .
Guitar solo

A G A C D A G A G A G A G A G A
sl.
F G A G A G A G A G A G A G
A
(Vocal ad lib)
sl.
3
3rd Verse
7
sl.
B5 A5 B5 A5 B5 A5 B5 A5 B5 A5 B5 A5
B5 A B5 D5 D♯5 E D E D E D E D E D E D
You
E D E D E D E D E D E
Free time (♩ = 88)
E7♯9
etc.
real - ly got me. . . .
sl.

You Shook Me

Written by Willie Dixon and J.B. Lenoir

To Coda
E7
you shook me all night long.
You shook me
1.
B7
A7
E7
so hard ba-by,
ba - by, ba - by, please come home.
B7
2.
B7
A7
2. I have a bird bird, won't do noth-in', oh, oh, oh,
E7
Organ Solo
B7
E7
with-out a dia-mond ring

A7
E7
B7
A7
E
Am
A♯°
E7/B
B7
Harmonica Solo
E7
A7
E7

B7
A7
E7
Guitar Solo
E7
A5
E7
B7
D.S. al Coda
A7
E7
B7
3. You _ know you

Coda

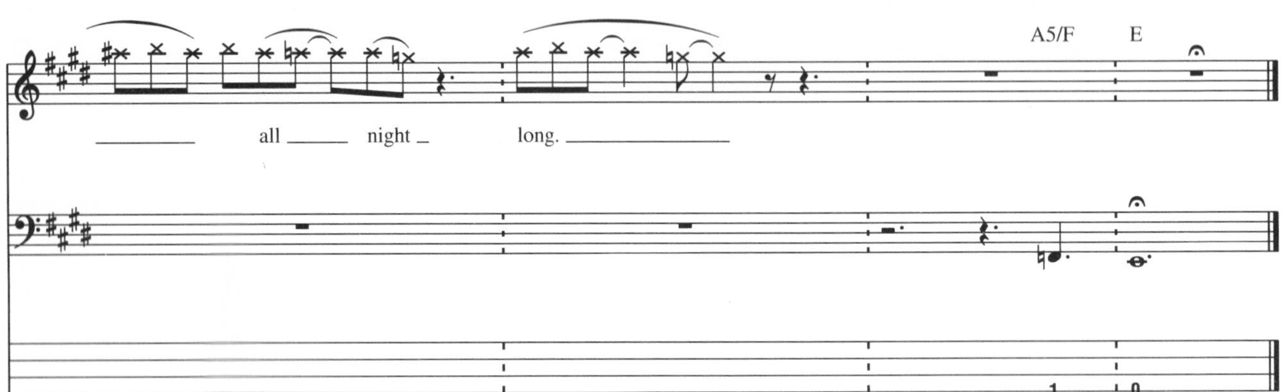

Additional Lyrics

2. I have a bird that whistles and
   I have birds that sing.
   I have a bird that whistles and
   I have birds that sing.
   I have a bird won't do nothin; oh, oh, oh, oh,
   Without a diamond ring.

3. You know you shook me, babe,
   You shook me all night long.
   I know you really, really did, babe.
   I think you shook me, baby,
   You shook me all night long.
   You shook me so hard, baby, I know.

Zero

Words and Music by Billy Corgan

Interlude
E5
Emp- ti- ness is lone- li- ness...
N.C.(Em)
D.S. al Coda
Coda
Guitar solo
N.C.(Em)
Pre-chorus
N.C.(Em)
D
You blame your - self
Chorus
She's the one...

Bass Notation Legend

Bass music can be notated two different ways: on a *musical staff*, and in *tablature*.

THE MUSICAL STAFF shows pitches and rhythms and is divided by bar lines into measures. Pitches are named after the first seven letters of the alphabet.

TABLATURE graphically represents the bass fingerboard. Each horizontal line represents a string, and each number represents a fret.

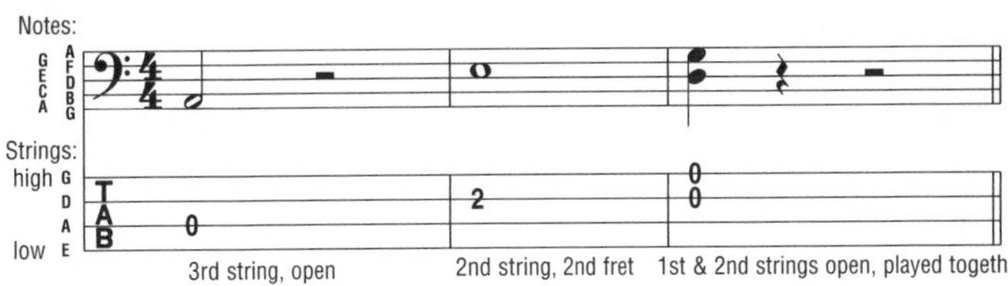

HAMMER-ON: Strike the first (lower) note with one finger, then sound the higher note (on the same string) with another finger by fretting it without picking.

PULL-OFF: Place both fingers on the notes to be sounded. Strike the first note and without picking, pull the finger off to sound the second (lower) note.

LEGATO SLIDE: Strike the first note and then slide the same fret-hand finger up or down to the second note. The second note is not struck.

SHIFT SLIDE: Same as legato slide, except the second note is struck.

TRILL: Very rapidly alternate between the notes indicated by continuously hammering on and pulling off.

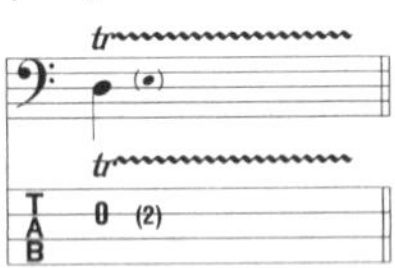

TREMOLO PICKING: The note is picked as rapidly and continuously as possible.

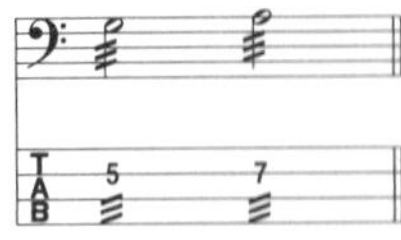

VIBRATO: The string is vibrated by rapidly bending and releasing the note with the fretting hand.

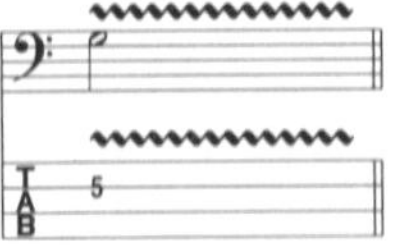

SHAKE: Using one finger, rapidly alternate between two notes on one string by sliding either a half-step above or below.

NATURAL HARMONIC: Strike the note while the fret hand lightly touches the string directly over the fret indicated.

MUFFLED STRINGS: A percussive sound is produced by laying the fret hand across the string(s) without depressing them and striking them with the pick hand.

BEND: Strike the note and bend up the interval shown.

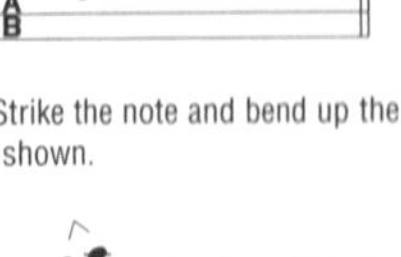

BEND AND RELEASE: Strike the note and bend up as indicated, then release back to the original note. Only the first note is struck.

RIGHT-HAND TAP: Hammer ("tap") the fret indicated with the "pick-hand" index or middle finger and pull off to the note fretted by the fret hand.

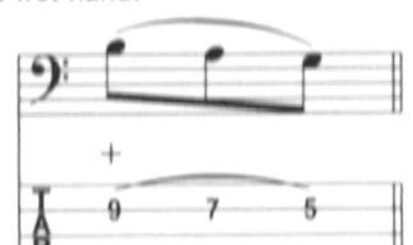

LEFT-HAND TAP: Hammer ("tap") the fret indicated with the "fret-hand" index or middle finger.

SLAP: Strike ("slap") string with right-hand thumb.

POP: Snap ("pop") string with right-hand index or middle finger.

Additional Musical Definitions

 *(accent)* • Accentuate note (play it louder)

 *(accent)* • Accentuate note with great intensity

(staccato) • Play the note short

⊓ • Downstroke

V • Upstroke

D.S. al Coda • Go back to the sign (𝄋), then play until the measure marked "***To Coda***," then skip to the section labelled "**Coda**."

D.C. al Fine • Go back to the beginning of the song and play until the measure marked "***Fine***" (end).

Bass Fig. • Label used to recall a recurring pattern.

Fill • Label used to identify a brief pattern which is to be inserted into the arrangement.

tacet • Instrument is silent (drops out).

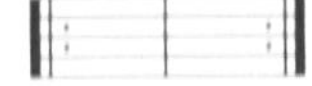

• Repeat measures between signs.

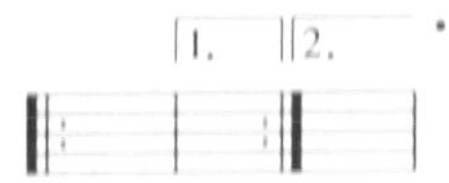

• When a repeated section has different endings, play the first ending only the first time and the second ending only the second time.

NOTE: Tablature numbers in parentheses mean:
1. The note is being sustained over a system (note in standard notation is tied), or
2. The note is sustained, but a new articulation (such as a hammer-on, pull-off, slide or vibrato begins), or
3. The note is a barely audible "ghost" note (note in standard notation is also in parentheses).

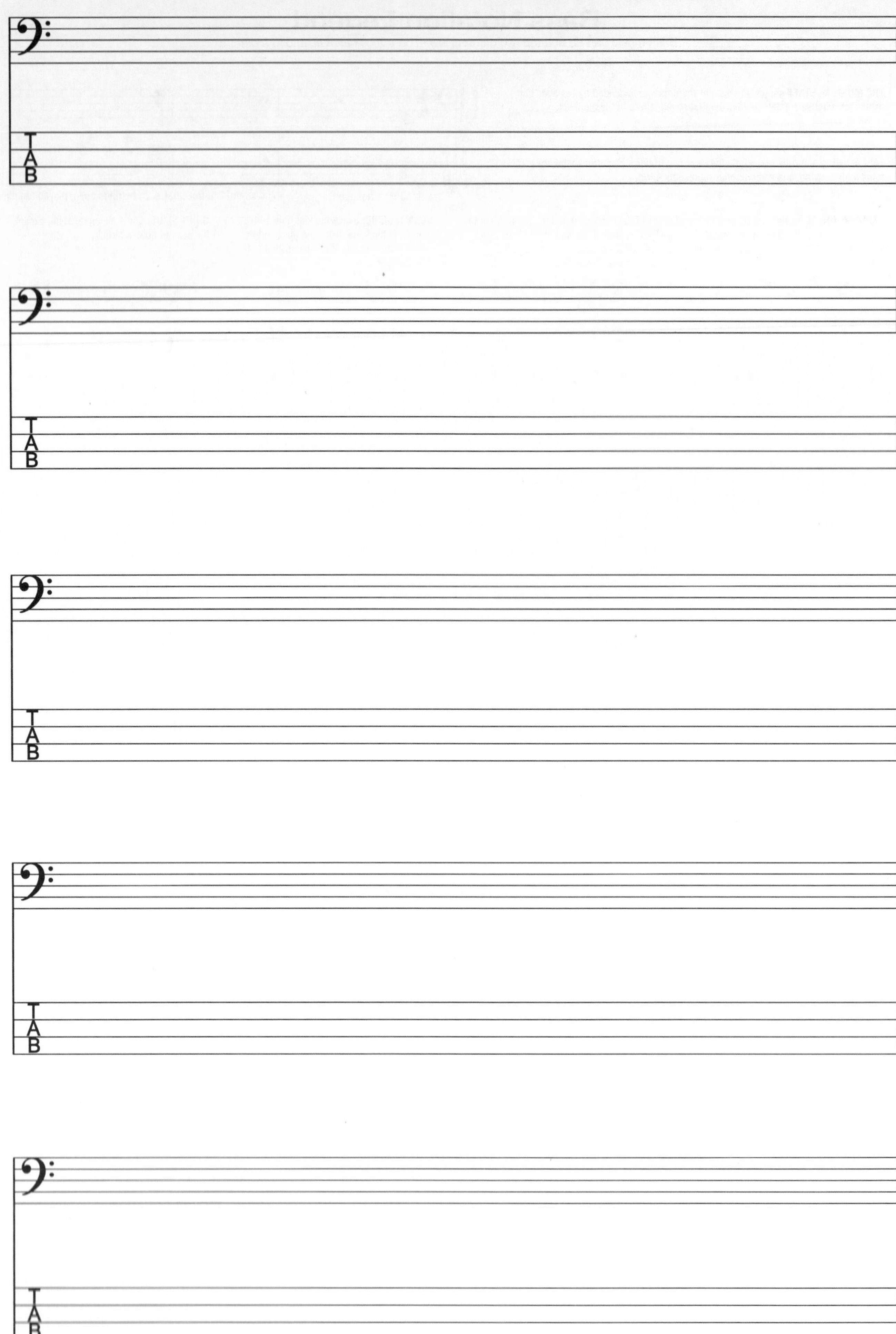

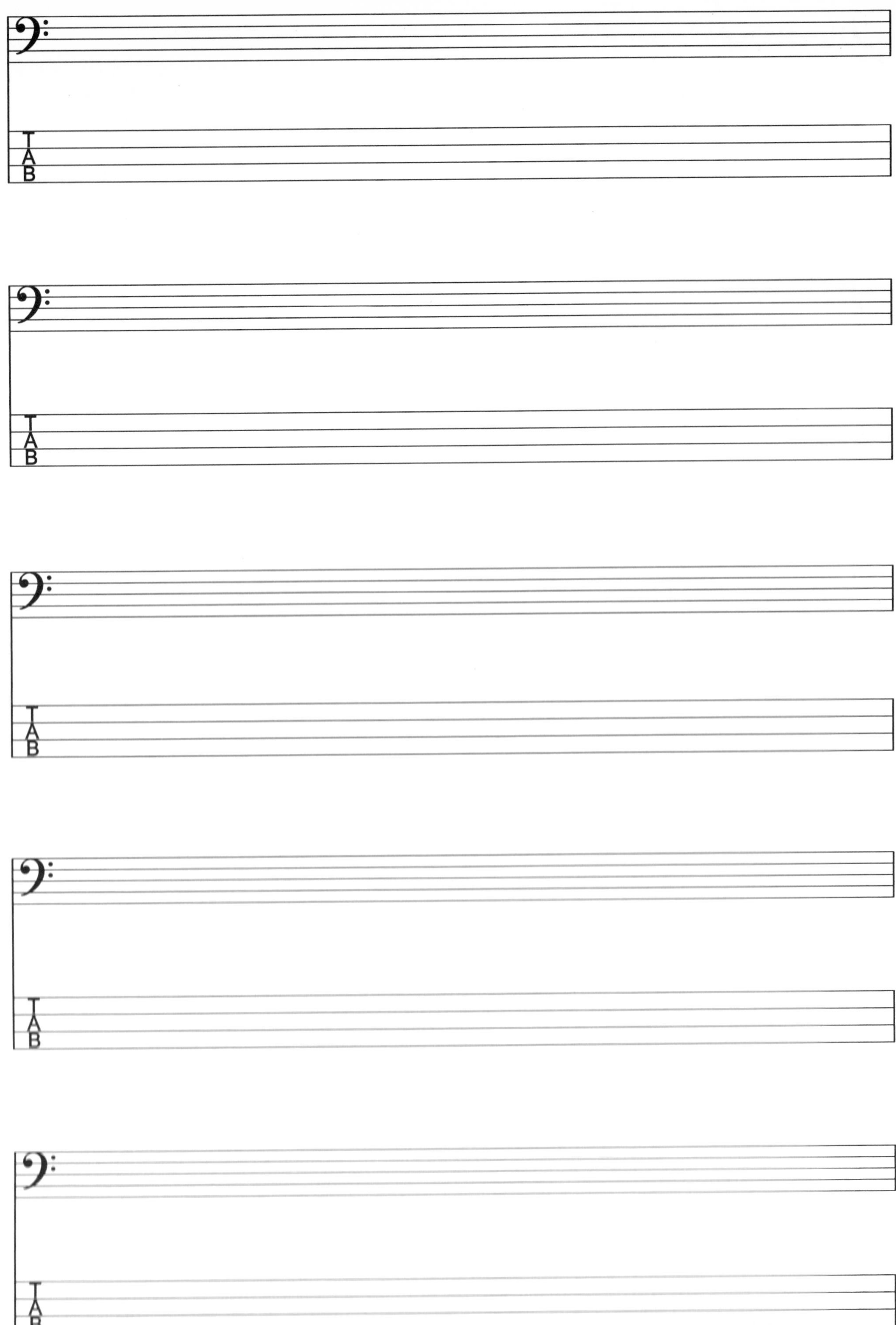

TAB

TAB

TAB

TAB

TAB

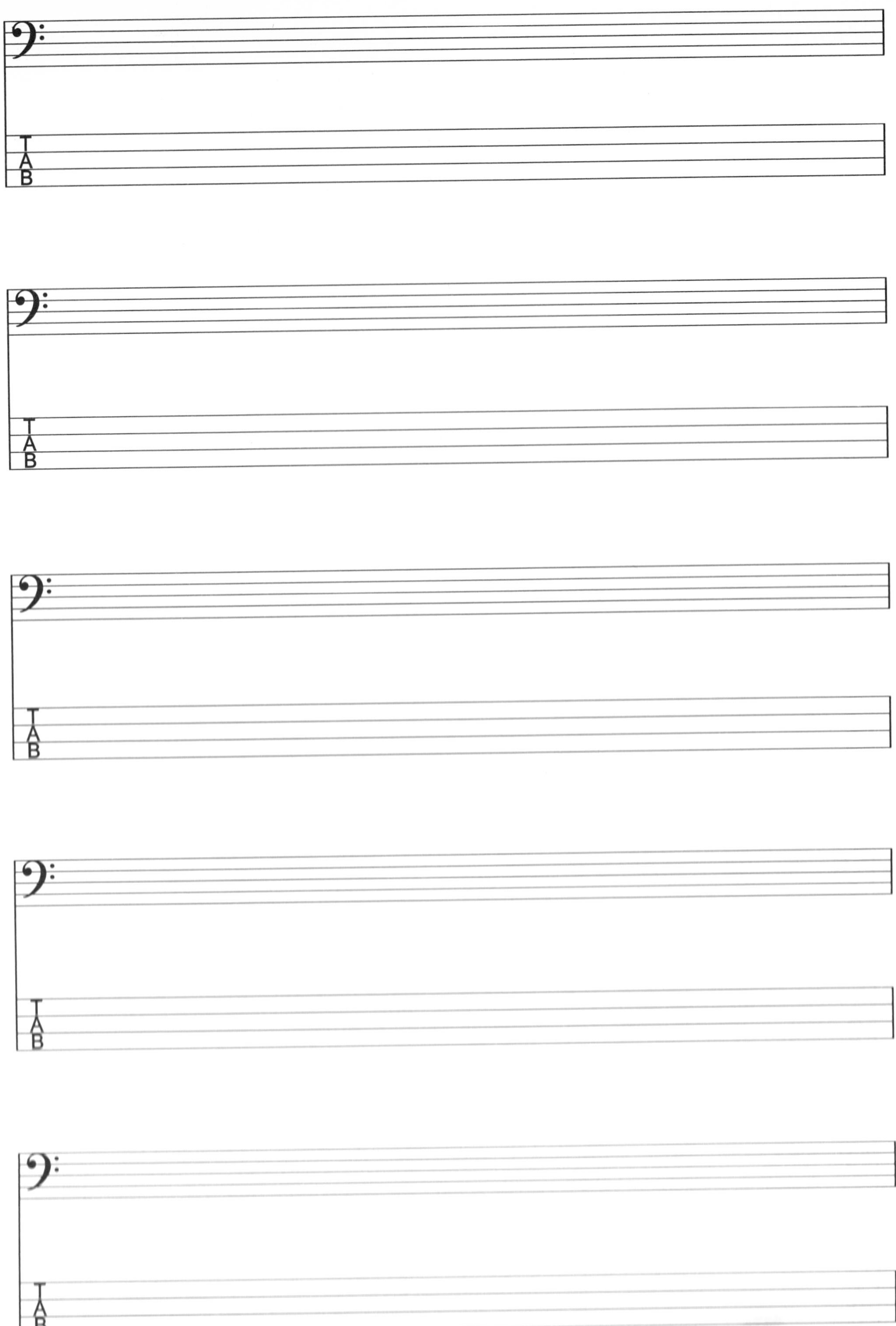
TAB
TAB
TAB
TAB
TAB

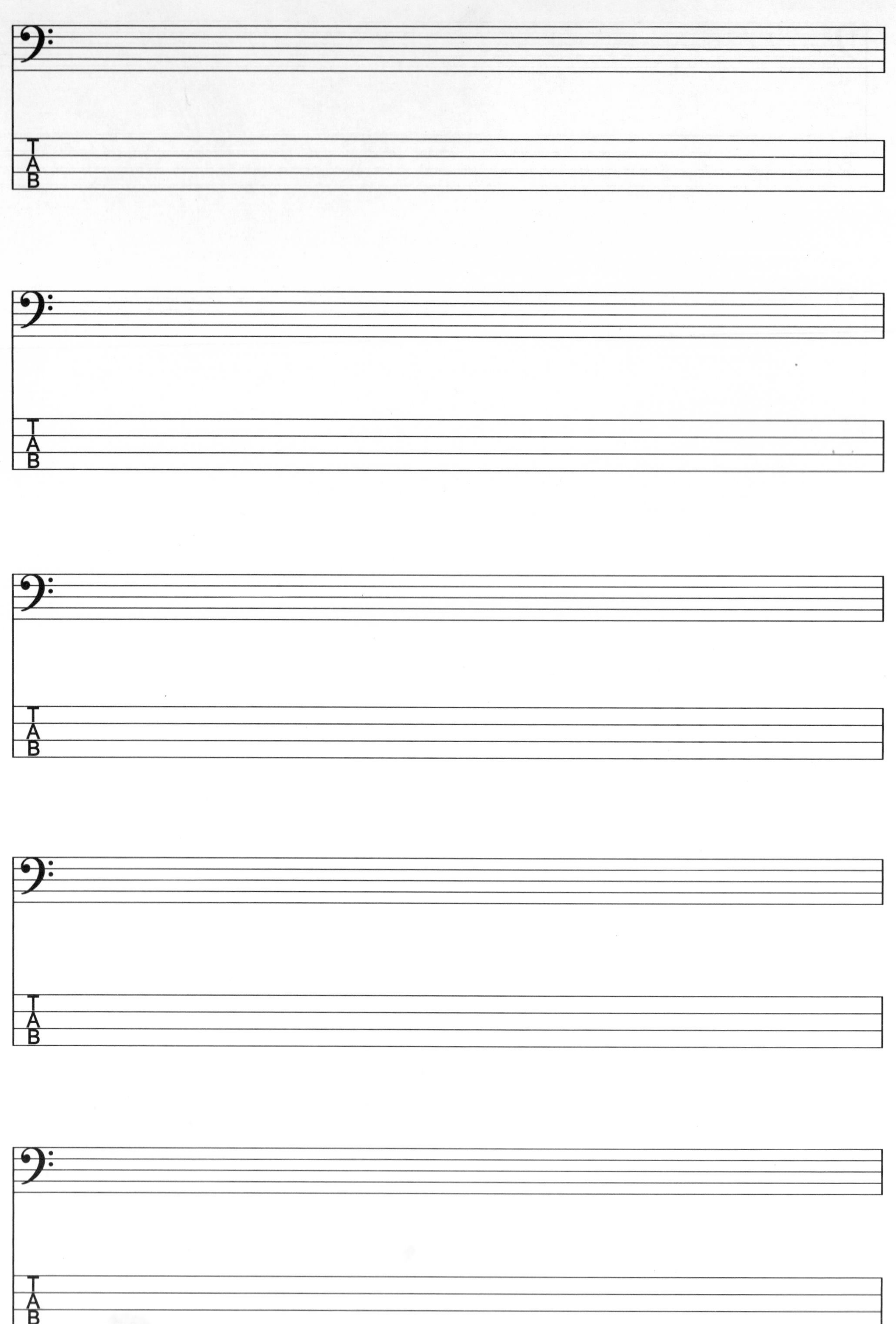
T
A
B
T
A
B
T
A
B
T
A
B
T
A
B